Fleet Safety

for Safety Professionals and Fleet Managers

Joel M. Haight Ph.D., P.E.
Editor

AMERICAN SOCIETY OF
SAFETY PROFESSIONALS

Disclaimer
While the publisher and authors have used their best efforts in preparing this book, they make no representations or warranties with respect to the accuracy or completeness of the contents, and specifically disclaim any implied warranties of fitness for a particular purpose.
The information herein is provided with the understanding that the authors are not hereby engaged in rendering professional or legal services. The mention of any specific products herein does not constitute an endorsement or recommendation by the American Society of Safety Professionals, and was done solely at the discretion of the author(s).

Notice of Name Change
The American Society of Safety Engineers (ASSE) is now the American Society of Safety Professionals (ASSP).

Library of Congress Cataloging-in-Publication Data
Fleet safety : for safety professionals and fleet managers / Joel M. Haight Ph.D., P.E., editor.
    pages cm
Includes bibliographical references and index.
ISBN 978-0-939874-00-2 (alk. paper)
1. Motor vehicle fleets--Safety measures. 2. Motor vehicle fleets--Safety measures--Economic aspects. 3. Motor vehicle fleets--Management. I. Haight, Joel M., editor. II. American Society of Safety Engineers.
TL165.F56 2015
388.3'40684--dc23

2015004103

Managing Editor: Michael F. Burditt, ASSP
Copy Editor: Jeri Ann Stucka, ASSP
Page Composition: Amnet Systems PLC
Cover: Reed Design Studio

Printed in the United States of America

24 23 22 21 20 19 18   2 3 4 5 6 7 8 9

Contents

Preface

The chapters in this book provide a 360° perspective on fleet safety: both OSHA and DOT regulations, accident investigation, sustainability, and making a business case for investing in safety, are just some of the subjects. Moreover the information provided is from the best sources available, as a quick review of the extensive chapter bibliographies will reveal.

We have also included selected papers from the ASSE Professional Development Conference as chapter appendices. The presenters' insights provide additional perspectives and valuable information.

Fleet Safety examines fleet safety from a business perspective as well. In the chapter, "Cost Analysis and Budgeting" Fran Sehn presents loss analysis methods, and analyzes direct and indirect costs of accidents. The chapter by Anthony Veltri and Jim Ramsay in turn discusses how to use that information to demonstrate to management the value of investing in safety. And for a broader and more global perspective, the authors of the chapter on sustainability discuss ISO 26000 and the strategic role OS&H plays in social responsibility. They go on to discuss employee participation in safety and health and two-way communication regarding safety and health.

Ergonomics and vehicle design are presented from an applied perspective. The author, Dennis Andrews, is an expert in biomechanics with over 30 years of experience. Issues related to transit busses as well as trucks are discussed.

Equally important is the chapter on vehicles and accidents, which discusses in-depth vehicle inspections and maintenance, as well as accident investigation procedures. Accident reporting is further discussed Ed Musal in the chapter, "Benchmarking and Performance Criteria"—as "the foundation on which a fleet's benchmarking and performance appraisal system is built... ."

In the final chapter, the authors, Phil Moser, Carmen Daecher, and Amy Stewart, begin their discussion of best practices in fleet safety with risk management of fleet operations and expected outcomes. They then present a ten-step outline for creating a fleet safety initiative. As the authors point out, "Many safety professionals are not familiar with the steps necessary to create a comprehensive fleet safety initiative within their organization." The steps outlined will be valuable to anyone with fleet safety responsibility who wants to better manage the risks of motor-vehicle crashes, which were responsible for 21 percent of all worker fatalities in 2010 according to the Bureau of Labor Statistics.

Introduction

Charlie Halfen

Workplace injuries take a tremendous toll on any organization. Not only are company employees injured and may miss work, the company may also face considerable costs associated with the injury. It has been estimated that employers pay almost $1 billion per week for direct workers' compensation costs alone. Costs include workers' compensation payments, medical and legal expenses, not to mention the indirect costs associated with worker replacement and damage to the organization's reputation. The Bureau of Labor Statistics (BLS) reported that there were 2,976,400 recordable injuries in 2012, resulting in 905,700 days away from work.

Auto crashes still account for the highest number of severe injuries and fatalities in the workplace. According to the "2012 Motor Vehicle Crashes: Overview" published by the U.S. Department of Transportation (DOT), the U.S. lost 33,561 people in crashes on roadways in 2012. Corresponding with the increase in behind-the-wheel distractions, there has been a 3.7 percent increase in the number of people killed in crashes involving large trucks. The BLS also stated in their "Census of Fatal Occupational Injuries Summary, 2012" that transportation incidents accounted for more than 2 out of every 5 (41 percent) fatal work injuries in 2012.

Workplace safety is essential to any organization's success. The successful reduction of injuries and crashes will always begin with management. Management's level of acceptance is the foundation of any successful safety process, and the motivating force for organizing and controlling activities throughout the organization. Management will ultimately determine the success of the safety process of the organization.

Companies should not tolerate unsafe actions in the work area or behind the wheel. By meeting high safety standards, an organization contributes to the well-being of its employees, its company, and the communities it serves.

Steps for creating a fleet safety initiative are discussed in the section "Best Practices" by Phil Moser, Carmen W. Daecher, and Amy Stewart.

MANAGEMENT INVOLVEMENT

For any organization to maintain an injury-free and crash-free workforce, policies and procedures must be defined companywide for management and non-management. Policies should establish the guidelines for how the company and its employees perform in any given situation.

Management should provide the means through which workers develop and confirm their own commitment to health and safety. Written policies must clearly establish procedures and methods that insist on employee involvement by providing visible top management support. Each level of management should be involved through its own allocation of people and resources. Management should be committed to encouraging the most effective safe practices in the workplace and on-road. Commitment must go beyond just discussing safety at the start of every meeting. Management must demonstrate by its actions how safety is a company core value.

In an effective process, management regards worker health and safety as an important value of the organization and applies its commitment to the environmental, health and safety process with as much strength as other organizational commitments. Explicit policies provide the outline for the management of the business. Defined policies are necessary so all company employees possess the same understanding of the philosophies, guidelines, procedures, and methods that shape the company's future.

Investments strategies are reviewed and details discussed in the section, "Basic Economic Analysis and Engineering Economics," written by Anthony Veltri and James D. Ramsay.

Whether management personnel believe in the final policy or not, each has an obligation to carry out the policy for the well-being of the organization. All levels of management should be expected to understand the policy and be able to explain the reasons for the policy. Policies will provide a guide to employees so that their decisions and actions will also reflect the best interests of the company. Like management, all employees must be expected to follow the policies even if they don't agree with them.

Long-term safety commitment to these policies should outline the company vision. Management, with non-management input, should set short-term safety goals for continuous improvement. These short-term accomplishments help the business to achieve its companywide objectives.

Minimum safety standards for a successful organization are based on the personal values, safety skills and knowledge required for both entry-level and experienced employees. Outlined procedures and methods explain how to accomplish those safety standards successfully. Safety training based on the safest and most efficient methods is an ongoing concern.

TRAINING

Training schools, workshops, computer courses, and other programs may be required to meet the needs of all employees. It is the responsibility of the management team to ensure that employees receive all of the necessary training, and that such training is effective in the prevention of injuries and auto crashes. Even though defined responsibilities are assigned to specific individuals, employees should always act as a cooperative team. While any safety training works to some degree, a one-on-one interaction on the safest methods will always be the most productive and meaningful. Through management's support, coaching and counseling, employees should be expected to develop the safety knowledge that is necessary for prevention of injuries and auto collisions.

The many costs associated with driver training are discussed in the section "Cost Analysis and Budgeting," written by Fran Sehn.

Once responsibilities have been established, a thorough review of the results will allow the organization to hold employees accountable for safety performance and compliance. The basic management skill of demonstrating the method and accountability for its performance will always produce the greatest comprehension.

Injury prevention policies and procedures should be communicated plainly and reinforced on a daily basis. Authority and resources must be delegated down to the front line for true accountability. Like management, all employees should have established goals and objectives. Responsibilities should be clearly assigned. The operational methods used in each job position throughout the organization should be adequately analyzed to identify any potential hazards that my cause an injury. Prevention techniques revealed for those potential injuries should then be merged into the current methods. If possible, always try to engineer hazards out of the workplace.

All new and existing employees should then be trained on how to use the safest methods and avoid the occupational hazards associated with their positions. Once trained, employees should be held accountable for their lack of use of these safe methods. Since failure to follow safe work methods will eventually lead to an injury, action must be taken to correct unsafe behavior before an injury occurs.

An organization must also maintain high standards of business conduct to ensure compliance with the applicable laws and regulations in which they operate. The amount of information that must be handled to effectively manage the health and safety of an organization has grown significantly over the last three decades. Increased regulatory activity by state and federal agencies has prompted many organizations to introduce several new internal programs designed to improve safety and reduce cost. No matter the agency, training and accountability are critical for compliance and prevention.

Nancy Bendickson outlines fleet exposure to these varied agencies in her section of this Guide, "OSHA and Other Regulations."

A careless driver takes more chances and is more likely to be involved in an auto crash. They have learned their driving habits through their own experiences or poor training and will continue to take those same chances until they have a significant emotional event (a crash where they accept responsibility), or they receive instructional training to correct their bad methods. Companies can no longer accept the liability that comes with a poor driver. Trainers must have the tools to be successful in training safe driving skills.

The goal of safe driver training and education is to have each individual understand what is needed to prevent an auto crash. While all driver training, whether computer-based, classroom or hands-on, works to some degree, drivers need on-road training. Mental and physical habits, such as driving, cannot be taught in a classroom. Much like any sport, safe driving calls for continuous improvement so even the most experienced drivers need re-training on-road in the safest driving methods.

There are several things every driver should know about the hazards they face behind the wheel. First, distractions are the number one cause of all crashes. Driving requires the driver's undivided attention from start to finish. In other words, if the driver just pays attention and look for hazards while driving, the chances of having a crash are cut in half. The most common crashes are backing up and hitting stationary objects. A driver should learn how to handle the vehicle, and pay attention even when doing the simplest maneuver, such as parking. The same is true with backing up. No one feels comfortable moving backwards but it's something a driver does every time they drive. Learn to use the mirrors. The most serious injury-producing collisions are at intersections or head-on, rear-ending another vehicle , and hitting pedestrians or cyclists. While any crash can be deadly, these crashes cause the most injuries. With limited resources, organizations should concentrate training in these most dangerous and most common areas.

While on-road safe driving can be started in a classroom, the safe habits that the driver will use will be behind the wheel. Safety rides are used to observe and correct the driver's ability to recognize the hazards faced while driving. A good trainer should take the wheel during this ride and show the student how to keep his or her eyes scanning, recognizing those hazards that may affect the travel path and how to react accordingly. Constructive feedback on the mental and physical driving skills demonstrated by the driver should be given, since there will always be areas of improvement needed.

Managers and supervisors should monitor and track unsafe driving behaviors by drivers and follow company policies, including those related to discipline and incentives. Managers and supervisors must also "Walk the Talk" by regularly communicating and demonstrating their commitment to safe driving. An employee will never be accountable to follow the safe methods by an immediate supervisor who does not follow those same methods.

Every commercial motor vehicle is subject to the laws and regulations of the jurisdiction in which it is operated. The Department of Transportation (DOT), through the Federal Motor Carrier Safety Administration (FMCSA), continues to hold motor carriers responsible for driver behavior and job performance.

Gregory L. Smith details the history and focus of this agency in his section of the Guide, "DOT Regulations."

The Compliance, Safety, Accountability (CSA) initiative is the FMCSA enforcement and compliance program used to reduce vehicle crashes, injuries, and fatalities. The program leverages the use of technology by using safety performance data collected during roadside stops and through crash reports to identify unsafe carriers and drivers and to identify safety performance problems. Within the CSA, the Safety Measurement System (SMS) quantifies the on-road performance of carriers and drivers to identify candidates for intervention, determine the specific safety problems exhibited, and to monitor whether safety concerns are improving. The SMS uses a motor carrier's data from roadside inspections, including all safety-based violations, state-reported crashes, and the federal motor carrier census to quantify performance in Seven Behavior Analysis and Safety Improvement Categories (BASICs).

HIRING GUIDELINES

Along with the implementation of safe work and driving methods, it is also important to provide hiring personnel with guidance on how best to attract, screen, and qualify applicants who are most likely to adhere to company safety policies. Organizations should develop a job description for every position. Individual employees should be assigned roles that will establish hiring compliance with the company safety procedures. Ongoing training will ensure that these hiring officials can be held accountable in their role and have the current knowledge, training, and experience regarding essential job requirements.

With fleets, creating a safe driving workforce starts at the front door. Crash history is one of the stronger predictors of future crashes. Past behavior almost always predicts future behavior. If you hire a bad driver, you have a bad driver. Hoping they'll get better doesn't work. A bad driver will always be a bad driver unless they have a significant emotional event, such as a crash, or they get significant constructive training to overcome years of poor driving habits.

As pointed out in Dennis R. Andrews' section of this manual, "Vehicle Engineering and Ergonomics," training begins with the CDL application.

A company orientation should be held for all new employees on the first day of employment. Expectations and accountability must be established from the beginning. New employees that are left to learn from fellow employees will pick up bad habits that are hard to break. Even though it may be very time consuming for management, that initial one-on-one interaction with the new employee will pay off with future accountability. Any job training should include hands-on demonstrations.

EMPLOYEE PARTICIPATION

With training tools in hand, employee participation should now be developed throughout the organization. This participation outlines employee responsibility and ensures involvement in safety awareness activities. Recognition and appreciation should be given where due to all employees for safety accomplishments.

One of the most important responsibilities of management is the development of the employees. Every employee must be fully prepared to perform the job assigned. Through training, support, coaching, counseling, and example, employees should be expected to develop the knowledge and skills that are necessary for success in their current job. When the time comes, this education will also help them assume positions of greater responsibility. Employees should be expected to take advantage of the training available throughout the organization. In turn, the company should provide employees with assignments and responsibilities that allow them to demonstrate their skills and develop their capabilities.

Employee involvement is the degree to which employees lead the process. Once clearly defined policies, procedures, and methods are in place, management must be able to shift ownership of the process to those with a vested interest, the employees. Roles and responsibilities are delegated to ensure compliance and involvement. Every employee should know what safe methods are needed to successfully implement the safety policies and procedures. Employees should also learn that the use of an unsafe method, such as not lifting properly or not clearing an intersection, assures a greater chance of having an incident. The ultimate objective for introducing a safety system for the organization is to empower the employees to hold themselves accountable for following the safest methods at all times, giving them total control of their own safety, as well as those around them.

Cooperation and teamwork are necessary among all employees for the continued safety success of any organization. It's important to keep all employees informed about company activities. This will help them to understand company objectives and perform their jobs more efficiently. The most effective way to involve employees in the prevention of workplace injuries and the use of safe driving skills is through their participation in local occupational safety and health (OS&H) committees.

Committees must be organized and maintained as they affect behaviors, attitudes, work processes, compliance, and the general work environment. A companywide safety committee must detail g the roles and responsibilities for each committee member in writing. These OS&H committees should consist of both management and non-management employees, equally sharing their thoughts and recommendations. Committee members are ultimately a conduit to the rest of the workforce.

Through local incident investigation, tracking and analysis, OS&H committees will see patterns and develop solutions for fellow employees. This education process will lead to the use of safer work methods and reduced injuries and crashes. Regulatory compliance will also improve significantly with OS&H committee involvement.

Immediate feedback on the outcome of prevention activities is important. As with any commitment, results matter. To maintain a viable OS&H committee, commitments must be obtainable. Even small, continuous gains should be applauded. A formal plan will lead to improved and sustainable results for the ever-changing committee membership.

There are some necessary traits for those on the OS&H committee. Members must be willing to listen to others. No matter how slight it may appear, every concern is important to some individual and should be addressed. Members must learn and use the safest work and driving practices at all times. Like management, committee members must "Walk the Talk". Leaders lead by example.

There should be an OS&H committee to cover all employees in all locations. Management should always encourage employee suggestions for safety improvements. In working together, employees create an environment of teamwork that will help to reduce injuries and crashes.

More on employee participation can be found in the section of this Guide, "Sustainability and the Safety, Health, and Environmental Professional," written by Kathy A. Seabrook, Robert Stewart, Jeffery Camplin, and Mike Taubitz.

Employees deserve recognition for accomplishments in their regular jobs. They also deserve recognition for the extra effort they make for the safety of their fellow employees. Management is responsible for recognizing the accomplishments of the employees. Recognition programs should be designed to reward and encourage safe behavior. While some employees may be motivated by public recognition or monetary gifts, some may just appreciate acknowledgement from their immediate supervisor or manager.

Organizations should make it a priority to recognize their employees and locations that follow safe work and safe driving methods leading to reductions in injuries and auto crashes. Operations should be allowed to provide recognition when certain group milestones of "safe work days" or "safe driving days" are reached.

Millions of people are licensed to drive on public roads. Some drive often and some drive well, but only a small group drive often and well, and they deserve recognition. The drivers in this group are on the road for many hours a day and never become involved in a crash. Most are professionals and drive accordingly. Accomplishing such driving records is not by chance but only by the continued use of safe driving techniques.

Employee involvement provides the means through which employees develop and express commitment to their own safety as well as those around them. Once personal responsibility has been defined for each employee, OS&H committees have the ability to engage all levels in the safety process. Direct involvement in their own well-being will increase job satisfaction and organizations that give recognition for following safe work and driving methods will see a reduction in injuries and crashes. After all, employees will always be an organization's most valuable assets.

ANALYSIS

Tracking injury, crash, and compliance indices enables the company to be aware of employees' safety performance and compliance with company policies, procedures, and methods. Starting with a baseline, safety performance measurements are required for sustained improvement. Analysis of this tracked information will lead to accountability for the results.

All companies should keep historical loss data, in terms of injuries and crashes. Employees should understand that history will repeat itself unless procedures procedures are developed to prevent a reoccurrence. The most successful organizations are those that have employees help track and analyze their own injury and crash data.

More information on record-keeping systems can be found in Edward Musal's section of this Guide, "Benchmarking and Performance Criteria."

An analysis of the worksite involves several investigation approaches designed to identify and reduce existing hazards that may cause an injury or crash. These approaches include: analysis of data, analysis of job hazards, an audit of the facilities, and investigation of injuries and auto crashes.

Data analysis is a process of scrutinizing the injuries and auto crashes that have occurred in an operation by identifying trends and developing controls for those types of injuries and crashes. Analyzing prior injuries and crashes helps to confirm the preventative measures currently in place. Some of the trends identified may include: injury or crash type; location; equipment used; prior training; job hazards; work process; employee behavior; and time of day. Once trends are identified, specific action plans are developed to address the main sources of injuries and crashes. Data analysis highlights the jobs or tasks that have produced the most injuries or crashes, and may lead to further investigation using a job hazard analysis.

Job hazard analysis (JHA) is a method that breaks specific occupations into their component actions to identify contributions to injuries or crashes. Observation forms based on the current methods should be developed to evaluate employee behavior. These observations, as well as the historical data, are used together in the analysis. By truly defining the specific behavior that causes an injury or crash, companywide procedures may be changed to improve the outcome. Additional observations of the specific component action will determine further steps to decrease unsafe actions. Once refined, the safest and most efficient methods should be formalized and taught to all employees. A review of basic methods may be needed if incidents still occur with the use of safe work and driving methods. In most cases, the analysis will show a failure to follow prescribed safety methods in which case, lack of training or front-line accountability is responsible.

The audit of facilities is a comprehensive examination of all equipment and work locations within a facility. The most effective audits are completed by cross-functional teams with representatives from all different work groups, including both management and non-management. From injury prevention to regulatory compliance, the OS&H committee plays a vital role in comprehensive audits. To ensure ongoing training necessitated by turnover and to avoid complacency, a system of internal auditing is needed. These audits will verify the effectiveness of the company's safety process.

Injury and auto crash investigations identify the underlying causes of injuries and crashes and develop controls to prevent reoccurrence. An effective safety process includes the investigation of "near misses." An injury investigation is the single most effective way to prevent future injuries. Unlike detailed company-injury prevention methods training on the job, driving habits, both good and bad, are set before the driver ever begins work at the company. To reduce risk, the company has an obligation to observe and retrain the new employee in the safest driving methods and any company-specific requirements.

While the DOT has its own definition of what's recordable, companies should set a high standard and demand accountability for any auto incident. The most important aspect of auto crash prevention starts with the company's definition of a "crash.. To eliminate any confusion, I would define the highest standard for an auto crash is as:

"Any occurrence in which a vehicle is in any way involved and which results in personal injury, property damage, or collision no matter how slight and regardless of fault."

Without documenting every incident, any thorough analysis as to cause will never accomplish the ultimate goal of preventing future crashes. To validate a fair and employee-backed recognition process, some discretion must be given to a small percentage of drivers that were using safe driving methods as taught and did everything possible to avoid the crash. Based on the root cause of the incident, the crash may then be judged as "unavoidable." Companies should always maintain high standards and work as hard to eliminate "unavoidable" crashes as they do "avoidable" ones, keeping in mind that almost all crashes can be avoided.

The objective of the investigation is to determine and point out any errors in judgment or driving made by the driver for the purpose of making him or her a better driver and avoiding future similar incidents. A report on prevention should refer back to previous documented training as well as future remedial training that this driver will receive to prevent a reoccurrence. For liability reasons, if remedial training is needed, then it must be completed in a timely manner.

In the event of a serious injury or fatal crash, an organization's standardized report format must be followed to document the investigation of the incident. The purpose of the investigation and report are to: (1) enable company attorneys to render legal advice; (2) provide information to assist company attorneys in anticipation of claims which may arise in connection with the incident; and (3) conduct a self-critical analysis with respect to company policies and procedures.

More information on accident investigation can be found in the "Vehicles and Accidents" section of this Guide, written by Jubal Hammernik and Peter M. Himpsel.

The goal of analyzing the worksite is to see injury and crash trends over time and develop patterns with common causes which can be identified and prevented. The OS&H committee, with management support and counseling, can make excellent use of this approach in overall safety prevention.

To feel the immediate impact of any incident, front-line operations should not only be held accountable for their automotive crash frequencies, they should also experience an immediate, one-time expense charge when any incident occurs. The allocation should be based upon an analysis of the current and prior year's data and projections of actual expenses incurred. This expense should be based on the closed-case historical cost of the specific type of injury or crash. The cost chargeback should be updated regularly to reflect a running expense based on the incident type.

ACCOUNTABILITY

The tracking and analysis of all injury and crash data gives an organization the ability to hold both management and non-management accountable for unsafe performance. With a comprehensive analysis of the tracked information, feedback is accurate and immediate, both which are required to change habits. The most successful results are correlated with management's desire to "Walk the Talk," and hold employees accountable for safety performance. Management must accept responsibility for its own compliance with the safety policies, which can easily be determined by visiting an operation and observing if unsafe behaviors are being corrected by management. Upper-level management may initiate the process of creating a safer workforce but making it a habit requires ongoing support from all levels of management 100 percent of the time. The one-time acceptance of an unsafe act by an employee in front of management will be seen by all employees as a sign of approval.

Like management commitment, employees should also be held accountable for their results. Frequent evaluations should be held with all employees about their safety performance, including the use of safety methods in the building and safe driving skills while behind the wheel. Follow-up evaluations should be conducted to ensure the continued development of a safety culture in the workforce.

The primary cause of all injuries and crashes is employee behavior. When an employee is injured or involved in a crash, in all probability, this is not the first time that the employee has performed the same task in an unsafe manner. In this situation, their unsafe behavior has eventually caused the incident. In all likelihood, management has witnessed this unsafe behavior before and said nothing. Management is partly to blame. Management must eliminate all doubt as to the appropriate safe behaviors.

Once it has been determined that the employee has the skills, knowledge, and ability to work safely, then further training is not the answer. At this time, the employee's behavior must be addressed. Accountability that addresses behaviors instills a culture that will make the employee think about using safe methods on their own when performing the job. It is very easy for management to tell employees that the company pays them not to have injuries, but expecting an employee not to get injured while continuing to use unsafe methods is not realistic. The same is true in taking unnecessary chances while driving. Injuries and crashes will continue until the employee changes unsafe behavior.

Getting an employee to change unsafe behavior can be a challenge to the most experienced management. Taking disciplinary action when an incident occurs may seem the easiest way to address the problem, but it does not solve the underlying issue of not using safe work methods. More incidents will occur. Management should focus on the behavior of the employee and the use of safe methods instead of the eventual outcome when unsafe methods are used. Chances of injury or crash escalate with the increased use of unsafe methods. The vast majority of the time, employees are working safely, and are not involved in an injury or crash. When employees are working safely, positive reinforcement can be a building block to discuss unsafe methods.

Giving an employee positive feedback will always increase the employee's job satisfaction and lead to a renewed organizational commitment. Not only will positive reinforcement make a favorable impact on the reduction of incidents at work but creating a personal safety attitude will reduce incidents at home. The safe driving skills at work are the same at home. A driver who uses safe driving methods will have fewer crashes, both on and off work. On the other hand, an employee who does not wear a seat belt at home will not wear a seat belt at work, thus increasing the chance of injury with any incident.

The majority of employees that do not follow safe methods on a consistent basis to prevent injuries and crashes will improve with one-on-one methods review. A small number of employees will require a more disciplinary approach to correct unsafe habits. The purpose of discipline, is not to punish the employee, but rather focus attention toward achieving improvement in the use of safe work and driving methods. An employee who uses unsafe methods will have more injuries and crashes than an employee who works safely all of the time. To maximize the safety process, everyone in every location should understand that unsafe actions will not be accepted at any time for any reason.

Company safety policies must address progressive disciplinary action through written procedures. The procedures must be focused on how management can take corrective actions to ensure employees comply with injury prevention methods, safe driving skills, and regulatory compliance. A progressive disciplinary policy should include, among other things, written warnings and suspensions that may lead up to termination. Any disciplinary measures should correspond to the risk posed, with violations associated with high-consequence incidents punished more severely. To ensure fairness across the organization, the steadfast use of disciplinary procedures for unsafe methods is necessary.

Accountability for results can be the impetus for change to any organization. Injuries and auto crashes are no longer a cost of doing business; they are a failure of business. While all safety improvement is seen in the bottom line, gains are a direct result of the increased use of injury prevention methods and safe driving skills. Accountability is essential for a safety process to thrive, and to ensure that history does not repeat itself.

The safety of the employees and the general public should always be the highest priority of any organization. Workplace injuries and auto crashes have long been major concerns for most companies. The prevention of incidents has been an ongoing battle for years. Without a comprehensive safety process, injury and crash trends will go up and down over the years with no consistent improvement or solution. While changing entrenched mindsets is not easy, business results will be sustainable once a safety process is implemented within the organization.

ABOUT THE EDITOR AND AUTHORS

Joel M. Haight, Ph.D., PE, CIH, CSP, is Associate Professor of Industrial Engineering, Swanson School of Engineering, University of Pittsburgh. Prior to joining the University of Pittsburgh in 2013, he was Branch Chief of the Human Factors Branch at the Centers for Disease Control and Prevention (CDC). In 2000, Dr. Haight received a faculty appointment and served as Associate Professor of Energy and Mineral Engineering at the Pennsylvania State University. He was employed as an engineer and manager for Chevron, where he worked both domestically and internationally for eighteen years. He received a Ph.D. (1999) and Master's degree (1994) in Industrial and System Engineering from Auburn University.

Dennis R. Andrews, Ph.D., PSP, CECD, WSO-CSS, is Principal of Accident & Safety Consultants. His B.S. and M.S. are in Safety and Health, and his Ph.D. is in Safety Engineering and Injury Biomechanics. He has 30 years' experience, including as an expert witness. He has published books, articles, and taught at universities. He is a Professional member of ASSP.

Nancy J. Bendickson, CSP, CDS, ARM, ALCM, is a Senior Consultant, Casualty Risk Control, with Aon Global Risk Consulting, Minneapolis, MN. She is the fleet safety thought leader for Aon–United States and works with clients to reduce the total cost of risk associated with fleet, general liability, and workers' compensation exposures.

Jeffery C. Camplin, M.S., CSP, CPEA, obtained a Safety degree in Industry and Technology from Northern Illinois University, and a Master's degree in Safety and Emergency Management from Eastern Kentucky University. He is President of Camplin Environmental Services, Inc., a safety and environmental consulting firm he founded in 1991.

Charlie Halfen retired from the United Parcel Service (UPS), where he was Corporate Fleet Safety Manager in charge of accident prevention, crash investigation, and regulatory compliance worldwide. Through his company, CHN Safety, LLC, he consults with organizations on analysis, design, and implementation of prevention activities to reduce auto incidents and insure DOT compliance.

Jubal D. Hamernik, Ph.D., P.E., is President/CEO of Hamernik & Associates, Inc., as well as a nationally qualified expert in many areas of engineering and accident reconstruction.

Peter M. Himpsel, P.E., is a professional engineer with Hamernik & Associates, Inc., and has provided extensive expert testimony regarding engineering and accident reconstruction. He is a member of ASSP, SAE, and the ICC.

Phil Moser is Vice President for Advanced Driver Training Services, Inc. (ADTS) in Trooper, Pennsylvania, and is certified in Pennsylvania courts in the field of accident investigation and reconstruction.

Edward A. Musal, M.A., M.S., CSP, CPEA, is the Environmental Health & Safety Officer for the State University of New York College at Purchase.

James D. Ramsay, Ph.D., M.A., CSP, received his Ph.D. from the University of Wisconsin in 1994 as a joint degree in Preventive Medicine and Industrial Engineering. He is currently the founding chair of the department of security studies and international affairs at Embry-Riddle Aeronautical University in Daytona Beach, Florida. He currently serves on the CDC/NIOSH Board of Scientific Counselors, is an ABET Board member, and the Chair of the ASSP Education Standards Committee. Dr. Ramsay is also the founding president of the International Society for Preparedness, Resilience, and Security.

Kathy A. Seabrook, CSP, CFIOSH (UK), EurOSHM, is president of Global Solutions, Inc., an advisor to the Center for Safety and Health Sustainability, and served on the 2005 and 2012 ANSI Z10 committee, and is the U.S. TAG Vice Chair and U.S. expert for ISO 45001 OHSMS.

Francis P. Sehn, M.S., CSP, ARM, is Vice President–Risk Control and Claims Advocacy for Willis of PA, of Pittsburgh, Pennsylvania. He has over 40 years of experience in providing risk control consulting services to a variety of clients in North America. He specializes in safety and risk management systems to enable clients to reduce the cost of risk.

Gregory L. Smith, CSP, is a principal and co-founder of Vector Risk and Safety, LLC. Greg has more than 30 years of experience in the safety field, working in both construction and general industry environments. He holds both B.S. and M.S. degrees in Industrial Hygiene and Safety from the University of Houston-Clear Lake. He has presented at numerous national, regional and local safety events, and was a contributing author to *Construction Safety Management and Engineering* and *The Safety Professionals Handbook*, both published by ASSP, as well as a variety of safety articles.

Amy Stewart, CSP, has more than 20 years' experience designing, implementing, and conducting safety and training programs. Specializing in transportation, she holds a current, fully endorsed Ohio Commercial Driving License (CDL), and is published with the ASSP among numerous other publications.

Robert R. Stewart, M.S., CIH, CSP, is EHS Director for Oldcastle Architectural Products, Atlanta, GA.

Michael Taubitz, B.S.M.E., M.A., is Secretary for the Michigan Lean Consortium Board of Directors, and provides expert testimony for FDR Safety. He spent 43 years at General Motors, holding a number of engineering, HR, and other positions in the company.

Anthony Veltri is an Associate Professor of environment, safety, and health in the College of Health and Human Sciences at Oregon State University. Dr. Veltri's current research is aimed at making the business case for environment, safety, and health.

Chapter 1

DOT Regulations

Gregory L. Smith

LEARNING OBJECTIVES

- Be able to define the rationale and scope of the Department of Transportation (DOT) Act.

- Describe areas where the DOT Act has cross-jurisdictional impact.

- Be able to interpret the goals of the DOT Act.

- Know how to differentiate between state and federal requirements.

- Be able to formulate strategies for transportation management.

- Estimate the impact of successful and unsuccessful company safety programs.

Before there was a Department of Transportation (DOT), transportation-related safety issues were often dealt with case by case. For example, on August 7, 1789, Congress federalized existing lighthouses built by the colonies and appropriated funds for lighthouses, beacons, and buoys. This was done to support the safety of the shipping industry by establishing a framework to provide continuity of maintenance, repair, and oversight. Shipping, and the rules governing it, grew and expanded throughout the country as expansion and population growth continued. Soon, roads and highways carried a significant portion of raw and finished goods to and from shipping points. Over time, the highway system and the regulations governing its use have grown and evolved significantly, requiring a much more comprehensive management effort than originally initiated. According to President Lyndon Johnson, when he signed the act creating the Department of Transportation on October 16, 1966 (DOT 1966):

> The Act which I sign today is the most important transportation legislation of our lifetime. . . . It is one of the essential building blocks in our preparation for the future. . . . Transportation has truly emerged as a significant part of our national life. As a basic force in our society, its progress must be accelerated so that the quality of our life can be improved.

The diversity of areas requiring oversight mandated a different approach to maintain an appropriate level of competency. This diversity was the impetus behind creating the Department of Transportation (DOT). The signing of this act marked the beginning of the national highway system as we know it today. To address growing needs, separate agencies were created within the DOT. The DOT is currently made up of several agencies with specific missions and responsibilities. Theses agencies are often mirrored by the states to add additional oversight in areas that require attention due to location, population, or other specific needs.

Leadership of the DOT is provided by the Secretary of Transportation, who is the principal adviser to the president in all matters relating to federal transportation programs. The secretary is assisted by the deputy secretary in this role. The Office of the Secretary (OST) oversees the formulation of national transportation policy and promotes intermodal transportation. Other responsibilities include negotiation and implementation of international transportation agreements, assuring the fitness of U.S. airlines and motor carriers, enforcing airline consumer-protection regulations, issuance of regulations to prevent alcohol and illegal drug misuse in transportation systems, and preparing transportation legislation. The following paragraphs describe the various agencies under the DOT banner.

Federal Aviation Administration

The Federal Aviation Administration (FAA) oversees the safety of civil aviation. Programs managed include Safety Hotline (maintenance improprieties, low-flying aircraft, aircraft incidents, and Federal Aviation Regulation (FAR) violations), safety advisories and alerts, data and statistics, the National Transportation Safety Board (NTSB), Security, and Awards.

Federal Railroad Administration

The Federal Railroad Administration (FRA) promotes safe and environmentally sound rail transportation with the responsibility of ensuring railroad safety throughout the nation. FRA's Office of Safety promotes and regulates safety throughout the nation's railroad industry. It employs more than 415 federal safety inspectors, who operate out of eight regional offices across the country. The inspectors specialize in five safety disciplines—hazardous materials, motive power and equipment, operating practices, signal and train control, track and structures, and industrial hygiene—and promote numerous initiatives under the Highway-Rail Grade Crossing and Trespasser Prevention programs.

Federal Transit Administration

The Federal Transit Administration (FTA) assists in developing improved mass-transportation systems for cities and communities nationwide. It currently covers areas including transit safety, emergency management, training and conferences, drugs and alcohol, safety and security, statistics, and publications.

Maritime Administration

The Maritime Administration (MARAD) is the agency within the U.S. Department of Transportation (DOT) that deals with waterborne transportation and ensures the viability of the U.S. Merchant Marine. Its programs promote the use of waterborne transportation and its seamless integration with other segments of the transportation system. The agency works in many areas involving ships and shipping, shipbuilding, port operations, vessel operations, national security, environment, and safety.

MARAD is also charged with maintaining the health of the Merchant Marine, since commercial mariners, vessels,

and intermodal facilities are vital for supporting national security. Thus, the agency provides support and information for current mariners, extensive support for educating future mariners, and programs to educate Americans about the vital role the maritime industry plays in their lives.

The Maritime Administration also maintains a fleet of cargo ships in reserve to provide surge sealift during war and national emergencies, and is responsible for disposing of ships in that fleet, as well as other noncombatant government ships, as they become obsolete.

MARAD recently realigned many of its functions to revitalize its role as an industry facilitator, and to bring greater focus to the areas of environment and safety.

National Highway Traffic Safety Administration

The National Highway Traffic Safety Administration (NHTSA) is responsible for reducing deaths, injuries, and economic losses resulting from motor-vehicle crashes. NHTSA sets and enforces safety performance standards for motor vehicles and equipment, and through grants to state and local governments enables them to conduct effective local highway-safety programs. Some of the areas managed by the NHTSA include aggressive driving, bicycles, child passenger safety, disabled drivers and passengers, drowsy and distracted driving, emergency medical services, enforcement and justice services, impaired driving, motorcycles, new drivers, occupant protection, older drivers, pedestrians, programs/grants, research and evaluation, safety materials catalogs, school buses, traffic tech publications, and the Safe Communities Program.

Pipeline and Hazardous Materials Safety Administration

The Pipeline and Hazardous Materials Safety Administration (PHMSA) oversees the safety of more than 800,000 daily shipments of hazardous materials in the United States and 64 percent of the nation's energy that is transported by pipelines. Areas of focus include training and outreach, special permits, approvals, rulemaking, state and local government partnerships, enforcement, security plans, drug and alcohol programs, and a pipeline-safety program.

Research and Innovative Technology Administration

The Research and Innovative Technology Administration (RITA) coordinates DOT's research programs and is charged with advancing the deployment of cross-cutting technologies to improve our nation's transportation system. RITA leads the DOT in coordinating, facilitating, and reviewing the department's research and development programs and activities; advancing innovative technologies, including intelligent transportation systems; performing comprehensive transportation statistics research, analysis, and reporting; and providing education and training in transportation and transportation-related fields.

Saint Lawrence Seaway Development Corporation

The Saint Lawrence Seaway Development Corporation (SLSDC) is a wholly owned government corporation created to construct, operate, and maintain that part of the St. Lawrence Seaway between the Port of Montreal and Lake Erie, within the territorial limits of the United States. The mission of the SLSDC is to serve the U.S. intermodal and international transportation system by improving the operation and maintenance of a safe, reliable, efficient, and environmentally responsible deep-draft waterway, in cooperation with its Canadian counterpart. The SLSDC also encourages the development of trade through the Great Lakes Seaway System.

Surface Transportation Board

The Surface Transportation Board (STB) is an independent, bipartisan, adjudicatory body organizationally housed within the DOT. It is responsible for the economic regulation of interstate surface transportation, primarily railroads, within the United States. The agency has jurisdiction over railroad rate and service issues and rail-restructuring transactions (mergers, line sales, line construction, and line abandonment); certain trucking-company, moving-van, and noncontiguous ocean shipping-company rate matters; certain intercity passenger-bus-company structure, financial, and operational matters; and rates and services of certain pipelines not regulated by the Federal Energy Regulatory Commission.

Federal Highway Administration

The Federal Highway Administration (FHWA) coordinates highway transportation programs in cooperation with states and other partners to enhance the country's safety, economic vitality, and quality of life, as well as the environment.

REGULATORY RULEMAKING

As federal entities, these agencies follow standard rulemaking processes. To create new regulations or execute revisions to existing regulations, a public notice of proposed rulemaking is published in the *Federal Register*. As an example from the DOT, the FHWA proposed a requirement for the use of high-visibility safety apparel for workers who are working within federal-aid highway right-of-ways. This was posted in the *Federal Register* on April 24, 2006, as a proposed rule. It would require

workers whose duties place them on or in close proximity to a federal-aid highway to wear high-visibility safety apparel.

Each of these agencies has specific agendas and regulatory requirements. It is impossible to give detailed insights into each agency's operations within the scope of this chapter. Specific details, ranging from organizational histories and mission statements to rules and regulations, may be found on the respective agencies' Web sites. Additionally, changes to regulations and the implementation dates for those changes may be found on the Web site by searching for "rulemaking changes" or similar terms. This type of search will deliver a synopsis of reports in chronological order under the heading of the "Rulemaking Management System." The primary agency involved with fleet safety operations, as discussed below, is the Federal Motor Carrier Safety Administration (FMCSA).

Federal Motor Carrier Safety Administration

The FMCSA was established within the DOT on January 1, 2000, pursuant to the Motor Carrier Safety Improvement Act of 1999 (FMCSA 1999). Formerly a part of the FHWA, the FMCSA's primary mission is to prevent commercial motor-vehicle-related fatalities and injuries. The FMCSA focuses heavily on commercial cartage operations, and specifically interstate commerce. The FMCSA Safety and Fitness Electronic Records (SAFER) System offers company safety data and related services to industry and the public over the Internet. Users can search FMCSA databases, register for a USDOT number, pay fines online, order company safety profiles, challenge FMCSA data using the DataQs system, access the Hazardous Material Route registry, obtain National Crash and Out of Service rates for Hazmat Permit Registration, get printable registration forms, and find information about other FMCSA Information Systems. The SAFER system may be accessed at www.safer.fmcsa.dot.gov. The remainder of this chapter will review those areas that commonly come under FMCSA oversight.

APPLICABILITY OF REGULATIONS

Operators of any of the following types of commercial motor vehicles in interstate commerce must comply with the applicable U.S. Department of Transportation (USDOT) safety regulations:

1. A vehicle with a gross vehicle weight rating or gross combination weight rating (whichever is greater) of 4537 kilograms (kg) (10,001 pounds (lb)) or more;

2. A vehicle designed or used to transport between nine and fifteen passengers (including the driver) for compensation;
3. A vehicle designed or used to transport sixteen or more passengers; or
4. Any size vehicle used in the transportation of materials that are considered hazardous under the Hazardous Materials Transportation Act and that require the motor vehicle to be placarded under the hazardous materials regulations.

These regulations include areas concerning commercial driver's licenses (CDLs): controlled substances and alcohol testing for all persons required to possess a CDL; driver qualifications (including medical exams); driving of commercial motor vehicles; parts and accessories necessary for safe operations; hours of service; and inspection, repair, and maintenance.

Pursuant to Title 49 CFR Part 107, Subpart G (§107.601–107.620), certain offerors and transporters of hazardous materials, including hazardous waste, are required to file an additional annual registration statement with the USDOT and to pay a fee.

AREAS OF INTEREST IN REGULATORY COMPLIANCE

Interstate Commerce

Interstate commerce is defined as *trade, traffic, or transportation involving the crossing of a state boundary.* Either the vehicle, its passengers, or its cargo must cross a state boundary, or the intent to cross a state boundary must exist in order for an activity to be considered interstate commerce. *Intrastate* commerce is *trade, traffic, or transportation within a single state.* Operations that include interstate commerce in addition to intrastate commerce must comply with applicable federal safety regulations and operating-authority rules in addition to state and local requirements. The state in which a vehicle is registered must be notified of the intention to operate it in interstate commerce to ensure that the vehicle is properly registered for purposes of the International Registration Plan (IRP), and International Fuel Tax Agreement (IFTA). The base state collects the appropriate fees and distributes a portion of those fees to the other states in which the commercial motor vehicle operates.

Intrastate Commerce

Companies that operate exclusively in intrastate commerce must comply with applicable state and local regulations. The only federal regulations that are applicable to intrastate operations are the commercial driver's license (CDL) for drivers operating commercial motor vehicles as defined in 49 CFR 383.5; controlled substances and alcohol testing for all persons required to possess a CDL; and minimum levels of financial responsibility for the intrastate transportation of certain quantities of hazardous materials and substances.

A USDOT number is required for vehicles over 10,000 lb if they are transporting between nine and fifteen passengers (including the driver) for compensation, if they are transporting sixteen or more passengers, or if they are hauling hazardous materials in interstate commerce. No fee is required. Carriers must complete the MCS-150, Motor Carrier Identification Report (FMCSA 2007), to obtain a USDOT number. The MCS-150 can be completed online or copies can be printed, completed, and mailed to the address indicated.

For-Hire Carrier

A *for-hire carrier* is a person or company that provides transportation of cargo or passengers for compensation. In addition to the USDOT number, for-hire carriers must obtain an operating authority [motor carrier (MC) number]. Generally, for-hire motor carriers of regulated commodities or passengers in interstate commerce must also obtain an interstate operating-authority (MC) number unless the operation is limited to the transportation of exempt commodities or is within a commercial zone that is exempt from the interstate operating-authority rules. Information about commercial-zone exemptions is in 49 CFR 372. Administrative Ruling No. 119 (FMCSA n.d. a). A list of commodities that are not exempt from the operating-authority rules can be found in 49 CFR 372.115. Both are also available online at the FMCSA's Web site (www.fmcsa.dot.gov).

Form OP-1, Application for Motor Property Carrier and Broker Authority (FMCSA 2013e), is required for a motor carrier of property. Form OP-1(P), Application for Motor Passenger Carrier Authority (FMCSA 2013d) is a proposed revision of the form designed to enhance safety for nondomestic carriers. Part of Section V (Safety Certifications) is the acknowledgment that the applicant will "maintain current copies of all U.S. DOT Federal Motor Carrier Safety Regulations, Federal Motor Vehicle Safety Standards, and the Hazardous Materials Regulations (if a property carrier transporting hazardous materials), *understands and will comply* with such Regulations, and has ensured that all company personnel are aware of the current requirements. . . ." An Application for Motor Passenger Carrier Authority is required for motor carriers of passengers.

For-hire carriers must have an operating-authority (MC) number. Carriers must (1) complete and file the appropriate OP-1 application along with the filing fee for each type of authority requested; (2) have their insurance company file the appropriate insurance forms for the type of authority requested with the FMCSA; and (3) submit or have a process-agent service submit a BOC-3, Designation of Process Agent form (FMCSA 2013a). (A *process agent* is a representative upon whom court papers may be served in any proceeding brought against a motor carrier, and creating this designation is one of the prelicensing requirements that must be met by the carrier before authority is issued.)

Passenger carriers who are Federal Transit Administration Grantees (Transit Benefit Operators) under 49 U.S.C. 5307, 5310, or 5311 are required to maintain liability insurance at least as high as the highest level required for any of the states in which the transit service is located. This is to ensure that both parties are protected in the event of an accident or incident. The filing fee is waived for the Transit Benefit Operator application. To travel within the United States as a for-hire motor carrier, a carrier must file for an operating authority (active MC number). The appropriate OP-1 application may be completed online at www.safer. fmcsa.dot.gov, and the required filing fee can be paid with a credit card; a copy of the application form can be downloaded from the DOT Web site, or a copy of the OP-1 application can be requested and an application will be mailed. A filing fee is currently required for each type of authority requested. No insurance information can be submitted until the carrier has been assigned its MC number.

Once the application is received and accepted, the MC number will be assigned. The applicant will receive a letter stating the MC number and detailing any additional information needed to achieve compliance. Once the carrier's insurance company has filed the correct insurance form and the process agent has filed Form BOC-3 (Designation of Process Agent), the official operating authority in the form of a certificate and/or permit will be issued (FMCSA 2013a). Operating a carrier is not permitted until this information has been submitted and the certificate and/or permit is officially issued. Leasing of services to a for-hire carrier with a valid number is permissible if there is full compliance with the requirements under Section 376.11.

The regulations currently state that if a company operates as both for-hire and private carriage, once the USDOT number is issued, the carrier may operate as a private motor carrier. Operation as a for-hire motor carrier is not permitted, however, until an operating authority (an active MC number) is issued.

Exempt and Regulated Commodities

If a company transports exempt commodities and possesses a USDOT number, it is permitted to operate as an exempt for-hire interstate motor carrier without an MC number.

Transport of regulated commodities in interstate commerce prior to having obtained operating authority (certificate and/or permit) and received the single-state registration is not allowed. Simply applying for operating authority is not sufficient; the certificate and/or permit must be issued.

Administrative Ruling No. 119 is a guide to what is and is not exempt (FMCSA n.d. a). The booklet is no longer in print, but the information is still correct. The list of exempt commodities changes frequently, but this booklet can be used as a general guide. Also, a list of commodities that are not exempt can be found in the FMCSR in section 372.115.

OPERATING-AUTHORITY ISSUANCE

To check whether operating authority has been issued, carriers can visit www.li-public.fmcsa.dot.gov. There is also a 24-hour automated phone verification system. FMCSA will fax the operating authority only if ten or more working days have passed since the service date and the operating authority has not yet been received. Once the operating authority has been issued, the regulations do not allow for its voluntary suspension; however, voluntary revocation of the operating authority is allowed. To accomplish a voluntary revocation, a carrier must (1) complete Form OCE-46, Request for Revocation of Registration (FMCSA n.d. b); (2) have it notarized; and (3) mail it back to the FMCSA. Upon receipt of the form, the information will be coded into the system. The date coding occurs is when the operating authority will be voluntarily revoked.

A carrier can reinstate an operating authority by requesting reinstatement of the authority and paying a fee. This can be done online at www.safer.fmcsa.dot.gov and paid for with a credit card. A carrier can also request reinstatement of the operating authority by mailing the MC number and the legal name of the carrier along with payment of the fee by check, money order, or credit card payable to FMCSA. The carrier's insurance company must file the BMC-91 (FMCSA n.d. c) or 91X (FMCSA n.d. d) and/or BMC-34 (FMCSA n.d. e), if necessary, to meet the proof-of-insurance requirement. A valid Designation of Process Agents (BOC-3) filing must also be in effect (FMCSA 2013a). The operating authority will not be reactivated until updated insurance filings have been received and accepted. The carrier will receive a reinstatement notification from the FMCSA after the operating authority has been reinstated. To validate the reinstatement or to validate any carrier's number, check the Web site under Carrier Search. There is also a 24-hour automated system.

Common, Contract, and Broker Authority

Common carriers provide for-hire truck transportation to the general public. Common carriers must file both liability (bodily injury and property damage—BI & PD) insurance and cargo insurance. *Contract carriers* provide for-hire truck transportation to specific individual shippers based on contracts. Contract carriers must file only BI & PD insurance. A *broker* is a company that, for compensation, arranges for truck transportation of cargo belonging to others using for-hire carriers to provide the actual transportation. Brokers must file either a *surety bond* or a *trust fund agreement*. A contract carrier cannot broker loads without first applying for and receiving a license to operate as a broker of freight.

Common Carrier Authority

A common carrier of property must file Form OP-1, Application for Motor Property Carrier and Broker Authority (FMCSA 2013e), and a common carrier of passengers must file Form OP-1(P), Application for Motor Passenger Carrier Authority (FMCSA 2013d). Carriers can file for operating authority online or can download a copy of the application forms. They may also call 1-800-832-5660 and request that an application be mailed or faxed.

Carriers are also required to file an MCS-150, Motor Carrier Identification Report (FMCSA 2007), to obtain a USDOT number. Carriers can file for the USDOT number online or call the toll-free number and request that the form be mailed or faxed. Form OP-1(P), Application for Motor Passenger Carrier Authority (FMCSA 2013d), is required for passenger authority. This reflects more stringent rules that are in effect for the transportation of personnel. Carriers can file for this authority or download a copy of the application online. They can also call the toll-free number and request that a copy be mailed or faxed.

Transfer of Operating Authority (MC Number) and USDOT Numbers

It is important to maintain an information chain to track training and liability issues. This information can be lost if proper transfer protocols are not followed. Transfer

applications can be faxed directly. A transfer application can also be requested via phone or mail.

USDOT numbers are not transferable. Carriers can file for a USDOT number online or call to request a copy of the MCS-150, Motor Carrier Identification Report (FMCSA 2007). If transporting regulated property from one state to another, for-hire carriers are required to have both a USDOT number (MCS-150) and an operating authority (active MC number, OP-1).

Brokers

To become a broker, one must file Form OP-1, Application for Motor Property Carrier and Broker Authority (FMCSA 2013c). This operating authority requires an entity to have on file with the FMCSA either a surety bond (BMC-84 form provided by an insurance company) or a trust fund. A BMC-85 form (FMCSA 2013b) may be obtained by request to the Insurance Compliance Division at FMCSA, as well as a Designation of Agents Form BOC-3 (FMCSA 2013a). It is important to ensure that the broker is a valid entity to maintain proper liability for shipment safety.

Freight Forwarders

A *freight forwarder* is a company that arranges for the truck transportation of cargo belonging to others, using for-hire carriers to provide the actual truck transportation. In the ordinary course of its business, a freight forwarder usually assembles and consolidates less-than-truckload (LTL) shipments at their origin and disassembles and distributes truckload (TL) shipments at their destination. The freight forwarder assumes responsibility, including responsibility for some safety issues, for the transportation from origin to destination, but it uses a for-hire carrier for the line-haul movement. Freight forwarders must register with the FMCSA by filing Form OP-1(FF), Application for Freight Forwarder Authority (FMCSA 2013c). This authority can be applied for or downloaded online or obtained by calling the toll-free number and requesting that a copy be mailed or faxed.

APPORTIONED TAGS

License plates and stickers are state matters. Companies can contact their state department of motor vehicles for requirements but must ensure that registrations and safety inspections are current prior to allowing movement. The correct department can usually be located on the Internet home page of the state government where licensing is desired.

INFORMATION CHANGES FOR MOTOR CARRIER OPERATIONS

Current information is important in the event of an accident or incident requiring notification of management. There are separate filing procedures for changing a carrier's name with or without a change in the ownership, management, or control of the company. There is a fee for a name change. If there is a change in ownership, management, or control of the company, a transfer application must be filed.

A company wishing to change its legal or trade name must send a letter to the FMCSA along with a check or money order. The letter must contain the current name, the new name, and a statement that there is no change in ownership, control, or management of the company. If the company is incorporated, it must send a copy of its articles of incorporation with the letter. A copy of the letter should be kept on file for verification of safety training for employees who worked under the former company name.

Some requests for name changes can be processed online, but they require additional documents for verification:

1. If an immediate family member is added or deleted, a notarized letter must be presented in order for the change to become effective. (*Immediate family member* means husband, wife, brother, sister, mother, or father.)
2. If a name is to be deleted from the operating authority because of the death of a spouse or a partner already on the operating authority, a copy of the death certificate is required.
3. If a partner is being added as a result of marriage, a copy of the marriage license must be presented.
4. If a partner currently on the operating authority is being deleted, a notarized letter from the partner being removed must be presented.

After a carrier receives a re-entitlement decision, it has a 30-day window to refile the proof of insurance and designation of agents (BOC-3) in its new name (FMCSA 2013a). Upon completion, the name will be changed on the MC number and USDOT number.

Address changes can be made online. A letter to the FMCSA Licensing Division will also be accepted. The letter must reference the MC number and include former and current addresses and telephone numbers and be signed by the applicant or applicant's representative. The address change will be updated for both the MC number and the USDOT number. No fee is currently required.

If a name change is executed, the company keeps its MC number. However, instead of receiving a new certificate or permit, it will receive a re-entitlement decision that should be attached to the original operating authority.

A USDOT number may be updated by filing an MCS-150, Motor Carrier Identification Report (FMCSA 2007). Carriers that update online need a personal identification number (PIN) and can apply for it online. The USDOT record may also be updated by filing an MCS-150 by mail. The carrier should make all necessary changes on the form and mark it "update." MCS-150 forms may be obtained by calling the toll-free number and requesting that a copy be mailed.

INSURANCE REQUIREMENTS

To apply for common carrier authority, carriers must have on file evidence of both BI & PD and cargo insurance. This requirement promotes a greater attention to safety issues because insurance costs are directly related to recorded incidents. To apply for contract authority, carriers are required only to have evidence of BI & PD insurance on file. Common carriers hauling low-value goods (49 CFR 387.301(b)) may request exemption from cargo-insurance requirements by requesting a cargo-exemption form. The forms BMC-91 (FMCSA n.d. c) and BMC-91X (FMCSA n.d. d) are both used to make liability insurance filings with the FMCSA. The insurance company making the filing maintains its own supply of forms. In fact, many insurance carriers are set up to make the required insurance filings electronically.

COMPLIANCE, SAFETY, AND ACCOUNTABILITY (CSA)

In December 2010, FMCSA rolled out a new safety program called Compliance, Safety, and Accountability (CSA). The purpose of the program is to identify high-risk motor companies and drivers, then deploy a range of corrective interventions to address specific safety concerns. The centerpiece of the program is the safety measurement system (SMS), which analyzes all safety-based violations from inspections and crash data to determine a commercial motor carrier's potential for unsafe outcomes during operations.

The system quantifies the on-road safety performance of both carriers and drivers to identify candidates for interventions, determines the specific safety problems that a carrier or driver exhibits, and monitors whether safety problems are improving or worsening. SMS has replaced SafeStat as the new review, assessment, and action process.

The data from roadside inspections, including all safety-based violations, state-reported crashes, and the federal motor carrier census is used to quantify performance in seven Behavior Analysis and Safety Improvement Categories (BASICs). These categories are:

1. **Unsafe Driving:** *Example violations:* Speeding, reckless driving, improper lane change, and inattention (FMCSR Parts 392 and 397).
2. **Hours-of-Service (HOS) Compliance:** *Example violations:* HOS RODS, and operating a CMV while ill or fatigued (FMCSR Parts 392 and 395).
3. **Driver Fitness:** *Example violations:* Failure to have a valid and appropriate commercial driver's license (CDL) and being medically unqualified to operate a CMV (FMCSR Parts 383 and 391).
4. **Controlled Substances/Alcohol**: Operation of CMVs by drivers who are impaired due to alcohol, illegal drugs, and misuse of prescription or over-the-counter medications. *Example violations:* Use or possession of controlled substances/alcohol (FMCSR Parts 382 and 392).
5. **Vehicle Maintenance:** *Example violations:* Brakes, lights, and other mechanical defects, failure to make required repairs, and improper load securement (FMCSR Parts 392, 393 and 396).
6. **Hazardous Materials (HM) Compliance:** *Example violations:* Release of HM from package, no shipping papers (carrier), and no placards/markings when required (FMCSR Part 397 and Hazardous Materials Regulations Parts 171, 172, 173, 177, 178, 179, and 180).
7. **Crash Indicator:** Histories or patterns of high crash involvement, including frequency and severity based on state-reported crash information.

Once a categorization is conducted, a carrier's measurement for each BASIC will depend on the following:

- The number of adverse safety events (violations related to the BASIC, or crashes)
- The severity of violations or crashes
- Timing of the adverse safety events (more recent events are weighted more heavily as being indicative of current trends)

After a measurement is determined, the carrier is then placed in a peer group (e.g., carriers with similar numbers of inspections). Percentiles from 0 to 100 are then determined by comparing the BASIC measurements of the carrier to the measurements of other carriers in the peer group. A percentile of 100 indicates the worst performance record. Many companies have similar internal programs to rate performance but may lack the benchmarking component of the peer group (FMCSA 2014).

CONCLUSION

The regulation of safety in transportation, as in other areas, is constantly changing. Companies should keep in mind that, regardless of the number and scope of regulations governing a subject, regulations are *de facto* minimums. There is no substitute for proactive pursuit of safety by the personnel involved in the tasks, the safety department as a real-time resource, and full support and commitment by all levels of management.

REFERENCES

Department of Transportation (DOT). 1996. Department of Transportation Act. P.L. 89-670, U.S.C. 1651–1659 (October 15, 1996).

Federal Motor Carrier Safety Administration (FMCSA).

_____. n.d. a. Administrative Ruling 119, *Composite Commodity List* (accessed September 12, 2014). www.fmcsa.dot.gov/administrative.pdf

_____. n.d. b. Form OCE-46, Request for Revocation of Registration.

_____. n.d. c. BMC-91, Motor Carrier Bodily Injury and Property Damage Liability Certificate of Insurance.

_____. n.d. d. BMC-91X, Motor Carrier Bodily Injury and Property Damage Liability Certificate of Insurance.

_____. 1971. Transportation of Hazardous Materials; Driving and Parking Rules. Regulations, 49 CFR Subtitle B, Chapter III, subchapter B, Sections 397.1–397.225. Uniform Safety Act. 49 U.S.C. 5101 et seq.

_____. 1999. Motor Carrier Safety Improvement Act of 1999. P. L. 106–159, 113 Stat. 1748 (December 9, 1999).

_____. 2007. MCS 150, Motor Carrier Identification Report. www.fmcsa.dot.gov/documents/forms/r-1/MCS-150-Instructions-and-Form.pdf

_____. 2010. Compliance, Safety, Accountability. www.csa.fmcsa.dot.gov/Documents/GeneralFactSheet.pdf

_____. 2013a Form BOC-3, Designation of Process Agents—Motor Carriers, Brokers and Freight Forwarders. www.fmcsa.gov/documents/Form-BOC-3-508.pdf.

_____. 2013b. Form BMC-85, Broker's or Freight Forwarder's Trust Fund Agreement Under 49 USC 13906 *or* Notice of Cancellation of the Agreement. www.fmcsa.gov/documents/forms/r-1/BMC-85-10-1.pdf

_____. 2013c. Form OP-1(FF), Application for Freight Forwarder Authority. www.documents/forms/r-1/op-1-ff.pdf

_____. 2013d. Form OP-1(P), Application for Motor Passenger Carrier Authority. www.documents/forms/r-1/OP-1(P).pdf

_____. 2013e. Form OP-1, Application for Motor Property Carrier and Broker Authority. www.documents/forms/r-1/op-1.pdf

RECOMMENDED RESOURCES

Federal Aviation Administration (www.faa.gov)
Federal Railroad Administration (www.fra.dot.gov)
Federal Transit Administration (www.fta.dot.gov)
Maritime Administration (www.marad.dot.gov)
National Highway Traffic Safety Administration
   (www.nhtsa.dot.gov)
Pipeline and Hazardous Materials Safety Administration
   (www.phmsa.dot.gov)
Research and Innovative Technology Administration
   (www.rita.dot.gov)

Saint Lawrence Seaway Development Corporation
   (www.seaway.dot.gov)
Surface Transportation Board Federal Highway
   Administration (www.stb.dot.gov)

ADDITIONAL READING

DOT COMPLIANCE AND AUTO SAFETY*

Charlie Halfen
CNH Safety, LLC
UPS Fleet Safety Manager (retired)
Austin, TX

Introduction

No matter the size of your fleet, you must have safety processes in place to ensure a reduction of on-road risk. Minimum safety standards for a successful fleet are based on the personal values, safety skills and knowledge required for both entry-level and experienced motor vehicle operators.

For a carrier to maintain a safe on-road fleet, policies and procedures must be defined companywide for management and non-management. Policies should establish the guidelines for how motor carriers and their employees behave in any given situation. Management commitment and employee involvement must be complementary. In an effective process, management regards worker health and safety as a fundamental value of the organization and applies its commitment to the health and safety process with as much vigor as to other organizational purposes. Management should provide the means through which workers develop and express their own commitment to health and safety. Written policies must also clearly establish procedures that insist on employee involvement by providing visible top management support. All levels of leadership should be involved through the allocation of people and resources.

Outlined procedures explain how to accomplish those policies successfully. Communication of these policies and procedures should outline a motor carrier's commitment so that everyone understands the expectations. Individual personnel will be assigned roles and responsibilities that will establish compliance with the company procedures. Subject matter training will then give personnel the adequate skills and knowledge to perform their assigned role. Once training has taken place and responsibilities have been established, then tracking results will enable the carrier to be aware of their employees' safety performance and compliance with its policies and procedures. With results in hand, the motor carrier now can take action to maintain or improve their employee's behavior, whether by positive reinforcement or disciplinary action led by refresher training.

Taken together, the Safety Management Processes, as outlined by the Federal Motor Carrier Safety Administration (FMCSA), help to provide a framework for motor carriers to identify and correct breakdowns or safety compliance issues before or after they have occurred. This framework can be applied to all of the seven Behavior Analysis and Safety Improvement Categories (BASICs): Unsafe Driving, Hours-of-Service Compliance, Driver Fitness, Controlled

Substances/Alcohol, Vehicle Maintenance, Hazardous Materials Compliance, and Crash Indicator.

Driver Selection

Prior to the implementation of these company processes, we must start with the initial selection of new employees, our future drivers. Creating a safe driving workforce starts at the front door. If you hire a bad driver, you have a bad driver. Hoping they'll get better doesn't work. A bad driver will always be a bad driver unless they have the significant emotional event, *the crash,* or they get significant constructive training to overcome years of poor driving habits. A safe workforce starts with the application.

It is important to provide hiring personnel with guidance on how best to attract, screen, and qualify applicants who are most likely to adhere to driver fitness regulations and company safety policies. Carriers should develop a job description for each position that requires driving. Individual employees should be assigned roles that will establish hiring compliance with the company safety procedures. Ongoing training will ensure that these hiring officials can be held accountable in their role and have the current knowledge, training, and experience regarding driver fitness regulations, both interstate and intrastate. I have listed some of the regulations below that require employment compliance with federal DOT regulations.

General qualifications of drivers (391.11)

A person shall not drive a commercial motor vehicle unless they:

- are at least 21 years old,
- can read and speak English sufficiently,
- can operate the vehicle safely,
- are physically qualified,
- have a current driver's license
- have furnished the carrier with a list of convicted traffic violations
- have successfully completed a road test

Application for employment (391.21)

Employment applications should capture all of the safety information that is required by the Federal Motor Carrier Safety Regulations (FMCSRs). That would include 3 years of history pertaining to employers and previous crashes and violations. For drivers applying for a Commercial Drivers License (CDL) position, applicants must supply 10 years of employment history. Review and evaluate gaps in employment and frequent job changes. The applicant must sign the application to certify that all of the information is true.

Investigation and Inquiries (391.23)

Carriers must request a Motor Vehicle Record (MVR) from each state where the applicant held a license during the preceding 3 years. A copy of the MVR must be placed in the Driver Qualification File (DQF). Carriers must also investigate the 3 year safety performance history of applicants for CDL positions. The results of the investigation must be placed in the Driver Investigation History File (DIHF).

The FMCSA has a program that helps motor carriers make more informed hiring decisions by providing electronic access to a driver's crash and inspection history. Pre-Employment Screening Program (PSP) records are available for commercial drivers and persons conducting pre-employment screening services for the motor carrier industry.

Prospective DOT regulated employers must investigate the required alcohol and substance testing and verify that applicants for safety-sensitive positions do not have a current controlled substance and/or alcohol problem by querying them and checking with their employers over the previous 3 years regarding controlled substance and alcohol violations, related background, conditions and behaviors indicative of controlled substance and/or alcohol abuse or misuse, and by conducting pre-employment testing as required by regulation and company policy. Create a detailed written record of each inquiry.

Pre-Employment Testing (382.301)

Prior to the first time a driver performs safety-sensitive functions (CDL), the driver shall undergo testing for controlled substances.

Road Test (391.31)

The road test assures the carrier that the driver can physically and safely operate a company vehicle. No person shall drive a commercial motor vehicle unless they have successfully completed a road test given by the carrier and has been issued a Certificate of Driver's Road Test. The road test should be signed by the person who gave it and if it is successfully completed then the Certificate should be completed and a copy given to the driver tested. The original road test and the original Certificate of Road Test must be kept in the driver's Driver Qualification File (DQF).

Equivalent of Road Test (391.33)

A motor carrier may accept a valid Commercial Driver's License (CDL) or a copy of a Certificate of Driver's Road Test completed within the last 3 years in place of the carrier's road test. If the carrier accepts the CDL or Certificate, then a copy of the CDL or Certificate must be kept in the driver's DQF. A carrier may always require a road test as a condition of employment.

Physical Qualifications for Drivers (391.41)

A person must not operate a commercial motor vehicle unless they are medically certified as physically qualified to do so. Once certified, they must have their current medical examiner's certificate on their person while on-duty.

Driver Investigation History File (DIHF) (391.53)

Carriers should ensure that prospective drivers will drive safely by querying applicants, checking with previous employers and references, and obtaining necessary documents regarding the drivers' safety performance going back three years. Detailed written records of each inquiry relating to the investigation into the safety performance history of prospective drivers for hiring decisions should be maintained in a secure location with limited and controlled access for as long as the driver is employed and for 3 years thereafter. The file must include:

- The driver's written authorization for the carrier to seek information about the driver's alcohol and controlled substance history
- Investigative responses received from previous employers or documentation that the carrier made good faith efforts to contact them.

Unsafe Driving

The FMCSA continues to hold motor carriers responsible for the job performance of those who work for them. Therefore, motor carriers are held accountable for their employees' poor driving.

Applicable Operating Rules (392.2)

Every Commercial Motor Vehicle (CMV) must be operated in accordance with the laws, ordinances and regulations of the jurisdiction in which it is operated. Speeding is a highly cited violation.

Use of Seat Belts (392.16)

A commercial motor vehicle which has a seat belt assembly installed at the driver's seat shall not be driven unless the driver is properly restrained. Failing to wear a seat belt is a very common violation.

Prohibition Against Texting (392.80)

No driver shall engage in texting while driving and no motor carrier shall allow or require its drivers to engage in texting while driving. While texting is a major driver distraction, something so simple as talking to passengers can divert a driver's attention from the task of operating a motor vehicle. Remember, driving needs your undivided attention. The consequences are not worth the risk.

Using a hand-held mobile telephone (392.82)

No driver shall use a hand-held mobile telephone while driving a CMV and no motor carrier shall allow or require its drivers to use a hand-held mobile telephone while driving. Like the prohibition on texting, mobile phones may not be used while stopped in traffic.

While on-road safe driving can be started in a classroom, the safe habits that the driver will use for life will be set behind-the-wheel. Safety rides are used to observe and correct the driver's ability to recognize the hazards they face while driving. A good trainer should take the wheel during this ride and show the student how to keep their eyes scanning, recognizing those hazards that may affect their travel path and how to react accordingly. Constructive feedback should be used on the mental and physical driving skills demonstrated by the driver since there will always be areas of improvement noted.

Getting employees involved in their own safety is critical. Safety committees should be developed and maintained since they can affect behaviors, attitudes, work processes, compliance, and the general work environment. A safety committee process should be outlined in detail as to how people at all levels can work together to make improvements for the good of their fellow employees. Daily, weekly and monthly commitments by safety committees should be outlined in writing for all to see. Immediate feedback on prevention activities with their results is important. As with any commitment, results matter. To maintain this process, commitments must be obtainable.

HOS Fatigued Driving

Hours of Service (HOS) regulations were developed to get tired drivers off the road before serious accidents could occur. These rules apply to those carriers with vehicles that have a gross vehicle weight of over 10,000 pounds or transport hazardous materials that require placarding. Both employers and drivers have an obligation to comply. The roles and responsibilities of all personnel as they pertain to HOS policies and procedures should be reviewed in new-hire, initial and refresher training.

Rest Breaks (395.3(a)(3)(ii))

After June 30, 2013, driving is not permitted if more than 8 hours have passed since the end of the driver's last off duty.

All drivers should be trained on the hours of service requirements and how to maintain a complete, legible, and accurate driver's daily log or how to enter data into electronic on-board recording system and perform all necessary calculations. Managers and dispatchers should be held responsible for reviewing the driver's Record of Duty Status (RODS) for accuracy and making sure that all RODS are collected and stored per regulations. Disciplinary measures, if needed, should focus on taking corrective action to ensure all personnel comply with hours of service regulations.

Driver Fitness

Motor carriers are required by law to use qualified drivers to move their passengers and goods. It is also in the best interest of the carrier since a safe, dependable driver can be their top asset.

Annual Inquiry and Review of Driving Record (391.25)

Carriers must, at least every 12 months, make an inquiry to the appropriate state agency to obtain the MVR for each employee that drives one of their vehicles. A note is required naming the person who reviewed the MVR. A copy of the new MVR and the review note must be kept in the DQF.

Record of violations (391.27)

Carriers must, at least every 12 months, require employees that drive one of their vehicles to furnish it with a list or certification of convictions of motor vehicle traffic laws for the preceding 12 months. A copy of this list or certification should be kept in the DQF.

Roles and responsibilities of managers and supervisors must be outlined for providing training and maintaining safe driving qualifications for all drivers. Serious consideration should be given to violations such as speeding, reckless driving, operating under the influence of alcohol or drugs, or any indication that the driver has disregarded the safety of the general public.

Controlled Substances/Alcohol

Drugs and Other Substances (392.4)

No driver shall be on duty and possess, be under the influence of, or use, any regulated controlled substance.

Alcohol Prohibition (392.5)

No driver shall use alcohol or be under the influence of alcohol within 4 hours before going on duty or operating a CMV.

Carriers must develop a written company policy incorporating all regulations regarding controlled substances and alcohol use, testing, training, and records retention for all employees. Personnel in safety-sensitive positions should receive the required training on the importance of responsible lifestyle behaviors and personal choices regarding controlled substance and alcohol use.

Vehicle Maintenance

A carrier's inspection and maintenance programs are critical to a carrier's on-road safety process. Vehicle maintenance helps to prevent crashes caused by vehicle deficiencies. Worn, failed or incorrectly adjusted components can cause or contribute to an incident. Preventive maintenance and periodic inspection procedures can help prevent mechanical failures from occurring while vehicles are being operated. Vehicle inspections help to ensure that vehicles are in a safe operating condition while being driven. Required inspection procedures and documentation assist the process.

Pre-trip Inspection (396.13)

The pre-trip inspection of your vehicle is required by state and federal regulations. It is forbidden to operate any vehicle in such condition that its operation would be hazardous or likely to result in a crash or breakdown. A quality pre-trip provides a safe operating vehicle for the driver and general public. Drivers must make a pre-trip inspection of their vehicle every day prior to going on the road to be satisfied that the vehicle is in safe operating condition.

Post-trip Inspection (396.11)

Every motor carrier must require its drivers to prepare a Driver Vehicle Inspection Report (DVIR) at the completion of each day's work on each vehicle that the driver operated. The DVIR should cover at least the following parts:

- Service brakes, including trailer brake connections
- Parking brake
- Steering mechanism
- Lighting devices and reflectors
- Tires
- Horns
- Windshield wipers
- Rear vision mirrors
- Coupling devices
- Wheels and rims
- Emergency equipment

A system of preventive automotive maintenance for compliant, safe, and efficient fleet operations, including a schedule for periodic maintenance, inspection, and recordkeeping should be developed. This system should be coordinated with the manufacturer recommendations, the carrier's own experience, and regulatory requirements.

Hazardous Material Compliance

Transporting hazardous material can be extremely dangerous, not only to the driver but the general public. The general public is subject to a greater safety risk if hazardous materials are involved in a motor carrier crash and any unmarked or poorly marked cargo can result in a less effective emergency response leading to injuries or fatalities for emergency responders.

Policies and procedures must be developed to address the regulatory requirements for HAZMAT transportation registration, recordkeeping, packaging, securement, marking, labeling, placarding, reporting, documentation, security, and emergency response. Roles and responsibilities must be defined of drivers, dispatchers, managers, and other designated personnel in relation to regulations and company policies and procedures. Disciplinary measures must be implemented to insure accountability.

Crash Indicator

Maintain high standards when it comes to crash avoidance. An auto crash is any occurrence in which a vehicle is in any way involved and which results in personal injury, property damage, or collision. While the DOT has its own definition of what's recordable, as listed below, a carrier should track and demand accountability on any incident no matter how slight and regardless of fault.

Definition (390.5)

An accident means an occurrence involving a commercial motor vehicle operating on a highway in interstate or interstate commerce, which results in:

- A fatality
- Bodily injury to a person who, as a result of the injury, immediately receives medical treatment away from the scene of the accident
- One or more motor vehicles incurring disabling damage as a result of the accident, requiring the motor vehicle to be transported away from the scene by a tow truck or other motor vehicle.

The driver and the local management team must investigate and fill out a detailed prevention report, detailing what should have been done to prevent the crash. The objective of the investigation is to determine any errors in judgment or driving made by the carrier's drivers, and to point them out to them for the purpose of making them better drivers, and thus, avoiding future similar incidents. These prevention reports should also refer back to previous documented training as well future remedial training that this driver will receive to prevent a reoccurrence. For liability reasons, if remedial training is needed, then it must be completed in a timely manner.

Not only should front-line operations be held accountable for their automotive frequencies, they should also experience an immediate one-time expense charge when an incident has occurred. Immediate feedback is required to change habits. This expense should be based on the closed-case historical cost of the specific type of accident. This cost chargeback should be updated regularly to reflect a running expense based on the incident.

Compliance Is Safety

DOT regulations and fleet safety are not mutually exclusive. Compliance is a matter of safety and must be used to reinforce policies and procedures that lead to a safer on-road fleet. Communication about concerns helps to disseminate the safety message throughout the company and reinforce upper level commitment. Documented training on roles and responsibilities throughout the ranks introduces accountability for the use of safe methods. Tracking results and taking corrective action where needed closes the loop for company-wide accountability.

Injuries and fatalities are no longer a cost of doing business; they are a failure of business. As carriers begin to use these Safety Management Processes, injuries and fatalities will decline.

Chapter 2

OSHA and Other Regulations

Nancy Bendickson

LEARNING OBJECTIVES

- Identify OSHA regulations that pertain to organizations with motor-vehicle exposures.

- Identify other federal agencies that address motor fleet safety, including DOT, FAA, PHMSA, EPA, CDC, and NIOSH.

- Explain commonly cited standards for SIC 4200 (Motor Freight Transportation and Warehousing).

- Be familiar with the regulations for construction vehicles.

- Know what rollover protective structures for material-handling equipment are required for construction and agricultural vehicles.

- Explain what is covered under the OSHA Marine Terminal Vehicle Regulations.

- Understand the expanded role OSHA has taken to address motor-vehicle safety as outlined in OSHA Motor Vehicle Guidance.

- Understand how OSHA has addressed distracted driving as a special focus initiative.

Organizations with fleet exposures are affected by a number of different regulatory agencies. This chapter will provide an overview of key regulatory issues and guidelines developed to address motor-vehicle safety. The Department of Transportation (DOT) regulations, history, and some other areas are covered in the first chapter of this section of the handbook. The primary focus of this chapter will be on the Occupational Safety & Health Administration (OSHA) and the jurisdictional role of federal agencies with regard to fleet exposures.

Data from the Bureau of Labor Statistics (BLS) showed that, in 2012, 1,923 fatal work injuries resulted from transportation incidents (BLS 2014), making them consistently the leading cause of occupational fatalities in the United States. In 2013, highway incidents accounted for one out of every five fatal work injuries—a total of 40 percent (see Figure 1). Risk of work-related motor-vehicle crashes cuts across all industries and occupations. Workers who drive on the job may be "professional" drivers whose primary job is to transport freight or passengers. Many other workers spend a substantial part of the work day driving a personal vehicle or one owned or leased by their employer. Considered to be hidden or grey, it is difficult to estimate the number of these fleets in operation. There is no specific percentage of hired/non-owned vehicle use documented in literature for the United States. Arval (a U.K. Fleet Management company) did a study within the U.K. that found one in four vehicles operated for business use was a non-owned vehicle (Road Safe Summer 2008).

Traditional fleet safety processes have typically addressed the driver of a company-owned vehicle. The historical approach to fleet safety has been to address company-owned vehicles and not to address non-owned vehicle exposures.

OSHA does not have specific standards that address passenger-vehicle operations. However, Section 5(a)(1) of the OSH Act, often referred to as the General Duty Clause, requires employers to "furnish to each of his employees employment and a place of employment which are free from recognized hazards that are causing or are likely to cause death or serious physical harm to his employees" (OSHA 1970). Occupational motor-vehicle operation does present a

15

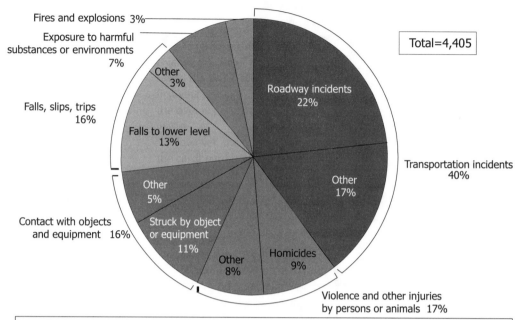

Fatal occupational injuries, by major event, 2013*

Total=4,405

Fires and explosions 3%

Exposure to harmful substances or environments 7%

Falls, slips, trips 16%

Other 3%

Falls to lower level 13%

Roadway incidents 22%

Other 17%

Transportation incidents 40%

Contact with objects and equipment 16%

Other 5%

Struck by object or equipment 11%

Other 8%

Homicides 9%

Violence and other injuries by persons or animals 17%

More fatal work injuries resulted from transportation incidents than from any other event in the 2013 preliminary counts. Roadway incidents alone accounted for nearly one out of every four fatal work injuries.

*Data for 2013 are preliminary.
Note: Transportation counts presented in this release are expected to rise when updated 2013 data are released in spring 2015 because key source documentation detailing specific transportation-related incidents has not yet been received. Percentages may not add to 100 due to rounding.
Source: U.S. Bureau of Labor Statistics, U.S. Department of Labor, 2014.

FIGURE 1. Manner in which fatal work injuries occurred, 2013 (*Source:* BLS 2014)

recognized hazard since it has been the leading cause of worker fatalities in the workplace year after year.

An initiative was launched on October 4, 2010, by the Department of Labor (DOL) and the Department of Transportation (DOT) to combat distracted driving. OSHA created a Web page directed at those employees whose workplaces are cars, vans, and trucks that deliver goods and services and their employers. The online resource provides information on workers' rights; employers' responsibilities to provide safe workplaces that extend to the operation of a motor vehicle; and best practices and policies to achieve safe workplaces in motor vehicles (OSHA 2007b).

OSHA's distracted-driving initiative addresses texting while driving. Employers are directed to prohibit any work policy or practice that requires or encourages workers to text while driving. Allowing the practice of texting while driving will violate the OSH Act.

Additional guidance for employers on fleet safety can be found on the "Motor Vehicle Safety" page of OSHA's Web site.

Reduction in transportation crashes requires implementation of motor fleet safety-management controls that combine traffic safety principles and fleet safety-management practices.

MAJOR JURISDICTIONAL AGENCIES

OSHA has jurisdiction over off-highway loading and unloading, such as would occur at warehouses, plants, retail locations, marine terminals, wharves, piers, and shipyards (OSHA 2007c).

In addition to federal OSHA regulations, there are OSHA state plans that incorporate motor-vehicle regulations. An example of this is Washington state. The Washington Administrative Code (Chapter 296-865 WAC) has regulations for Motor Vehicle Statutory Authority (WISHA Rules–Motor Vehicles 2007).The regulations cover motor-vehicle operation, transportation of passengers, motor-vehicle equipment, trucks and trailers, dump trucks, semitruck brakes, and truck/trailer loads. Trucking companies that have operations in states with OSHA state plans need to review their specific rules to determine if there are additional regulations that would pertain to a fleet operation.

DOT has jurisdiction over interstate highway driving, hours of service, driver qualification standards, and roadworthiness of vehicles. The Environmental Protection Agency (EPA) has jurisdiction over the natural environment and pollution prevention programs. OSHA can be preempted for jurisdiction by another federal agency *only* for a specific task or activity. The ultimate responsibility for the safety and health of all employees rests with OSHA.

OSHA has developed an "OSHA Assistance for the Trucking Industry" page on its Web site that provides information about preventing occupational illness and injury in the trucking industry through links to summaries, training presentations, publications, and other resources. It also offers a one-stop location to find applicable DOT and EPA compliance requirements related to worker protection (OSHA 2007c).

OTHER AGENCIES: AN OVERVIEW

When a federal agency other than OSHA has regulated a working condition, OSHA is preempted by Section 4(b)1 from enforcing its regulations. Some examples of this are provided below:

- Department of Transportation (DOT) regulates driving over public highways, the health and safety of drivers involving their use of drugs and alcohol, hours of service, and use of seatbelts. In addition, states have additional regulations for intrastate trucking. Most states adopt many, if not all, of the federal regulations regarding a driver's qualifications, hours of service, drug and alcohol testing, and more.
- DOT also regulates the roadworthiness of trucks and trailers and has specific requirements for the safe operation of trucks.
- DOT has jurisdiction over *interstate* trucking operations, while OSHA has jurisdiction over *intrastate* motor vehicles operated in the workplace and not on public roads, except those handling hazardous materials. DOT has issued regulations regarding the shipping, packaging, and handling of these materials. However, if a truck driver becomes an emergency responder in the event of a spill, then OSHA has jurisdiction.
- Interstate versus intrastate highway driving operations: DOT preempts OSHA's jurisdiction if a vehicle is traveling on public roads. OSHA has broader jurisdiction over intrastate trucking operations. Intrastate is defined as *operating strictly within a single state*. Examples of this type of trucking operation include: gravel/sand haulers, logging, agriculture, cement and concrete mixers. DOT has jurisdiction over the transportation of hazardous materials for both an interstate or intrastate trucking operation.
- Federal Aviation Administration (FAA) regulates flight crews and some aspects of the safety of ground crews. For example, if there is a working condition in an operational plan negotiated between the carrier and the FAA, FAA has jurisdiction over that working condition. Otherwise, OSHA covers most working conditions of ground crews and baggage handlers.

- Environmental Protection Agency (EPA) works with industries and all levels of government on pollution prevention programs. They have developed a number of environmental screening checklists and workbooks that can be used to screen and evaluate an industry or government agency's compliance with EPA environmental regulations. The *Environmental Screening Checklist and Workbook for the Trucking Industry* (August 2000) and *Profile of the Ground Transportation Industry: Trucking, Railroad, and Pipeline*, EPA Office of Compliance Sector Notebook Project (September 1997), provide examples of screening checklists that the transportation industry can utilize (see Figure 2).
- The Pipeline and Hazardous Materials Safety Administration (PHMSA) has public responsibilities for the safe and secure movement of hazardous materials to industry and consumers by all modes of transportation, including the nation's pipeline. PHMSA is part of the U.S. Department of Transportation. This function was previously the responsibility of the Research and Special Programs Administration (RSPA). RSPA ceased operations on February 20, 2005. RSPA programs were moved to the following agencies: Pipeline and Hazardous Materials Safety Administration, Research and Innovative Technology Administration, and the Office of Emergency Transportation moved to the Office of the Secretary. The regulations governing hazardous materials are complex. Specific information about the regulations for hazardous materials can be found at www.phmsa.dot.gov.
- The Centers for Disease Control (CDC) recognize motor-vehicle-related injuries and deaths as a serious public health problem. The agency, which is part of the Department of Health and Human Services (DHHS), supports research and prevention efforts. The CDC has developed fact sheets on a number of motor-vehicle safety topics, including: child passenger safety, teen drivers, older adult drivers, impaired driving, distracted driving, Native American road safety, pedestrian safety, and global road safety (NIOSH 2010).
- National Institute of Occupational Safety and Health (NIOSH), which is a part of the CDC, was established to assure safe and healthful working conditions for working men and women by providing research, information, education, and training in the field of occupational safety and health. The NIOSH Workplace Safety and Health Topic: "Motor Vehicle Safety" offers comprehensive information on subjects such as general crash statistics and prevention, vehicle safety for fire fighters and emergency responders, highway work zones, research initiatives, and motor-vehicle injuries (NIOSH 2010).

ENVIRONMENTAL CHECKLIST FOR TRUCKING INDUSTRY

1.0 WASTE MANAGEMENT**

Hazardous Waste Generation, Storage, and Transport*	Does the facility have an EPA hazardous waste generator ID number? (p. W-6)	Y☐ N☐ NA☐
	Does the facility store hazardous waste in appropriate storage containers? (p. W-6)	Y☐ N☐ NA☐
	Does the facility meet all hazardous waste storage (quantity and time) requirements? (p. W-7)	Y☐ N☐ NA☐
	How does the facility dispose of its hazardous waste? (p. W-7)	Ships haz waste off site / Disposes of hazardous waste on site and is a RCRA-permitted TSDF / Other / NA
	Does the facility have a written contingency plan or basic contingency procedures in place for responding to spills and releases of hazardous waste? (p. W-8)	Y☐ N☐ NA☐
Used Oil and Filters*	Are used oil containers/tanks and associated piping labeled "used oil?" (p. W-10)	Y☐ N☐ NA☐
	Are used oil containers/tanks and associated piping leak free? (p. W-10)	Y☐ N☐ NA☐
	Does the facility prevent the mixing of used oil with hazardous waste? (p. W-10)	Y☐ N☐ NA☐
	How does the facility manage/dispose of used oil? (p. W-11)	Sent off site for recycling / Burned in on-site space heater / Burned off site / Other / NA
	How does the facility manage/dispose of used oil filters? (p. W-13)	Recycle / Srvc Co / Other / NA
	How does the facility manage/dispose of used fuel filters? (p. W-14)	Recycle / Srvc Co / Managed as haz waste / Other / NA
Used Antifreeze*	In terms of storage, is used antifreeze contained, segregated, and labeled? (p. W-15)	Y☐ N☐ NA☐
	Has the facility determined if it generates any antifreeze that is hazardous waste? (p. W-16)	Y☐ N☐ NA☐
Used Battery Storage and Disposal*	If storing used batteries, does the facility protect them from storm water contact? (p. W-19)	Y☐ N☐ NA☐
	How does the facility manage/dispose of used batteries? (p. W-19)	Return to supplier / Recycle / Srvc Co / Sent to Universal waste handler / Sent to hazardous waste landfill / Other / NA
Used Shop Rags/ Towels*	How does the facility manage/dispose of used shop rags and towels? (p. W-21)	Laundry service / Burned for heat / Other / NA
Absorbents*	Does the facility determine if used absorbents are hazardous before disposal? (p. W-22)	Y☐ N☐ NA☐
Used Tires	How does the facility manage/dispose of used tires? (p. W-23)	Resale / Retread / Recycle / Other / NA
Brake Repair*	How does the facility manage asbestos brake pads and asbestos-containing material (ACM) waste? (p. W-25)	Recycled off site / Disposed of by vendor / EPA-approved disposal site / Other / NA

FIGURE 2. Environmental screening checklist for the trucking industry (*Source:* Environmental Protection Agency 2000, www.epa.gov)

ENVIRONMENTAL CHECKLIST FOR TRUCKING INDUSTRY (cont.)

2.0 WASTEWATER AND STORM WATER MANAGEMENT**

Wastewater and Storm Water Management*	Can the facility identify the final destination of all its drains? (p. W-29)	Y☐ N☐ NA☐
	If the facility discharges to a surface water does it have an NPDES permit? (p. W-31)	Y☐ N☐ NA☐
	Does the facility have a storm water permit?	Y☐ N☐ NA☐
	If Yes, does the facility have a storm water pollution prevention plan (SWPPP)? (p. W-32)	Y☐ N☐ NA☐
	If discharging to a municipal sanitary sewer, has the facility notified the publicly owned treatment works (POTW) and received approval for discharges? (p. W-32)	Y☐ N☐ NA☐
	If discharging to an underground injection control (UIC) well, does the facility comply with UIC program requirements? (p. W-33)	Y☐ N☐ NA☐
	How does the facility manage the sludge from an oil/water separator? (p. W-34)	Off-site disposal as haz waste/Off-site disposal to other facility/On-site disposal/NA
Activities Generating Wastewater/Storm Water*	If the facility stores materials outside, are they protected from contact with storm water? (p. W-35)	Y☐ N☐ NA☐
Equipment Cleaning and Spent Solvents*	If halogenated solvents are used in cleaning equipment, has the facility submitted a notification report to the air permitting agency? (p. W-39)	Y☐ N☐ NA☐
	How does the facility manage/dispose of spent solvents? (p. W-40)	Third-party vendor/Permitted discharge to storm sewers or surface waters/Sanitary sewer with POTW approval/Other/NA
Fueling*	Do fuel delivery records indicate compliance with appropriate fuel requirements? (p. W-42)	Y☐ N☐ NA☐
	Does the facility use overfill protection measures, spill containment methods, and spill response equipment during fueling? (p. W-44)	Y☐ N☐ NA☐
Asbestos Concerns*	Has the facility assessed all buildings and structures built prior to 1980 for their potential for containing asbestos and treated accordingly? (p. W-45)	Y☐ N☐ NA☐
Construction Activities*	Are there any endangered species which may be affected by construction activities? (p. W-47)	Y☐ N☐ NA☐
	Has the facility obtained a Section 404 permit for any projects that may impact wetlands? (p. W-47)	Y☐ N☐ NA☐
Pesticide Use*	Are restricted use pesticides (RUPs) applied only by a certified commercial applicator? (p. W-49)	Y☐ N☐ NA☐
Yard Dust Control*	Does the facility prohibit the use of used oils or other liquid wastes to suppress dust? (p. W-51)	Y☐ N☐ NA☐
Painting/Paint Removal*	Does the facility have air permits? (p. W-52)	Y☐ N☐ NA☐
	How does the facility manage/dispose of paint stripping wastes and baghouse dusts? (p. W-53)	Municipal or hazardous landfill/Other/NA
	When not in use, does the facility store paints in labeled container? (p. W-54)	Y☐ N☐ NA☐
	How does the facility manage/dispose of used paints and painting waste products? (p. W-55)	Return to supplier/Reuse/Recycle/Other/NA

FIGURE 2. Environmental screening checklist for the trucking industry (*Source:* Environmental Protection Agency 2000, www.epa.gov)

ENVIRONMENTAL CHECKLIST FOR TRUCKING INDUSTRY (cont.)

Air Conditioning Repair*	How does the facility dispose of appliances containing ozone-depleting refrigerants? (p. W-61)	Landfill/Waste hauler/Scrap metal recycler/Other/NA

4.0 STORAGE TANKS, SPCC, AND EMERGENCY RESPONSE

Underground Storage Tanks	Has the State/Tribal UST program office been notified of any USTs located on site? (p. W-64)	Y☐ N☐ NA☐
	Does the facility conduct leak detection for tank and piping of all on-site USTs? (p. W-64)	Y☐ N☐ NA☐
	Do USTs at the facility meet requirements for spill, overfill, and corrosion protection? (p. W-65)	Y☐ N☐ NA☐
Aboveground Storage Tanks*	Does the facility inspect ASTs on a periodic basis for leaks and other hazardous conditions? (p.W-67)	Y☐ N☐ NA☐
SPCC and Emergency Response*	Does the facility have a Spill Prevention, Control, and Countermeasures (SPCC) plan signed by a professional engineer? (p. W-69)	Y☐ N☐ NA☐
	Is the phone number for the National Response Center posted on site for immediate reporting of oil spills? (p. W-70)	Y☐ N☐

5.0 RECORDKEEPING

Recordkeeping*	**NPDES:** Does the facility keep accurate records of monitoring information for the minimum requirement of 3 years? (p. W-71)	Y☐ N☐ NA☐
	Air: Does the facility meet the recordkeeping requirements of its air permit(s)? (p. W-72)	Y☐ N☐ NA☐
	Air: If the facility owns/operates appliances that contain ozone-depleting refrigerants, does the facility maintain all required records? (p. W-73)	Y☐ N☐ NA☐
	RCRA: Does the facility keep copies of its manifests for the 3-year minimum requirement? (p. W-73)	Y☐ N☐ NA☐
	USTs: Does the facility maintain leak detection records? (p. W-75)	Y☐ N☐ NA☐
	USTs: Does the facility maintain corrosion protection records? (p. W-75)	Y☐ N☐ NA☐

*For additional questions regarding these environmental compliance issues, refer to the workbook.

**In addition, the workbook includes environmental compliance questions regarding metal machining (p. W-26), on-site disposal of nonhazardous waste (p. W-49), and PCB-containing equipment (p. W-56).

FIGURE 2. Environmental screening checklist for the trucking industry (*Source:* Environmental Protection Agency 2000, www.epa.gov)

- NIOSH Transportation Initiative: This initiative coordinates NIOSH-wide activities in all industry sectors to reduce motor-vehicle crashes, the leading cause of traumatic occupational fatalities. The initiative currently supports: (1) collaborative work with the National Center for Injury Prevention and Control (NCIPC) to address both occupational and nonoccupational issues related to motor-vehicle safety; and (2) efforts promoting global road safety, including a NIOSH-sponsored "International Conference on Road Safety at Work" (NIOSH 2008), and NIOSH participation in the United Nations Road Safety Collaboration and in the federal agency, Global Road Safety Roundtable (NIOSH 2007a), coordinated by the U.S. Department of State. NIOSH houses the global online library for resources related to the prevention of road traffic injuries and deaths while at work.

Reference the Road Safety at Work Library of Training Materials and Practice Tools (Geolibrary 2005).

OSHA STANDARDS FOR THE TRUCKING INDUSTRY

OSHA regulations govern the safety and health of workers and the responsibilities of employers to ensure their safety at docks, warehouses, construction sites, and other places where truckers deliver and pick up loads. Even self-employed truckers, who are not regulated by OSHA, are covered by OSHA regulations when they enter workplaces to deliver or receive goods. Organizations that operate commercial motor vehicles need to be familiar with OSHA standards and take appropriate action to implement any relevant regulations.

Trucking companies must comply with General Industry Standard (29 CFR 1910). The ten most frequently issued citations for SIC 4200-*Motor Freight Transportation* from October 2008 to September 2009 involved (OSHA 2007c):

- Powered industrial trucks: 1910.178;
- Hazard communication: 1910.1200;
- Electrical—general requirements: 1910.303;
- Wiring methods, components, and equipment for general use: 1910.305;
- Portable fire extinguishers: 1910.157;
- Forms: 1910.29;
- Abrasive wheel machinery: 1910.215;
- Annual summary: 1910.2;
- Oxygen-fueled gas welding: 1910.253; and
- Guarding floor and wall openings and holes: 1910.23

ADDITIONAL STANDARDS COMMONLY CITED FOR THE TRUCKING INDUSTRY

In addition to the frequently cited standards discussed above, the following list highlights other standards that address common hazards in the trucking industry:

- 1910.151, Medical Services and First Aid
- 1910.176, Materials Handling, General
- 1904.7, Recordkeeping
- 1910.120, Hazardous Waste Operation and Emergency Response
- OSHA Act of 1970, General Duty Clause
- 1904.2, Log and Summary of Occupational Injuries and Illnesses
- 1910.146, Permit-Required Confined Spaces
- 1910.141, Sanitation
- 1910.106, Flammable and Combustible Liquids
- 1910.272, Grain Handling Facilities
- 1910.177, Servicing Multi-Piece and Single Piece Rim Wheels
- 1910.266, Logging Operations

These regulations can be found on the OSHA Web site at www.osha.gov/SLTC/trucking_industry/index.html (OSHA 2007a).

OSHA CONSTRUCTION-VEHICLE REGULATIONS

Motor-vehicle standards have been promulgated for the construction industry. These standards are found in CFR 1926, Subpart O, *Motor Vehicles, Mechanized Equipment, and Marine Operations* (OSHA 2007e). An overview of these regulations is provided below:

- 1926.600 Equipment – This section covers general requirements for parking unattended equipment at night, use of a safety tire rack or cage for work on tires with split rims or rims with locking devices, blocking of equipment parts when work is performed under elevated parts, parking brake use, cab glass construction, battery charging, procedures to follow when work is performed near energized power lines, and blocking of railroad cars on spur tracks.

- 1926.601 Motor Vehicles – Coverage applies to those vehicles that operate within an off-highway job site, not open to the general public. General requirements for this section include: brake systems; lighting standards; audible warning devices at operator's station; reverse alarms and use of observers for equipment with an obstructed rear view; windshields with powered wipers and defrosting system; cab shield or canopy to protect operator from falling or shifting cargo when it is loaded by crane, backhoe, or power shovel; tool securement within the cab; secured seats with adequate number for employees carried; seatbelts installed and used to meet federal motor-vehicle safety standards; means of supporting elevated dump body during inspection/maintenance; means to prevent accidental tripping of levers for dumping or hoisting devices; trip handles located so operator is in clear; fenders or mud flaps on rubber-tired equipment; and equipment inspection done before each shift to assure parts, equipment, and accessories are in safe operating condition.

- 1926.602 Earthmoving Equipment – This section applies to scrapers, loaders, crawlers or wheel tractors, bulldozers, off-highway trucks, graders, agricultural and industrial tractors, and similar equipment. Specific rules for compactors and rubber-tired, skid-steer equipment is not included in this standard, pending development of standards for this equipment. General requirements are outlined for: seatbelts, with an exemption for seatbelts when equipment is for stand-up operation or where a rollover protective structure (ROPS) is not provided; access roads and grades; brakes; fenders; audible horns; reverse alarms; and powered industrial truck rules, including operator training. The section states that equipment must meet CFR 1926, Subpart W, requirements for ROPS and overhead protection.

- 1926.1000, Subpart W – This section covers rollover protective structures (ROPS) for material-handling equipment and outlines requirements for ROPS. Key performance criteria include: ROPS shall be designed, fabricated, and installed in a manner that will support, based on ultimate strength of metal, at least two times the weight of the prime mover applied at the point of impact. The design objective is to minimize the likelihood of a complete overturn and thereby minimize the possibility of an operator being crushed as a result of a rollover or upset.

OSHA Agricultural Vehicle Regulations

Safety for agricultural motor vehicles is addressed in CFR 1928.51, *Rollover Protective Structures for Tractors Used in Agricultural Operations*. This agricultural standard defines what type of tractor is required to have ROPS and their design requirements. Where ROPS are required, employers should provide each tractor with a seatbelt, ensure that the employee tightens the seatbelt sufficiently to confine him/her to the protected area provided by ROPS, and ensure that the seatbelt meets the requirements set forth by the Society of Automotive Engineer Standard, SAE J4C, 1965 Seat Belt Assemblies (2), except when the seatbelt is used on a suspended seat. Then, the seatbelt should be fastened to a movable portion of the seat. Additional information is provided on material for seatbelt webbing, ROPS marking, different styles of tractors and ROPS requirements, operating practices, and ROPS remounting requirements (OSHA 2009).

OSHA Marine Terminal Vehicle Regulations

The requirements of vehicle safety regulations for marine terminals are outlined in CFR Part 1917.44, *Marine Terminals, General Rules Applicable to Vehicles*. This is a comprehensive standard that covers signs for traffic control, distance of vehicles at check-in, securement of vehicles/trailers, employee transport-vehicle rules, servicing of multi-piece and single-piece rim wheels, and cargo securement of pipe or other rolling stock cargo while it is being loaded or unloaded from flatbed trailers (OSHA 2009).

Traffic accidents are a serious problem at marine terminals, and OSHA developed a guidance document in 2007 to help improve traffic safety in terminals. Marine terminal operations need to go beyond complying with the OSHA standards on powered industrial trucks and vehicle operations to also develop traffic safety programs for vehicle and pedestrian safety. The guidance document on the OSHA Web site is "Traffic Safety in Marine Terminals" (OSHA 2007c).

Factors that Contribute to Traffic-Related Injuries and Fatalities in Marine Terminals

There are many factors that can contribute to traffic accidents in marine terminals. Often, accidents are caused by a combination of factors. The following points illustrate common traffic safety problems:

- *Unsafe equipment.* Broken, improperly maintained, or missing safety equipment, such as lights, seatbelts, brakes, and horns, can lead to accidents and injuries.

- *Inadequate traffic controls.* Inadequate traffic controls, such as lack of proper signage or marking, may lead to accidents.

- *Condition of terminal driving surfaces.* Many marine terminals, particularly larger ones, have paved terminal driving surfaces. Paved surfaces, which are smoother, are desirable because they reduce the potential for vehicle tipovers, cargo and equipment shifting, and operator bouncing, and allow for improved road markings, such as lane markings. However, smoother driving surfaces also require heightened awareness because they can become slippery when wet and contribute to excessive vehicle speed. Road surfaces need to be maintained properly because, over time, paving material can settle and result in uneven surfaces, potholes, and sinkholes that can lead to tipovers or other vehicle accidents.

- *Driving obstacles.* Vessel equipment, stacked materials, containers, and repair crews are some of the driving obstacles that increase the risk of traffic accidents at marine terminals.

- *Weather.* Ice, fog, and rain can create hazardous conditions, including slippery surfaces and poor visibility, in marine terminals. Also, the sun may cause glare on certain types of driving surfaces and vehicle windshields.

- *Inadequate illumination.* Poor lighting, particularly at night, as well as shadows, can make it difficult for drivers to see and avoid pedestrians, hazardous driving surfaces, and other obstacles.

- *Welding.* Welding flashes can distract vehicle and crane operators.

- *Unsafe vehicle operation.* Factors such as improperly loaded equipment, speed, and distractions (such as cell phones) can contribute to traffic accidents.

- *Improper parking.* Hazards can be created by improper parking of personal or company-provided vehicles and powered industrial trucks in areas where cargo is being worked on or heavy machinery is being used.

- *Lack of communication.* Accidents often occur because of poor communication. Technicians, mechanics, and other employees fail to alert vehicle operators of their location, and employers fail to notify employees of changes to traffic routes. In addition, noisy terminal environments can hinder effective communications. In some cases, there may be inadequate accommodations for persons with hearing impairment or language barriers.

- *Lack of training and awareness.* Accidents can occur when drivers and equipment operators do not have adequate training in the safe operation and maintenance of equipment and vehicles. Likewise, pedestrians walking in marine terminals are at risk of injury if they do not receive training on the potential for traffic accidents and how to avoid them.

- *Shift changes.* Marine terminal employers report that accidents often occur just before the end of a work shift or while employees are parking equipment at the end of the work shift.
- *Fatigue.* Marine terminal employees often work long and irregular hours, which can lead to fatigue and sleepiness. Fatigue and sleepiness can impair operator performance and contribute to workplace accidents and fatalities.
- *Substance abuse.* Substance abuse may contribute to vehicle accidents in marine terminals (OSHA 2007c).

OSHA SAFETY GUIDANCE FOR MOTOR VEHICLES

Since the roadway is a not a closed environment, employers need to develop strategies that combine traffic safety principles and sound safety-management practices. An employer cannot control the roadway condition; however, he or she can promote safe driving behavior by providing safety information to workers and by setting and enforcing driver safety policies. Crashes are *not* an unavoidable part of doing business.

OSHA highlights resources available through the National Safety Council (NSC), the National Highway Traffic Safety Administration (NHTSA), the National Institute for Occupational Safety and Health (NIOSH), the Institute for Highway Safety (IHS), and the Network of Employers for Traffic Safety (NETS).

A suggested prevention strategy for crash reduction is provided on the policies page of OSHA's Motor Vehicle Safety Web site. This prevention strategy is based on a publication by NIOSH (2004a) and includes the following steps:

- Policies
    - Assign a key member of the management team responsibility and authority to set and enforce a comprehensive driver safety policy.
    - Enforce mandatory seatbelt use.
    - Do not require workers to drive irregular hours or drive far beyond normal work hours.
    - Do not require workers to conduct business on a cell phone while driving.
    - Develop work schedules that allow employees to obey speed limits and to follow applicable hours-of-service regulations.

- Fleet Management
    - Adopt a structured vehicle maintenance program.
    - Provide company vehicles that offer the highest levels of occupant protection.
- Safety Programs
    - Teach worker strategies for recognizing and managing driver fatigue and in-vehicle distractions.
    - Provide training to workers operating specialized motor vehicles or equipment.
    - Emphasize to workers the need to follow safe driving practices on and off the job.
- Driver Performance
    - Ensure that workers assigned to drive on the job have a valid driver's license and one that is appropriate for the type of vehicle being driven.
    - Check driving records of prospective employees and perform periodic rechecks after hiring.
    - Maintain complete and accurate records of workers' driving performance.

ADDITIONAL RESOURCES FOR PREVENTION STRATEGIES

The "Best Practices" chapter within this section of the handbook provides extensive information about prevention strategies and resources, such as ANSI/ASSE Z-15.1 2006, *Safe Practices for Motor Vehicle Operations*. This standard sets forth practices for safe operation of motor vehicles owned or operated by organizations, including:

- definitions
- management, leadership, and administration
- operational environment
- driver considerations
- vehicle considerations
- incident reporting and analysis

These practices are designed for use by those having the responsibility for the administration and operation of motor vehicles. This is an excellent resource that should form the basis of an organization's fleet safety-management system (ANSI/ASSE 2006).

SUMMARY

This chapter provided an overview of OSHA and the jurisdictional role that other federal agencies have with regard to fleet safety. Motor-vehicle safety is a concern for many agencies because the risk of roadway crashes affects millions of U.S. workers and continues to be the leading cause of occupational fatalities in the United States.

The following federal agencies have initiatives or regulations that address fleet safety exposures: Department of Transportation (DOT), Federal Aviation Administration (FAA), Pipeline and Hazardous Materials Safety Administration (PHMSA), Centers for Disease Control (CDC), National Institute of Occupational Safety and Health (NIOSH), and the Environmental Protection Agency (EPA). NIOSH is involved in a global partnership on road safety at work and is housing an online library devoted to global road safety resources.

Distracted driving is the subject of several safety initiatives and regulation in 2010. OSHA considers texting to be a recognized hazard, and enforcement action will be taken against organizations that do not manage this exposure (OSHA 2007b).

Fleet safety initiatives within the regulatory agencies are changing. Safety professionals will need to monitor the Web sites of the federal agencies to stay current on motor-vehicle safety prevention strategies and regulations.

REFERENCES

American National Standards Institute (ANSI) and American Society of Safety Engineers (ASSE). 2006. *ANSI/ASSE Z-15.1 2006: Safe Practices for Motor Vehicle Operations*. Des Plaines, IL: ASSE.

Bureau of Labor Statistics. 2014. "Revisions to the 2012 Census of Fatal Occupational Injuries (CFOI) counts" (retrieved December 20, 2014). www.bls.gov/iif/oshwc/cfoi/cfoi_revised12.pdf

_____. 2014. *2013 Census of Fatal Occupational Injuries–Preliminary Data* (retrieved December 20, 2014). www.bls.gov/news.release/pdf/cfoi.pdf

Environmental Protection Agency (EPA). 2000. *Environmental Screening Checklist and Workbook for Trucking Industry* (retrieved July 10, 2010). www.epa.gov/compliance/resources/publications/assistance/sectors/truckwrkbk.pdf

Geolibrary. n.d. *Specialty Road Safety at Work Library of Training Materials and Practice Tools* (retrieved October 15, 2010). www.geolibrary.org/library/default/aspx?categoryID=627.

National Institute for Occupational Safety and Health (NIOSH). 2004a. *Work-Related Roadway Crashes: Prevention Strategies for Employers*. NIOSH Publication No. 2004-136 (retrieved July 10, 2010). www.cdc.gov/niosh/doc/2004-136/default.html

_____. 2004b. *Work-Related Roadway Crashes: Who's at Risk?* NIOSH Publication No. 2004-137 (retrieved July 10, 2010). www.cdc.gov/niosh/docs/2004-137/default.html

_____. 2007a. *Global Collaborations in Transportation, Warehousing and Utilities* (retrieved October 7, 2010). www.cdc.gov/niosh/programs/twu/global

_____. 2007b. *Motor Vehicle Safety* (retrieved October 7, 2010). www.cdc.gov/nioshtopics/motorvehicle

Occupational Safety and Health Administration (OSHA). 1970. Occupational Safety and Health Act of 1970 (retrieved October 15, 2010). www.osha.gov/pls/oshaweb/owadisp.show_document?ptable=OSHACT&p_id3359

_____. 2007a. *Safety and Health Topics: Motor Vehicle Safety* (retrieved July 10, 2010). www.osha.gov/SLTC/motorvehiclesafety/html

_____. 2007b. *Safety and Health Topics: Distracted Driving* (retrieved October 7, 2010).www.osha.gov/distracted-driving/index.html

_____. 2007c. *Safety and Health Topics: Marine Terminal* (retrieved September 11, 2010). www.osha.gov/SLTC/marineterminals/index.html

_____. 2009a. *OSHA Assistance for the Trucking Industry* (retrieved September 12, 2010). www.osha.gov/SLTC/trucking_industry/index/html

_____. 2009b. *Safety and Health Topics: Agricultural Operations* (retrieved September 11, 2010). www.osha.gov/SLTC/agriculturaloperations/index.html

_____. 2010. *Safety and Health Topics: Construction Motor Vehicles* (retrieved September 12, 2010). www.osha.gov/SLTC/constructionmotorvehicle/index.html

Pipeline and Hazardous Materials Safety Administration (PHMSA) n.d. (retrieved July 10, 2010). www.phmsa.dot.gov.index/html

Road Safe Summer. 2008. "A Grey Area of Fleet Safety" (retrieved July 28, 2011). www.roadsafe.com/magazine/2008summer/grey.html

Chapter 3

Vehicles and Accidents

Jubal Hamernik and Peter M. Himpsel

LEARNING OBJECTIVES

- Utilize vehicle-selection criteria to properly choose fleet vehicles.

- Establish and carry out proper vehicle maintenance programs and procedures for fleet vehicles.

- Understand and implement recommended practices for accident investigation.

Practicing fleet safety is an active, ongoing process, not just a policy statement. Each step, from purchase to salvage, should be undertaken with safety concerns in mind. Fleet safety can be improved through educated vehicle selection, proper vehicle maintenance, and thorough accident investigations. This chapter seeks to address these issues and give insight into good fleet safety practices.

VEHICLE CONSIDERATIONS

For any new fleet of vehicles or addition to an existing fleet, vehicle selection is important. When selecting new fleet vehicles, issues such as safety, cost, crashworthiness, and environmental friendliness should be considered. The first step is to determine the type and class of vehicle needed. Essentially, the fleet should be tailored to use so that it can accommodate the expected range, load, and so on required of the vehicle. The Federal Motor Carrier Safety Administration's (FMCSA) Commercial Driver's License Program (CDL/CDLIS) outlines the different classes of commercial vehicles. This information may be useful in determining the class of vehicle needed and the associated license requirements for fleet drivers. Vehicle classes A through C are determined by vehicle weight, towing capacity, and passenger size. Vehicle type can be found at the Federal Highway Administration (FHA) Web site under *FHWA Vehicle Types*. Once fleet use is determined and the type and class of vehicle have been identified, the practices outlined in this chapter may be referenced to help select a specific vehicle.

Safety Features

Vehicle selection should include consideration of the following safety features: seatbelts, airbags, antilock brakes, traction and stability control, tire-pressure monitoring system, head restraints, and a design that provides visual clarity for the driver.

Seatbelt System

Seatbelts are a critical component of vehicle safety. Seatbelt type and proper seatbelt usage are both crucial factors for proper safety compliance and injury prevention. A three-point seatbelt system is preferred to a lap-only system (see Figure 1). A fleet may have more than one driver operating a vehicle. To accommodate all drivers, look for vehicles where belt height is adjustable (see Point 1 in Figure 1). If the seatbelt is comfortable, a driver may be more likely to wear it—and if it is not, the driver might be deterred from using it. Avoid passive, automatic seatbelts. Passive seatbelt systems may be by default a two-point belt system in which the lap belt must be attached separately from the shoulder belt (automatic). Sometimes the driver will not attach the lap portion; utilizing only the automatic portion increases the risk of injury. Some vehicles are equipped with an innovative seatbelt reminder system, indicating to the driver when seatbelts are not buckled. Such indicators are good for safety monitoring.

Airbags

Driver and passenger airbags have been standard equipment in all passenger vehicles since 1998 and in light trucks since 1999. In order for an airbag to function properly, the occupant must be wearing a seatbelt, and the occupant's chest should be located ten inches or more away from the steering wheel (see Figure 2). Because an airbag inflates over a short time interval, being too close to the airbag may cause injury or death. Some newer vehicles are equipped with advanced airbag systems, which utilize extra sensors to monitor vehicle and passenger characteristics and compute the specific output force of the airbag, in an attempt to reduce the chance of airbag-induced injuries. If the fleet is intended to transport children under the age of twelve, then it is recommended that the children sit only in the rear passenger seats. The National Highway Traffic Safety Administration (NHTSA), in the "Airbags" section on its Web site (www.nhtsa.dot.gov/people/injury/airbags/airbags03/page3.html), provides useful resources on airbag safety and risks. The FMCSA does not currently have any rules or regulations mandating airbags in commercial vehicles (www.fmcsa.dot.gov/rules-regulations/rules-regulations.htm).

Vehicles equipped with side airbags offer protection to the torso and head in the event of a side-impact collision (see Figure 3). These airbags can deploy from the vehicle's roof rail, door, or seat. In addition to side-impact safety tests, many side airbag systems have been tested to determine safety in the event that the driver or occupant is out of position. Vehicles that have passed a battery of tests regarding safety in the event of

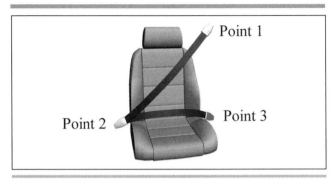

FIGURE 1. Three-point seatbelt system refers to three anchor locations for the seatbelts.

FIGURE 2. Driver and passenger airbags (*Source:* IIHS)

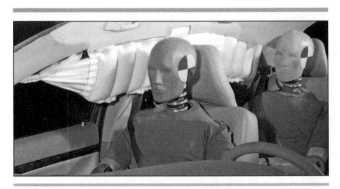

FIGURE 3. Side curtain airbags (*Source:* IIHS)

out-of-position occupants are listed in NHTSA's *Buying a Safer Car* publication available for download as a pdf file at www.safercar.gov.

Antilock Brake System (ABS)

When used properly, antilock brake systems can aid in maintaining control of a vehicle on slippery surfaces and assist in retaining steering capabilities during full braking. In order for ABS to be effective, the driver must know how to properly apply the brakes. In an ABS-equipped vehicle, when the ABS system engages, it modulates brake-line pressure and causes the brake pedal to counteract a force on the driver's foot. In such instances, the driver should continue to depress the pedal as necessary to reduce speed or stop. In an ABS-equipped vehicle, the driver must not pump the brakes.

Traction Control and Stability Control

Successors to the antilock brake system, both traction and stability control systems are based on the components and concepts of the ABS system. Traction control systems available in cars today offer electronic monitoring and control of wheel spin, essentially doing for acceleration what the ABS does for braking. Traction control systems monitor wheel spin and prevent excessive wheel spin (slip) under heavy acceleration or when roadway conditions offer limited traction. When slip is sensed, the system can cut engine power and/or apply braking to maintain traction and control.

Stability control systems take this concept one step further with the addition of a yaw rate sensor. *Yaw* can be defined as the rotation about a vertical axis that passes through the car's center of gravity. The addition of a yaw rate sensor gives the stability control system the ability to sense and mitigate vehicle yaw by activating individual brakes or by applying a combination of brake and throttle in order to maintain the steering angle the driver inputs.

The presence of both traction control and stability control in a wide range of consumer vehicles continues to increase. Both systems can be useful in accident prevention and safety by assisting the driver in maintaining control of the vehicle under a variety of conditions.

Tire-Pressure Monitoring System

Tire-pressure monitoring systems, when available, work by monitoring the individual pressure of each tire. Accessible indicators can warn the driver of over- or underinflated tires. Overinflated tires can reduce vehicle traction, whereas underinflated tires can affect the vehicle's fuel efficiency and stability.

Head-Restraint Design

Head-restraint systems are important for the prevention and reduction of whiplash-type injuries, which are discussed later in this chapter. A head restraint should be sufficiently tall to reach the upper portion of the driver's or passenger's cranium (see Figure 4). Second, if possible, the head restraint should be nonadjustable. Although an adjustable head restraint may sit high on the occupant's head, in the event of a large force acting on it, the adjustable head restraint may collapse and may result in adverse loading of the head and neck.

Visual Clarity

Vehicles should be chosen so that drivers have a clear view of the roadway and surrounding areas of the vehicle (see Figure 5). Avoid placing obstructions within the driver's field of view that reduce sight capabilities (e.g., large devices mounted to the windshield). In California, a device such as a GPS unit may only be mounted at the corners of the windshield. Alternative options include dashboard mounts, vent mounts, and adhesive discs. Vehicles should be equipped with two sideview mirrors and one rearview mirror. Additional convex mirrors can be added to existing sideview mirrors for visual assistance on larger vehicles.

Crashworthiness

In selecting a vehicle, one should also consider its crashworthiness. *Crashworthiness* encompasses how a vehicle will perform in an accident, how the vehicle will protect the occupants, and how the vehicle will resist costly repairs in low- to moderate-speed accidents. The Federal Motor Vehicle Safety Standards' (FMVSS) *Quick Reference Guide to Federal Motor Safety Standards* is a set of standards and regulations to which manufacturers of motor

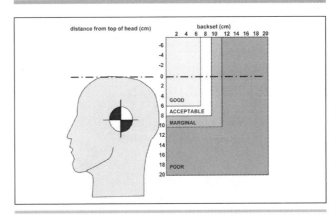

FIGURE 4. Head-restraint positioning ratings (*Source:* IIHS)

vehicles must conform (FMVSS 2011). The adherence to and surmounting of such standards may improve the crashworthiness of a vehicle. The FMCSA's *Regulatory Guidance for Federal Motor Carrier Safety Regulations* sets out regulations for large trucks and buses. Note that when evaluating vehicle crashworthiness ratings, comparison should be made between vehicles of the same class.

Low-Speed Collisions

Low-speed collisions account for a substantial portion of all reported traffic accidents. Occupant protection and minimal vehicle damage are concerns when evaluating a vehicle's low-speed crashworthiness. Vehicle bumpers can protect the vehicle from excessive damage during low-speed collisions. Quality safety belts and proper head restraints can minimize the likelihood of occupant injury during such accidents.

- *Bumpers:* Bumper systems are designed to protect the vehicle's body and structure in order to minimize expensive repair costs. Bumper systems can reduce induced damage to vehicle components such as fenders and quarter panels, which can occur by the transfer of mechanical forces. Preferably, these bumper systems and cosmetic covers should wrap around the corners of the vehicle and extend to the wheel wells, creating a larger area of protection. The FMVSS standard for passenger vehicles requires a minimum bumper strength of 2.5 miles per hour (mph), meaning at any speed below 2.5 mph, the bumper should resist permanent damage apart from minor scuffs and scraps. However, sport utility vehicles (SUVs), vans, and trucks are not required to comply with this standard. Vehicles that exceed this standard are preferred. Bumper systems that incorporate energy-absorbing material or piston isolators are preferred to simple bumpers made of stamped metal.

- *Whiplash:* Rearend-type accidents can result in biomechanical movement that leads to bodily injury. When a vehicle is hit from the rear, the vehicle will accelerate forward. If the head of the occupant is not adequately supported by the vehicle head restraint, it will lag behind the forward motion of the torso. This unsynchronized movement (see Figure 6) will cause neck extension and may produce whiplash-type injuries. Thus proper design and positioning of the head restraint is important in reducing whiplash-type injuries.

High-Speed Collisions

In case of high-speed vehicle accidents, vehicles should be designed to aid in the protection of the occupant(s). Components such as crumple zones, occupant compartments, rollover ratings, and restraint systems are all important in protecting the occupant in the event of a high-speed collision.

- *Crumple Zones and Occupant Compartments:* Crumple zones are areas that crumple or crush upon vehicle impact in order to reduce the deceleration experienced by the occupant(s). By testing and design, these zones can absorb a significant amount of energy during collisions. An occupant compartment

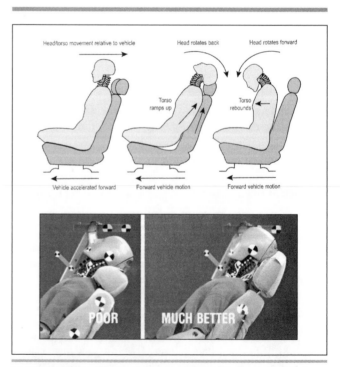

FIGURE 6. Occupant response when hit from behind with different head restraint designs (*Source:* IIHS)

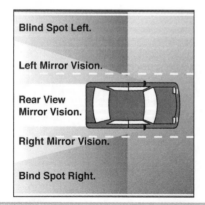

FIGURE 5. Blind spots (*Source:* Colorado Department of Revenue)

or protection cage is important in absorbing damage during a crash while keeping the occupant safe. Offset frontal crash tests performed by the Insurance Institute for Highway Safety (IIHS) are helpful in assessing the performance of vehicle structure and can be viewed at the institute's Web site.

- ***Rollovers and Side Impacts:*** Different vehicles have varying susceptibility to rolling, which is often termed vehicle rollover. A vehicle with a low center of gravity is preferred to reduce the chance of a rollover. The NHTSA provides rollover ratings for test vehicles based on a five-star rating system. These ratings and other information about rollovers can be viewed at the NHTSA Web site. Good rollover ratings are important for helping prevent the chance of rollover occurrence. The best form of occupant protection in the event of a rollover is proper seatbelt usage. A large percentage of occupant deaths due to rollover collisions resulted from occupants being ejected from the vehicle. Newer technology available in some vehicles includes rollover airbags or side curtain airbags, which stay inflated longer in an attempt to keep the occupant in the vehicle during a rollover.

Economic Considerations

Economic considerations almost always play a role in vehicle selection. Besides examining initial vehicle costs and overhead, attention should be paid to the long-term benefits and shortcomings of the prospective vehicle. Some considerations are outlined in the following paragraphs.

Fuel Efficiency: Estimated miles per gallon for city and highway driving should be considered with regard to the types of conditions under which the vehicle will be operating. A cost-benefit analysis should be performed to evaluate the economic impact of purchasing a more fuel-efficient vehicle. Information regarding estimated miles per gallon, fuel-saving tips, and alternatively fueled vehicles can be found at the Department of Energy Fuel Economy Web site. Also, the American Trucking Association offers a guide to fuel-saving practices for fleet managers.

Historically Low Maintenance: A good vehicle should have a reliable and low-maintenance engine, transmission, electrical system, and so on, often based on previous models or manufacturer projections. The vehicle's part-replacement costs, service fees, reliability, and expected life should also be considered.

Engine Type: The type of engine that is chosen (diesel, gasoline, or hybrid electric) will affect the overhead, maintenance, and fueling costs. Diesel engines generally have a longer life expectancy, are better suited for pulling heavy loads, and are generally more fuel-efficient

in comparison with an equivalent gasoline engine. Gas engines, on the other hand, are quieter and cheaper to purchase and have a fuel supply that is more readily available. Hybrid electric vehicles may have a higher initial cost, but lower fuel consumption per mile may be preferred in stop-and-go driving environments.

Depreciation and Salvage Value: Current vehicle depreciation and salvage value projections must be considered in order to recapture capital upon fleet retirement.

Upgrades Based on Change in Usage: Vehicle upgrades should be made specific to terrain, load, mileage, and similar factors. For example, if the fleet is used in an area that is consistently snowy, then snow tires for the fleet should be considered. If the maximum vehicle load or towing capacity is insufficient, then larger, more capable vehicles should be added to the fleet, or more vehicles should break up the transportation of heavy loads. If the fleet is consistently required to travel long distances, then more fuel-efficient vehicles should be considered.

Other Considerations

Environmentally Friendly Vehicles: A vehicle should produce emissions that are below minimum Environmental Protection Agency (EPA) limits and state emission requirements while minimizing noise pollution. Emission ratings for passenger vehicles manufactured from 2000 to 2011 can be found in the EPA's *Green Vehicle Guide* (EPA 2011).

It should be noted that, for every class of vehicles, there are differences with respect to safety features, failure properties, and crashworthiness. One can reference the IIHS Web site to verify which of these safety features are included in the prospective vehicle. Consumers may also refer to other safety sources mentioned previously, along with the *Automotive Safety Handbook* (Seiffert and Wech 2003) and *Consumer Reports*, for vehicle safety, cost, and reliability information. An in-person evaluation of the vehicle being considered is recommended as well. A sample evaluation checklist is outlined here.

IN-PERSON VEHICLE EVALUATION CHECKLIST

1. Ask the manufacturer or retailer about the existence and status of the following:
   a. Airbags
   b. Antilock brake system (ABS)
   c. Tire-pressure monitoring system
   d. Stability control and/or traction control
   e. Automatic or manual seatbelt system
2. Enter the vehicle and use the seatbelt. Take note of its condition, whether it is adjustable, and whether it is comfortable.

3. See if the driver and passenger seats are adjustable in height and/or lateral distance to accommodate for different drivers. See if the steering wheel is adjustable.
4. Test-drive the vehicle.
5. Check for available warranties.
6. If the vehicle is used, hire a mechanic to perform a safety inspection.
7. If the vehicle is used, perform a vehicle history report to determine accident involvement, previous owners, and so on. (www.carfax.com).

FLEET MAINTENANCE

Fleet maintenance is important for safety, efficiency, and the cost-effective operation of a fleet. All vehicles must be properly maintained at all times. The vehicle should undergo two types of inspections: daily inspections and biannual inspections. Fleet maintenance requirements vary depending on the vehicle type. The FMCSA requires a minimum annual inspection on all operated carrier vehicles. For normal passenger vehicles, check with state regulations for applicable requirements. It is recommended for passenger and carrier vehicles alike that in-depth inspections be performed more than once a year to serve as a safety check for preventive maintenance and to determine whether a vehicle should be deemed out-of-service. An out-of-service "red flag" indicates when a fleet vehicle is in need of maintenance and is unsafe to operate.

Record Keeping

Each vehicle should have an individual record of its history that is accessible and can be easily referenced if necessary. It is important to keep records for all maintenance performed on the vehicle and previously existing problems so that diagnostics and repair are more easily addressed. For carrier vehicles, record keeping must follow part 396.3 of the FMCSA regulations. For passenger vehicles, similar applicable procedures should be followed.

Daily Inspection

Daily inspections are important. They serve as preventive measures to ensure safe daily operation of the vehicle. These inspections should become a habitual part of fleet operation. The following list outlines safety criteria that should be performed before and after operating a vehicle.

PRE-OPERATION INSPECTION LIST

1. Review the last driver inspection report; sign it if any defects were noted to indicate that the current driver has reviewed the report and verified that defects were repaired.

2. Exterior:
   a. Check for body or glass damage. If any exists, check with maintenance before use to determine if the damage is old or new.
   b. Check the operation of all turn signals, brake lights, headlights, and taillights. Do not use the fleet vehicle until all defective lights and signals have been repaired.
   c. Examine tire condition, wear, and tire pressure. Add air if needed. If tire wear is beyond manufacturer specifications, deem the vehicle out-of-service and in need of replacement tires.
3. Safety Equipment: Make sure the vehicle's spare tire and emergency equipment are accessible and in working condition.
4. Under the Hood (after each refueling): Check fluid levels and refill as necessary. Make note of any fluid added.
5. Interior: Check for proper operation of seatbelts, starting system, fuel level, instruments, mirrors, and so on. If any problems exist, check with maintenance before use.
6. During Operation:
   a. Look for properly operating instruments.
   b. Smell for any strange or unusual odors.
   c. Listen for any unusual or abnormal sounds.
   d. Feel for any unusual vibrations or abnormal handling of the vehicle.
   e. Monitor fuel consumption and make note of any excessive or unusual fuel usage.

POST-OPERATION INSPECTION LIST

(Required for all carrier vehicles; recommended for passenger vehicles)

Check the following components:
1. Service brakes, including trailer brake connections
2. Parking (hand) brake
3. Steering mechanism
4. Lighting devices and reflectors
5. Tires
6. Horn
7. Windshield wipers
8. Rearview mirrors
9. Coupling devices
10. Wheels and rims
11. Emergency equipment

Other inspections unique to specific fleet vehicles should also be performed. If the vehicle is excessively dirty, the vehicle should be washed to ensure proper operation of instruments, full visibility of lights and signals, and ease in recognizing new damage to the vehicle. When any unusual or abnormal conditions exist, report such cases to fleet maintenance as soon as possible so that the issue can be further inspected before the vehicle is allowed back in service.

Unscheduled or Unanticipated Maintenance

Sometimes required maintenance cannot always be predicted. In the event of a roadside breakdown or tire failure, follow the procedure outlined in the driver's manual for bringing your vehicle to a stop. Make sure to turn on the emergency hazards and place triangle reflectors and flares (if visibility is poor) behind the vehicle. Call fleet management to alert them to the problem. If the fleet employee is capable, and it is safe to do so, he or she may change the vehicle's wheel. Depending on the spare tire available, it may be necessary to service the vehicle as soon as possible, in which case the vehicle should be driven to the appropriate maintenance location. If the vehicle or tire is unserviceable, tie something white to the vehicle antenna and raise the hood to let emergency personnel know you need assistance. Then stand away from the vehicle and roadway and call for assistance.

In-Depth Inspections and Maintenance

More in-depth, thorough inspections of components and systems should be performed two to three times per year by a qualified mechanic. For carrier vehicles, appendix G of part 396.6, FMCSA regulations, lists the necessary maintenance procedures. For passenger vehicles, applicable procedures based on these regulations should be followed. Thorough inspections and maintenance should be scheduled so that downtime is minimized and fleet productivity is maximized.

These inspections should assess overall vehicle condition and review feedback from driver reports and any potential problems. Maintenance should meet or exceed manufacturer recommendations. The minimum requirements for annual inspections on carrier vehicles set forth by the FMCSA are outlined in the following list. Fleet managers should perform an in-depth review of criteria for an out-of-service vehicle. The FMCSA or other professional organizations, such as the Commercial Vehicle Safety Alliance, with its *Out of Service Criteria*, provide these criteria. Certain organizations and companies, such as the state associations of the American Trucking Association, or private industry groups, such as J. J. Keller and Associates (*2011 Transport Catalog*), offer preprinted inspection forms that can assist the mechanic with inspection procedures and record keeping.

Minimum Periodic Inspection Standards

(Required for all carrier vehicles; recommended for passenger vehicles)

Check the following:
1. Brake systems
2. Coupling devices
3. Exhaust system
4. Fuel system
5. Lighting devices
6. Safe loading
7. Steering mechanism
8. Suspension
9. Frame
10. Tires
11. Wheels and rims
12. Windshield glazing
13. Windshield wipers

If repairs are required, all manufacturer warranties that apply should be considered. It is recommended that all repairs be made using OEM or OEM-equivalent parts. After repairs have been performed, vehicles should be road-tested to check that all parts and systems operate as expected and that no other problems exist.

If a vehicle is in need of major repairs, then a cost-benefit analysis should be performed to determine whether repair or replacement is more appropriate.

Industry and Manufacturer Recalls: Check for safety- and performance-related recalls of the specific fleet vehicle on a regular basis. Information regarding recalls can be found at the NHTSA's Office of Defects Investigation Web site (www-odi.nhtsa.dot.gov). If necessary, contact the manufacturer for details so that required repairs can be performed.

ACCIDENT INVESTIGATION

When a fleet vehicle is involved in an accident, a thorough investigation should be conducted. Accident investigation is important to understand the cause(s) of the accident and to see if any preventive steps can be implemented to reduce the likelihood of reoccurrence. In the event of litigation, scene evidence collected by fleet employees can assist in assessing fault.

To aid in proper accident investigation, each vehicle should be equipped with all documentation required by law: driver's license, vehicle registration, and proof of insurance. In addition, a disposable camera, tape measure, investigation checklist (see the following list), notepad, and pen can assist in evidence collection.

Vehicles should also carry relevant contact information and emergency daytime and nighttime phone numbers for appropriate company personnel. Persons in charge of receiving accident-related calls should have easy access to all driver emergency-contact and medical history information.

Should an accident occur, depending on severity, the following procedure should be considered.

ACCIDENT PROCEDURE

1. Activate emergency four-way flashers (hazard lights), evaluate safety of vehicle's position, and move vehicle to safe location if it is safe and legal to do so.
2. Stop vehicle immediately, turn the ignition off, and set the parking brake.
3. Exit the vehicle if it is safe to do so.
4. Take reasonable precautions to prevent further accidents through proper use of emergency flares, triangle reflectors, and so on.
5. Contact authorities and emergency personnel (follow state regulations regarding accident procedures and reporting, often outlined in the state driver's manual).
6. Report accident to fleet vehicle management.
7. Collect evidence (see next section).

Evidence Collection

Initial evidence should be collected by the driver if it is safe to do so. The following information should be obtained/collected by the driver if it is safe to do so. The following information should be obtained.

EVIDENCE COLLECTION PROCEDURE

(Perform only if not injured and it is safe to do so.)

1. Write down driver name, vehicle make and model, insurance information, and license plate numbers for all vehicles involved.

FIGURE 8. Photograph the vehicle from multiple angles.

2. Take notes and witness statements, with witnesses' names and contact information included.
3. Examine the vehicle where the contact or collision point occurred. Mark the damage, if any, on a diagram similar to the example in Figure 7 for all vehicles involved.
4. Examine other parts of the vehicle to determine whether other damage is related to the accident or previously existed and document any new damage.
5. Write down any damage descriptively (e.g., shattered light, 2-inch circular dent, 5-inch scrapes/scuffs).
6. Take pictures of the vehicle(s) from a distance and from multiple angles (see Figure 8), including the total roadway and intersection in the field of view.
7. Take pictures of the damaged section from multiple angles with an extended tape measure in the photos (see Figure 9).
8. Take pictures of the skid marks, starting from the beginning of the skid marks until the final vehicle location.

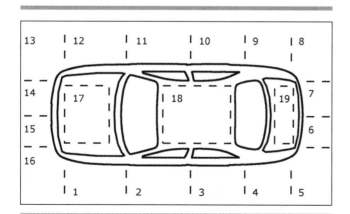

FIGURE 7. Example vehicle-damage diagram

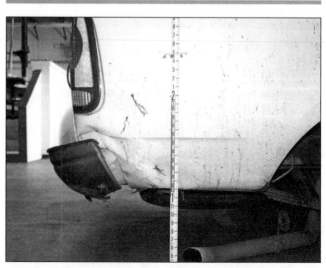

FIGURE 9. Example photo of vehicle damage

FIGURE 10. Proper photographic technique

- Vehicle ending point is visible
- Total skid mark is visible
- No people in the picture

FIGURE 11. Improper photographic technique: Vehicle ending point is not visible

FIGURE 12. Improper photographic technique: Total skid mark is not visible

9. Photograph the accident scene (e.g., tire marks, gouges, obstructions, vehicle ending positions, roadway) (See examples in Figures 10–12).
10. Make note of weather and road conditions.
11. Describe the accident and events preceding and following the accident.
12. Get a copy of the police report of the accident from the local precinct for fleet records.

All of the evidence collected at the scene should be maintained by the fleet and submitted to the insurance company. The fleet vehicle involved should be checked for government or factory recalls. The driver should also document any vehicle defects or conditions that may have contributed to the accident as well as defects occurring after the accident.

For serious accidents, a trained staff of independent or in-house accident investigators should be sent to the accident site as soon as possible. This is to make sure that all available scene evidence is collected and preserved. These trained investigators will be able to obtain relevant data from the roadway, vehicles, and witnesses.

Proper collection of accident-related information and, when appropriate, additional investigation and analysis will provide the best means of managing the economic impact of a motor-vehicle accident involving a fleet vehicle.

Event Data Recorders (EDRs)

Many vehicles are equipped with Event data recorders (EDRs) that may provide data relevant to an accident (www.NHTSA.gov/EDRs). Fleet vehicle management should note which vehicles are equipped with EDRs and take the appropriate steps to have a qualified technician download and evaluate any available data in the event of an accident. United States Code of Federal Regulations, Title 49, Part 563, specifies:

> . . . uniform, national requirements for vehicles equipped with event data recorders (EDRs) concerning the collection, storage, and retrievability of onboard motor vehicle crash event data. It also specifies requirements for vehicle manufacturers to make tools and/or methods commercially available so that crash investigators and researchers are able to retrieve data from EDRs.

REFERENCES

American Trucking Association. *Marketplace*. www.truck line.com

Autoliv Inc. *Illustrations* (retrieved August 2001). www.autoliv.com

Carfax Vehicle History Reports. www.carfax.com

Colorado Department of Revenue. *Colorado Driver Handbook*, Part 3 (retrieved August 2011). www.colorado. gov/cs/Satellite/Revenue-MV/RMV/1212657832969

Commercial Vehicle Safety Alliance. *Out of Service Criteria* (retrieved August 2011). www.cvsa.org

Consumer Reports. www.consumerreports.org

Federal Highway Administration (FHWA). *FHWA Vehicle Types* (retrieved August 2011). www.fhwa.dot.gov/ policy/ohpi/vehclass.html

Federal Motor Carrier Safety Administration (FMCSA). *Commercial Driver's License Program (CDL/CDLIS)* (retrieved August 2011). www.fmcsa.dot.gov/ registration-licensing/cdl/cdl.html

———. *Part 396: Inspection, Repair, and Maintenance*. www. fmcsa.dot.gov/rulesregulations/administration/fmcsr/ fmcsrguidedetails.asp?menukey=396

———. *Regulatory Guidance for Federal Motor Carrier Safety Regulations* (retrieved August 2011). www.fmcsa.dot.gov/ rules-regulations/administration/fmcsr/fmcsrguide.html

Insurance Institute for Highway Safety (IIHS). *A Procedure for Evaluating Motor Vehicle Head Restraints* (Volume 2), Research Council for Automobile Repairs. www.rcar. org/papers.htm

———. April 1997. *Status Report* 32(4):2.

———. October 2002. *Status Report* 37(9):2.

J. J. Keller & Associates, Inc. 2011. *2011 Transport Catalog*. www.issuu.com/jjkeller/docs_2011_transport

National Highway Traffic Safety Administration (NHTSA). Office of Defects Investigation. www-odi.nhtsa.dot. gov/cars/problems/recalls

———. *Buying a Safer Car 2007*. www.safercar.gov/ BASC2007

———. *Airbags*. www.safercar.gov/airbags/index.html

———. *Buying a Safer Car* (retrieved August 2011). www. safecar.gov

———. *Event Data Recorders (EDRs)* (retrieved November 8, 2011). www.nhtsa.gov/EDRs

———. *Rollovers*. www.safercar.gov/Rollover/Index.html

Seiffert, U., and L. Wech. 2003. *Automotive Safety Handbook*. London: Professional Engineering Publishing.

United States Department of Energy Efficiency and Renewable Energy and United States Environmental Protection Agency. *Quick Reference Guide to Federal Motor Vehicle Safety Standards* (retrieved September 23, 2005). www.fueleconomy.gov

United States Department of Transportation. *Quick Reference Guide to Federal Motor Vehicle Safety Standards* (retrieved March 2004). www.nhtsa.gov/cars/rules/ standards/FMVSS-Regs/index.html

United States Environmental Protection Agency. 2011. *Green Vehicle Guide*. www.epa.gov/greenvehicles

ADDITIONAL READING

SAFE DRIVING FOR EVERY SEASON*

Philip Moser
Advanced Driver Training Services
Trooper, PA

Introduction

Have you ever heard of an affliction known as "Seasonal Driving Amnesia" (SDA)? Don't feel bad if you haven't; it was "invented" for the purposes of this article. However, just because it was made up does not mean that it doesn't really exist. Think about it. For those of you who drive in areas that receive snow, have you ever noticed that there are an inordinate number of vehicle crashes during the first snowfall of the season? Why does this happen!? Do people forget how to drive in the snow from one year to the next? Do they forget that, when the roads are slippery, they need to slow down and leave a greater following distance? There is a case here to substantiate the existence of SDA.

In reality, there are specific driving dangers and challenges associated with all four of the seasons. This article covers each of these seasonal issues and provides solutions that will help drivers remain safe throughout the entire year.

Spring

Spring is such a wonderful time of year. For many, this is the season of renewal. The weather isgetting warmer, flowers are blooming, the rain is falling and, as a result, cars are hydroplaning.Spring brings a set of specific driving dangers and challenges.

Rain

April showers bring May flowers and hazardous driving conditions. The steady and prolongedrainstorms associated with spring create challenges on the roadways. Each of these will beaddressed separately.

Lights

Many vehicles have daytime running lights (DRLs). This is fantastic. Having lights on in the front of the vehicle decreases the risk of a vehicle-to-vehicle daytime frontal collision by 25%. If you do not have DRLs, turn on your headlights. If you have a vehicle that has the "auto" position on your light switch, you need to be cautious during inclement weather. If you have an "auto" position, all you need to do is place the switch in this position and the lights turn on automatically when it begins to get dark. There is a sensor on the dashboard that detects darkening conditions and automatically turns on the vehicle's headlights and taillights. What you need to be aware of is that, during normal lighting conditions, only the DRLs will be illuminated in the front of the vehicle. If it begins to rain, or if there is fog, it may not get dark enough for all of the lights to turn on automatically. In bad weather. you definitely want your taillights lit. You want to be visible to those who are approaching from behind. A simple rule to follow is: Wipers on/Light switch on. For those areas that have a "lights on during bad weather" law, DRLs do not fulfill the requirement. You must turn on all of your lights.

Wipers

Most drivers realize that they need to replace their wiper blades when they turn on their wipers and they aren't getting the job done. There are streaks and gaps and the wipers are jumping across the windshield like a squirrel that has just downed a double-shot espresso. Typically, the next time that these same drivers remember that they need to replace their wipers is the next time it rains and they can't see a thing. Get into the habit of replacing your wipers at the beginning of each season. By doing so, you will be assured that you will be able to see where you are going when there is bad weather. This will help you avoid all of those other drivers with worn out wiper blades.

Tires

If we all lived in areas where we always had dry clean road surfaces to drive on, the safest tires we could have on our vehicles would be racing slicks; in other words, smooth tires that have no tread. These tires provide a greater amount of tire to road surface contact and therefore provide more traction. The reason we have tread on our tires is because we do have to drive in rain, fog, slush and snow.

The tread design helps the tire to cut through and dissipate the moisture, snow, mud, slush etc. This tread design will only work properly if the tire is inflated properly. Check your owner's manual, the inside of the vehicle's door jam, or the sidewall of the tire to determine what the proper air pressure is. To avoid a false high reading, always check the tire when it is cold. Considering that a tire's air pressure can change with the hit of every chuck hole on the road, it is important to get into the habit of checking your vehicle's tire air pressure on a weekly basis. Also, you want to be certain that the depth of the tread is sufficient. You may have heard of using a typical U.S. penny to check the tread depth. If you place the penny into the tire tread and the top Lincoln's head is exposed, there is not enough tread for the tire to work effectively in bad weather. Replace that tire.

Hydroplaning

Hydroplaning occurs when one, two, three or all four of your vehicle's tires ride on top of the water, thus losing contact with the road surface. If all four of your tires are hydroplaning, unless you have a rudder for your vehicle, you have lost control. The two tires that typically hydroplane first are the front tires. This stands to reason, considering that they are the first to encounter the water. The rear tires usually track behind the front tires after the water has been dissipated by the front tires.

Hydroplaning occurs for a number of reasons. The most common cause of hydroplaning is speed. The faster a vehicle travels, the more water it encounters and the less time the tread has to disperse the water. A simple solution is to slow down. This seems simple enough. However, the mistake that many drivers make is not allowing more time to arrive at their destinations when it is raining. As a result, they will drive at the same speed on the wet road as they would on a dry road. To make matters worse, in the likely event of a weather-related crash, the traffic is going to be backed up, and once the driver clears the crash area, will now drive even faster to make up for the time lost due to the heavy traffic. All of this was probably created by a driver who failed to allow more travel time, even though it was raining. It's all one big, ongoing weather-related crash zone.

Another reason hydroplaning occurs is due to improperly inflated tires. As stated earlier, it is very important to check the vehicle's tire pressure. If a tire is underinflated, the center of the tire will suck in allowing only the edges to touch. If the tire is over inflated, only the center of the tire will make contact.

High water is another reason why vehicles hydroplane. Avoid driving in puddled areas, especially at higher speeds. Scan well ahead and look for water being thrown up by other vehicles in order to determine where these areas of high water are located.

Do not use cruise control when it is raining. If a vehicle hydroplanes, and the cruise control is set, it may give the cruise control a false reading and the vehicle will actually accelerate at a time when power should be decreased to the drive wheels of the vehicle.

If you find yourself in a hydroplane, come off the gas, do not over steer the vehicle and reduce your speed gently. You do not want to apply heavy brake pressure. Stab lightly at the brakes in quick successions in order to reduce the vehicle's speed.

Allergies

Another challenge created by the spring season is allergies. Every year, there are reported instances of "sneeze accidents." These collisions occur when a driver experiences a series of sneezes in a row while they are driving. Drivers involved in these incidents have been known to swerve off the road, into other traffic lanes and have struck other vehicles from behind. If you find yourself sneezing, try to hold the wheel steady and avoid any unintended quick steering maneuvers.

Another situation that is created by allergies is impaired driving due to allergy medications. These medications may be purchased over the counter or they may be prescribed medications. Either way, they can, and do cause impairment behind the wheel. Many drivers are surprised that they can be charged for driving under the influence by simply taking an allergy medication. Read all warnings on all medications. Ask your doctor or pharmacist about the risk of impairment. Lastly, if you are taking a medication for the first time, take it at a time when you do not have to drive. You want to see what effect the medication has on you prior to getting behind the wheel.

Summer

AHHH—The good old summertime! For many, this is the time for vacation. The time of year when you can get away from work and get some much needed rest and relaxation. You spend time with your family and recharge your battery. This is also a time for drunk driving due to summer holidays, sporting events and backyard barbeques. During the summer you can also count on sudden and severe weather, more pedestrians on the roads and fatigue-related crashes. Not exactly a Beach Boys song, but it is the reality of this season.

Vacation

Driver safety typically does not come to mind when people are thinking of vacation. However, understanding the risks associated with driving to, from and while on vacation can prevent a vacation from turning into a nightmare.

Fatigue

There are many drivers who, when driving to a vacation destination, refuse to stop for a rest. They believe that any time spent stopping will decrease the amount of their expected vacation "fun" time. The fact that the rest of their family requires a much-needed break means nothing to this marathon driver. This is not only inconsiderate; it is just plain unsafe. Fatigue can come upon a driver very rapidly. A fatigued driver is just as dangerous as an alcohol, or drug-impaired driver. There are a number of tricks fatigued drivers will utilize in order to combat their impaired condition. Rolling the windows down and turning the air conditioning to the arctic setting, turning up music to high levels, and consuming mass quantities of caffeinated beverages are all very common. Drivers who utilize these methods are commonly cold, suffer hearing loss and urgently need to utilize restroom facilities, but they are still tired. The only true way to combat fatigue is to rest. If you have not had enough sleep, do not drive. Even if you have had enough rest, you should stop at least every two hours. Some will argue that, if they stop that often, they will never get to their destination. If they don't stop, they may very well not arrive at their destination at all. Vacation crashes related to fatigue are unfortunately all too common.

Sudden and Severe Weather

Summer thunderstorms create obvious and unique driving hazards. If you encounter a torrential downpour, turn your light switch to the full on position, slow down, and consider finding a safe place to legally park. Get off the road at the nearest exit and find a safe parking lot to sit in until the storm blows over. For obvious safety reasons, do not park under trees and power lines. Avoid stopping along the side of the road. Crashes occur when other drivers see vehicles on the side of the road, and due to the decreased sight distance caused by the storm, assume that this is a travel lane. If conditions are so severe that you are having difficulty seeing the hood of your vehicle, you must understand that other drivers are going to have trouble seeing you. In these conditions consider turning on your vehicle's emergency flashers. Some areas have laws that forbid the use of emergency flashers while driving. Common sense must prevail here. Consider your conditions and decide what the safest course of action is.

Summer Events and Alcohol

Parties, picnics and sporting events are very common summer activities. For many of these, alcohol is included as the beverage of choice. As a society, we are geared towards this. Think of all of the advertisements that depict people at summertime gatherings having a great time as they drink down icy cold alcoholic beverages. They all appear to be having the time of their lives, and the beverages play a large role in these fun festivities. At the end of many of these advertisements, there is a quick statement that tells us to "Please drink responsibly." These notices are similar to car alarms; nobody pays attention to them. Every driver has to make the decision to not drink and drive. It is truly a personal decision. The difficulty with summertime gatherings is that consuming alcoholic beverages is the norm. Many people feel left out if they don't participate. This leads to drunk driving, and this leads to motor vehicle crashes and all of the associated hardships.

Judgment is one of the first things affected by alcohol. There are numerous accounts of people who become aggressive and loud after drinking. These people won't back down and have been known to pick on the biggest, meanest and strongest person they can find. Many times these people have their heads handed to them, but at the time, due to their alcohol related impaired judgment, these inebriated pugilists actually thought they would win. The same is true with impaired judgment regarding driving. People who drink think that they are capable of safe driving. The think they are "all right" to drive. This is the alcohol talking. Considering that judgment is impaired as soon as we begin to drink, arrangements need to be made prior to the first drink. Plan to stay at the location of the event, have a designated driver, or have it arranged that a cab will be called for you. If you are hosting an event, it is your responsibility to make sure others do not attempt to drive after they have consumed alcohol. Let your guests know ahead of time that this is a requirement at your event.

As drivers, we need to be on the lookout for impaired drivers. This is especially true during the holidays and when driving in the vicinity of sports venues. If you see any of the following driving activities, it is very possible that you are witnessing a drunk driver:

- Weaving within a lane from the center line to side marker line
- Fluctuations in speed for no apparent reason
- Erratic braking
- Last-second stops for red lights and stops signs
- Failure to pull away when a light turns green
- Cutting corners wide and cutting corners short
- Failure to dim high beam lights at night
- Driving with no lights or just parking lights at night
- Tailgating you and following your every move

If you spot a suspected drunk driver, and they are in front of you, keep them there. You do not want to pass a suspected impaired driver. If they in front of you, they can't hit you. If you want to notify the police, pull off to a safe place and provide a description of the vehicle and the route of travel. Do not get too close. Drunk drivers are dangerous and unpredictable.

Motorcycles, Bicycles and Pedestrians

With warm weather, there is an increase in the number of motorcyclists, bicyclists and pedestrians using our streets. The best advice that can be given to avoid conflict with these individuals is to look more than once. In other words, when you come to an intersection, get into the habit of scanning often to make sure that you have not missed seeing an approaching motorcycle, bicycle or pedestrian. They are much harder to see than a typical car, and they may blend into the surroundings. Be aware of this and be diligent. Also, use caution when driving in areas where there may be increased pedestrian activity, such as parks and pool areas.

Autumn

Fall is such a wonderful time of year. For many there is a change in the weather. The leaves are changing, there is a crisp coolness in the air and the holiday season is approaching. This season also means that school is back in session, leaves are on the roadways, frost is on windshields, and the deer are on the move.

Schools in

This means buses, increased pedestrian traffic in school zones and overloaded and stressed schedules for parents that have children who are involved in school activities.

Learn the school bus routes in the areas where you drive. Plan your route accordingly so that you can avoid getting behind a bus that makes frequent stops to pick up and drop off school students. Besides not being delayed by the bus, you can avoid the inevitable likelihood of a kid in the back seat of the bus making faces at you.

Watch for children going to and from school. May times they are distracted by one another and they may not be doing everything necessary in order to remain safe. Use extra caution.

If you are the parent of a child who is involved in school activities, you understand the stress associated with making sure that the kids are dropped off and picked up from their activities in a timely manner. If you have more than one child involved with school activities, you may want to consider being cloned. Since cloning is not a viable solution, consider arranging your work schedule so that you minimize those times where schedules are tight. Also, enlist the help of relatives, neighbors and other parents. You cannot be at two places at once. Ask for help.

Leaves

The fall foliage is very pleasant to look at. However, when the leaves begin to fall they can mix with moisture on the roadway and create slick conditions. Be aware of this and adjust your driving accordingly. Slow down on curves where there are overhanging trees and watch for leaf-covered intersections where it may be difficult to stop.

Frost

Frost on vehicle windows drastically cuts down on visibility. The obvious solution is to scrape your windows and/ or let the vehicle run until they are defrosted. However, how many Times have you seen somebody driving down the road with the only cleared-off area directly in front of the driver, and it is about the size of an orange? Take the time to clear your windows. Get up earlier if you have to make sure you have the time to accomplish this task. The few minutes it takes to clear off the windows of your vehicle could save you or someone else a life.

Deer

Autumn is the time of year when deer go into rut. In other words, this is their breeding season. During this time, they are more active, and, as a result, they are on roadways a great deal more. Also, in many areas, this is the time of year when deer hunting season occurs. This will also cause deer to be on the move. If you encounter a deer on the road, avoid the urge to swerve. Many drivers have become involved in more severe crashes as a result of trying to avoid a deer collision. Slow down in the areas where you know there are higher deer populations. Many times these areas are indicated by deer crossing signs. Use your high beam lights as much as legally possible at night and watch for their reflective eyes. If you see one deer, expect more. They are herd animals.

Winter

Winter is such a wondrous time. The joys associated with the holidays, the cool weather and all of the year-end events. Winter also brings issues with weather, impaired driving associated with holiday parties", snow birds" and year-end work related pushes.

Slipping and Sliding

With the onset of frozen precipitation, there is an obvious increase for the risk of skid related crashes. There are basically three skids that are associated with winter driving. They are the oversteer, the understeer and the all-wheel skid. Each of these will be addressed separately.

The Oversteer

This is the situation where the rear of your vehicle spins to the left or right. In this situation, come off the gas and don't touch the brake. Turn your steering wheel in the direction of the skid. In other words, if the rear of your vehicle slides to the right, turn the steering wheel to the right. If it turns to the left, turn the steering wheel to the left. Turn the wheel far enough to bring the vehicle back to a straight path. As soon as the vehicle is straight, recover your steering back to center. This will prevent you from going into a secondary skid.

The Understeer

An *understeer* occurs when you try to turn your vehicle but the front end plows out in a straight line. This happens at bends in the road, on ramps and when attempting to make turns. In this situation, look where you want to go. This may sound unimportant, but if you look where you want to go, you will react. If you stare at the area where the vehicle is plowing out towards, you may freeze up. Come off the gas. You can attempt to slow down by stabbing lightly at the brake. Do not apply heavy brake pressure and do not oversteer the vehicle.

All-wheel Skid

This type of skid has been pretty much eliminated now that most vehicles come equipped with anti-lock brakes as standard equipment. An all-wheel skid occurs with a vehicle has standard brakes and a driver applies too much brake pressure and the tires lock up. Simply release brake pressure and the skid will end.

Holiday Parties

As with summer parties and picnics, winter holiday parties increase the risk of impaired driving. Follow the same guidelines discussed earlier in this article to avoid being an impaired driver and to avoid drunk drivers.

"Snow Birds"

For those who live in warm weather climates, you probably have an increase in population during the winter months. Just as the robins and geese migrate south, there is a migration of people who head south in order to avoid the cold winter weather of the north. Be aware of this increased traffic, of people who are driving in unfamiliar areas and of drivers who may have reduced skill levels due to age related reductions in hearing, sight and reflexes.

Year-end Push

For those who drive as part of their work, the end of the year often brings with it an increase in activity in order to meet year-end work demands. This increase in activity can lead to overloaded schedules, and distracted driving. Be realistic with your schedule and remain focused when you are behind the wheel. Understand that the most important task you accomplish each day is arriving home safely.

Final Thoughts

Realizing that every season presents certain challenges, understanding those challenges and preparing accordingly will assist you with being safe. This article pointed out some of the hazards associated with each of the seasons. The areas where you drive may have specific hazards that you need to address. Driving is a skill that must be worked on every time you get behind the wheel. Be diligent, be safe and don't forget that you must adjust your driving to all of the seasonal conditions. You don't want to be accused of being afflicted with SDA.

Identifying and Changing Behaviors That Contribute to Truck Driver Injuries*

Peter Van Dyne, MA, CSP, CFPS

Technical Director

Liberty Mutual Insurance Milwaukee, WI

Introduction

The cost of worker injuries has a significant impact on trucking operations. The impact goes beyond the cost workers compensation medical and indemnity. Injuries are a significant disruption to the lives of the workers and can take a good driver off the road. The cost of your worker compensation insurance could be double that of a competitor with the same size of operation. Not being able to control the costs of injuries has caused some trucking companies to go out of business.

Liberty Mutual's best practice studies, meeting with individual truckers, and comparing programs shows us companies can be run differently and have successful programs. Management styles and practices vary but common styles or safety program elements exist at companies with lower crash or injury rates. These are:

- Select drivers based on their history and ability to perform the job
- Establish and communicate expectations on how jobs should be performed
- Monitor performance against the expectations
- Provide feedback on performance
- Change behavior that does not meet expectations
- Document their policies and actions

This report will provide you with an understanding of the:

- Work activities responsible for injuries in the trucking industry
- Work activities your employees were engaged in when they were injured
- How your injury rates compare to other trucking operations
- Steps you can take to reduce the risk of injuries with your work force

Management actions, programs, policies, and involvement in the day to day activities provide you with a greater chance of reducing the potential for injuries compared with "driver training". Our report focuses on specific steps you can take to reduce your cost of risk. Each company will need to identify tasks their drivers perform and have expectations for performing those tasks that reduce the potential for injuries. The report is intended to lay out a basic framework for a process to identify risk and reduce exposure.

Trucking Industry Loss Sources

Liberty Mutual conducted a study of trucking injuries for the Standard Industrial Classification code 42XX. The study reviewed 5 years of injury data valued shortly after the end of the 5 year time period. There were 37,000 injuries with costs in the study. The 7,000 injuries with incurred costs (current paid and reserved) greater than $9,999 were reviewed. The injury description allowed us to identify the task the worker was preforming when the injury occurred.

Some injury activities have the same exposure across all types of trucking. The frequency of the task will vary by operation, such as LTL drivers, who enter and exit their vehicles more frequently than long haul drivers. Some tasks, such as tarp work, will be limited to specific types of operations and specific loads. Each of the activities identified should have a control plan when the work activity is part of the operation.

The tasks that were responsible for 2% or more of the total incurred costs are shown in Table 1.

Comparing Injury Rates

Injury rates cannot be compared across all trucking companies due to the different work tasks and frequency of the common tasks. To understand how your injury frequency and costs compare to other truckers the comparison must be made to truckers doing the same type or types of work. This presents challenges when a trucking company has multiple operations or divisions.

To provide you with as close of a comparison as possible, we looked at trucking companies we insure and assigned a primary type of trucking based on our

TABLE 1

Injury Work Tasks by % of Cost and Frequency Ranked by % of Costs

Activity	% of Injuries	% of Incurred Costs
Crashes (driving or riding)	17%	20%
Handling cargo	14%	12%
Tractor entry and exit	11%	11%
Snow and ice fall	5%	5%
Parking lot or yard fall	5%	5%
Load securement	5%	5%
Landing gear	4%	4%
Trailer doors	4%	3%
Maintenance	4%	3%
Driving (in cab ergonomics)	3%	2%
Trailer entry or exit	2%	2%
Forklift incident	2%	2%
5th wheel	2%	2%
Flatbed falls	1%	2%
Tandems	2%	2%
Main Loss Source Totals	**80%**	**81%**
Grand Total	**100%**	**100%**

information, company web sites and public sources. This information was used to calculate benchmarks for each of the major types of trucking.

Measuring injury rates will show what has happened and may not be a valid measure of risk. Performance measures discussed in the next section can will help you measure risk based on observing behaviors.

The data shown below represents the most recently completed policy year for the truckers with workers compensation coverage. This is the most complete data that would represent all truckers insured by our Commercial Market. The % of truckers by type will change from year to year and injury exposures can vary by year based on weather, business conditions and other factors. Mixed types of truckers will include multiple types of equipment and will frequently have other operations such as

dock and or warehousing. The loss valuation date will vary slightly by company which can impact the incurred loss rate but should have minimal impact on the claims frequency rates.

Tracking injury rates should be part of your internal process for establishing and tracking goals. Injury rates can be measured using miles, stops or loads. When your operations (type of equipment, length of haul, number of stops per load, etc.) have not changed, miles, stops or loads can be used. When operations change, the exposure measurements can be changed to allow you to measure injuries based on your operations. Goals should be set using a rate to adjust for an increase or decrease in business activity. The example below shows how injury rates could be tracked to show progress or changes over time.

TABLE 3

Injury Rates in Miles

Calendar Year	Miles driven	Total Injury Count	Lost Time Injury Count	Injuries per Million	Lost Time Injuries per Million
2009	10,000,000	12	4	1.20	0.40
2010	9,500,000	12	5	1.26	0.53
2011	11,000,000	12	3	1.09	0.27

TABLE 4

Injury Rates in Loads hauled

Calendar Year	Loads hauled	Total Injury Count	Lost Time Injury Count	Injuries per 1,000 Loads	Lost Time Injuries per 1,000 Loads
2009	16,667	12	4	0.72	0.24
2010	15,833	12	5	0.76	0.32
2011	18,333	12	3	0.65	0.16

TABLE 2

Injury Benchmark Comparison

Type of Trucker	% of Truckers accounting for 5% or more of total	Total Claims w/ Cost Per Million Of Payroll	Indemnity Claims Per Million Of Payroll	Total Incurred Loss Per Million Of Payroll
Full Load Vans	34%	1.02	0.60	$18,096
Mixed Types	20%	1.67	0.83	$6,877
LTL	12%	2.33	0.94	$15,097
Tanker and Dumps	11%	1.47	0.79	$30,992
Moving and storage	7%	1.25	0.60	$10,538
Flatbed	5%	1.10	0.60	$23,311
All Other Types Combined	12%	1.76	0.79	$24,050
Overall Weighted Average		1.43	0.72	$16,534

Reducing Exposure to Injuries

Reducing the exposure to injuries requires attention in many areas. The headings outlined in the Executive Summary provide a framework for developing a strategy to compare your current programs and practices to those found at companies with lower injury rates.

Select drivers based on their history and ability to perform the job

Crashes have a significant impact on the cost and frequency of injuries. Driving records have been shown to be a strong indicator of which drivers are more likely to be involved in crashes. Having selection criteria that uses past driving record histories, violations from the FMCSA PSP (Pre Screening Program) and work histories (number of companies worked for, references, past experience) help assure that drivers with a disregard for motor vehicle safety and company policies are not placed into positions that require the operation of motor vehicles.

In addition to operation of motor vehicles most driving jobs have physical demands. Some tasks are required by the FMCSA or state DOT such as conducting pre-trip inspections. In addition to the required tasks, drivers must be able to get in and out of the vehicles, open trailer doors, climb into or on to the trailer and perform tasks associated with securing loads or handling cargo. Trucking companies that identify the task, develop and communicate steps to be used to complete the task and verify drivers offered positions can perform the tasks have lower exposure to injuries have lower exposure to injuries.

Have and communicate expectations on how jobs should be performed

Having and communicating work task expectations is more complex than providing training. The concepts and theories outlined in commercially available training materials must be an integral part of your company expectations. Drivers engage in a variety of tasks that use the same part of the body. To reduce the potential for drivers sustaining injuries from overuse that occurs over a working lifetime, tasks must be performed in a way that reduces the impact on their bodies. Drivers that jump from a vehicle or off the last step of the vehicle are more likely to sustain injuries over time than those that face the vehicle and step down while maintaining 3 points of contact. In addition drivers that do not exit a vehicle put additional stress on the body when reaching behind them as the climb down facing away from the vehicle.

Each work task a driver is expected to perform should be reviewed and the steps of that task outlined and documented. Tasks that have higher risk should be avoided when possible. Not all tasks can be eliminated

and injuries from tasks such as entering and exiting the vehicle are typically a result of how the task is performed. Identifying the task components, documenting how the tasks should be performed and effectively communicating the task expectations helps assure drivers understand the risk and how they are expected to complete the task required of them.

Monitor performance against the expectations

Once expectations have been developed, documented and effectively communicated actual work practices must be compared to the expectations in a quantifiable way. Monitoring performance with observations or through the use of technology allows you to measure risk. This can be on an individual level or to measure overall compliance with the expectations. Observations on a larger scale can be used to identify compliance with a group of expectations to identify task to focus on during future observations.

Some driving behaviors that can contribute to serious types of crashes can be identified by looking at driver performance data. The data can be gathered by downloading ECM data or using GPS tracking data. Some satellite systems will combine the two data sources. When data is available it can be used to look for the following:

- Compliance with route plans to identify drivers that are off route using additional fuel or taking routes that have higher crash potential.
- Speeding- speeds above posted may be a stronger indicator of crash potential than total speed on a freeway. Drivers traveling at 50 MPH in a 35 MPH zone may have higher crash potential than drivers operating at the top governor speed. Relying on governors may not be effective in reducing speed related crashes.
- % of time in cruise control when combined with brake actuations per 1,000 miles may identify drivers with frequent speed changes that can be an indicator of drivers that do not maintain adequate following distance
- Sudden decelerations or hard braking incidents can be another indicator of drivers which do not have adequate look ahead when driving

When driver performance data is available and can be used to compare drivers operating similar equipment, with similar loads on similar routes, drivers with habits that use extra fuel or make crashes more likely can be identified.

Observations on your property, on streets near your property or during in-vehicle observations can also be used to identify performance that does not meet expectations. If drivers are not performing tasks as expected when in your yard or on your property it is unlikely they will perform tasks as expected once they leave your property or lot. The tasks to be observed should be based on the main injury producing tasks identified in our study, on past observation results and work task activities identified in a review of your past injuries. Key areas to observe would typically include tasks outlined below and can be summarized in a spreadsheet program to measure the % safe.

Provide feedback on performance

Noticing or measuring driver performance will have little impact on performance unless drivers receive feedback on how their performance compares to the expected performance. Driver scorecards can be used for vehicle operation performance to show a driver how they compare to the median or middle of the pack driver.

Driver feedback on work tasks is typically most effective when the task is being done or as soon after as possible. Conversations and follow up actions should be documented so drivers not performing tasks as expected can be identified. Some performance will be more and should have stronger actions or consequences. The tolerance for performance that does not meet expectations will vary by task. Performance that would indicate stronger responses from management include texting while driving, following too close or failure to use vehicle restraints.

Not observing performance or not addressing behaviors not meeting the documented expectations is a form of feedback. This feedback tells drivers how they are performing a task is acceptable. Managers and supervisors must be engaged in the process of providing feedback to reduce the risk of injuries.

Change behavior that does not meet expectations

Most crashes and injuries in the trucking industry are caused by behaviors rather than a lack of knowledge.

Addressing performance that does not meet expectations with "retraining" is not likely to have significant impact on behaviors or injury rates. Coaching drivers on how to perform tasks helps reduce the risk of injury from accumulated abuse or overuse of parts of their bodies. Where drivers will not perform tasks as expected, a progressive discipline system should be used to reduce the risk of injury for their sake and the companies.

Document policies and actions

Performance measurement and improvement systems function best when the expectations, measurements and coaching discussions are documented. Expectations which are kept brief enough to tell the story and illustrated with pictures showing how task should be performed help assure drivers understand how they are expected to perform their work tasks. Practical or written tests help assure the knowledge was gained and show workers the company believes an understanding of the knowledge is an important job skill. Pre-injury risk measures (% safe behaviors) help identify risk prior to an injury occurring and will change over time and as operations and equipment changes. Documenting your expectations and activities help assure drivers receive a consistent message.

Program Elements

Program policies and practices typically found at companies with lower crash and injury rates include:

Select drivers based on their history and ability to perform the job

- Has MVR driving record criteria for current and prospective drivers that does not allow more than 3 moving violations in the past 3 years.

TABLE 5

Sample Driver Observations				
Observed work task	Desired performance	# of times performed as expected	# of times not performed as expected	% performed as expected
Tractor entry and or exit	Driver has 3 points of contact, faces equipment, does not carry things when climbing and has proper foot and hand position on steps and grab bars.	8	2	80%
Use of seat belts	Seat belts are worn when vehicle is in motion or while on public roads.	12	0	100%
Raising/ lowering landing gears	Driver uses wide stance, has firm grip on handle, keeps face away from handle and does not use 2 finger spin technique.	4	1	80%
Post trip inspections	Driver walked around rig prior to dropping trailer and looked at condition of the tractor and trailer.	6	2	75%
Opening trailer doors	Driver taps door to check for fallen cargo, stands to the side when opening the door, walks to the side of the door and secures the door to the trailer.	3	1	75%

TABLE 6

Sample Driver Scorecard

Driver Name	Sample Driver
Date of Review	10-Nov-08

	Median	Your Results	% of Median
Vehicle ID #		108	
Trip end date		9/24/2008	
Trip miles	26516	98183	370%
Fuel economy	7.34	7.11	97%
Avg. drive load	50%	56%	112%
Avg. vehicle speed	37.55	50.7	135%
Driving %	71.62%	74.49%	104%
Driving economy	7.56	7.26	96%
Veh. Speed limiting %	6.03%	14.62%	243%
Speeding A (66-71 MPH)	2650	60673	2290%
Speeding B (>71 MPH)	20	28295	141475%
Highest Speed	75.75	83.0	110%
Idle %	28.4%	25.5%	90%
Stop idle %	12.1%	13.4%	110%
Hard brake count	32	95	302%
Brake count	27626	55576	201%
Speeding B per 1,000 miles	0.75	288.19	38208%
Hard brakes per 1,000 miles	1.19	0.97	81%
Brake count per 1,000 miles	1042	566	54%

	Miles per year	MPG	Fuel cost per gallon	Total Fuel cost per year
Median	80,000	7.34	$4.00	$43,626
You	80,000	7.11	$4.00	$45,007
			Difference	**-$1,381**

- Has MVR criteria that does not allow for serious violations in the past 5 years.
- Has identified essential job functions and includes a driver's ability to do the job as part of the post offer pre-hire qualification process.

Have and communicate expectations on how jobs should be performed

- Company has a drivers handbook or manual that illustrates how driver tasks should be performed and covers all driver tasks shown in the trucking industry loss source section that are performed by their drivers.
- Driver handbook or manuals show company equipment and drivers performing tasks as expected and illustrates actions to be avoided to reduce the potential for injury.
- Driver handbook or manual training uses a knowledge checker or practical application test to verify drivers have gained needed knowledge with documented testing protocols.
- Driving expectations include speed, following distance, use of seat belts and mirror alignment sections.
- Use care and inspections for of tools, personal protective equipment and work materials are addressed in the expectations.
- Driver expectations include equipment inspections and process for reporting defective equipment.

Monitor performance against the expectations

- Driving performance is measured using in-vehicle technology to verify drivers follow route plans, comply with posted speed limits and do not violate company policies on hours of operation.
- Observations are conducted to verify drivers are performing tasks as expected when working in yards or other areas of the property.
- Observations off site or at property entrances/exits are made to verify driver compliance with seat belt policies.
- Observations are a combination of working directly with drivers and observations conducted at a distance when drivers do not know they are being observed.
- Driver performance is evaluated in multiple areas to identify drivers most in need of attention or closer supervision.

Provide feedback on performance

- Observations are summarized to measure the % of drivers observed performing tasks as expected.
- Goals are established for % of safe (i.e. performing tasks as expected) behavior.
- Drivers receive individual feedback on observations to coach them on performance that does not meet expectations and on performance that meets expectations to reinforce performing tasks as expected.
- Making observations is part of all managers and supervisors jobs to identify performance that does not meet expectations.

Change behavior that does not meet expectations

- A progressive discipline system exists to assure that repeat performance that does not meet expectations is addressed.

- The progressive discipline system involves actions in addition to "retraining" when performance issues have been identified.
- Coaching sheets or other documented materials are used to verify that all managers or supervisors providing feedback are delivering a consistent message on how work tasks should be performed.

Document their policies and actions

- Work task expectations are documented using company equipment to show how work tasks should be performed.
- The observation process has records showing when they were conducted and actions taken to follow up on performance meeting and not meeting expectations.
- Training and policy communication are documented to show names, date and content of the communication.
- Equipment and facility inspections are documented and corrective action is documented when actions are needed to reduce exposure to injuries.

Chapter 4

Vehicle Engineering and Ergonomics

Dennis R. Andrews

LEARNING OBJECTIVES

- Be able to describe the dynamics of the fleet vehicle.

- Mathematically determine the safe operations of fleet vehicles.

- Identify safe human factors for fleet operations in different environments.

- Learn defensive driving maneuvers and methods.

- Recognize the safety implications presented by a workspace environment.

- Identify safety criteria for fleet operators and drivers.

- Understand occupant protection and the biomechanics that can cause injuries.

- Learn about safe operations during the material-handling process in fleet operations.

This chapter contains information relating to the commercial (trucks and buses) motor-vehicle fleet industry and loading and unloading facilities. The information included, while not all-inclusive, was obtained from the industry literature, articles, and the author's experience. The chapter has four major sections: Vehicle Engineering and Tests, Traffic Safety Principles, Vehicle Defensive Driving Tactics, and Ergonomic Issues.

The objective of this chapter is to supply information about and data for the fleet industry as researched by the author. Readers will gain useful new and supplementary knowledge of the fleet industry. The reference section and recommended reading section contain books and articles of interest to motor fleet operators and safety personnel concerning both fleet vehicles and fleet facilities.

The chapter includes information and data on roadway incidents (vehicle accidents), safety, and information for safety programs that will be of interest to fleet owners, fleet safety managers, fleet operations managers, fleet insurance managers, depot operations managers, and anyone else with an interest in motor-vehicle fleet operations and safety.

VEHICLE ENGINEERING AND TESTS

Vehicle Offtracking and Swept-Path Width

Special skills are required to operate commercial and fleet vehicles safely. Large vehicles such as multiaxle trucks and buses operate much differently from passenger vehicles, and their drivers must have special training and maintain concentration while driving to avoid accidents and injury. For example, drivers must learn how to turn and back up articulated vehicles because they require additional space for these maneuvers. Drivers must also be aware of *offtracking*, a term used to describe the difference between the radius of the path of the center of the steering axle and the center of the rear axle for box-type trucks. For articulated vehicles such as tractors and trailers, the spacing along the longitudinal axles of the hitch point must be considered during low-speed turns because the rear wheels do not follow the same path as the front wheels.

The *swept-path width* is the difference between the lateral distance of the inside rear wheels and outside front wheels during a turning maneuver for both box-type and articulated vehicles. The radius of the turn determines the offtracking and swept-path width. The offtracking amount is always less than the swept-path width since offtracking is a measurement from the center of the front and rear axles and the swept-path width is a measurement of the distance between the outside front wheel and the inside rear wheel during a turning maneuver. Buses and similar large vehicles have comparable maneuvering movements but smaller space requirements than do articulated vehicles such as tractors and trailers. Formulas are used to calculate the swept-path width and offtracking of large articulated vehicles and box-type trucks or buses. These formulas supply the necessary data for roadway design. They are particularly important for designing off-ramps for interstate highways and turnpikes as well as for training vehicle operators on proper turning maneuvers (see Figures 1 and 2 for more details).

The formula for low-speed offtracking of a standard two-axle, box-type truck with dual rear wheels is

$$OT \text{ (in feet)} = r_1 - r_2 \qquad (1)$$

where

r_1 = the turning radius of the front axle
r_2 = the turning radius of the rear axle

To determine the rear-axle turning radius use the following formula:

$$r_2 = \sqrt{(r_1^2 - l^2)} \qquad (2)$$

where

l = the wheelbase of the vehicle (the distance between the front and rear axles).

Consider a box-truck vehicle with a front-axle turning radius of 50 feet and a wheelbase of 10 feet (l), the radius of the rear axle is 49 feet (r_2). The calculated offtrack distance is equal to 1 foot (50 – 49). If the wheels of the rear axle are wider than those of the front axle, an adjustment must be made by dividing the difference in the width of the axles by two and adding that number to the result above. For example, if the outside width of the rear wheels is 8 feet and the outside width of the front wheels is 6 feet, the adjustment is 1 (8 – 6 = 2 ÷ 2 = 1). Adding this result to the 1 foot of calculated offtracking distance noted above, the offtracking amount is 2 feet. (Fricke 1990, 78-15–78-16). Since offtracking represents the difference in radius between the centers of both axles, the swept-path width is calculated by adding one-half of the width of each axle to the offtracking result.

A more complicated approach is necessary when dealing with the offtracking of large articulated tractor-trailers and similar vehicles. The formula for a tractor-trailer with ten wheels (3 axles) is

$$OT = r_1 - r_3 = r_1 - \sqrt{(r_1^2 + l_{ko}^2 - l^2 - l_2^2)} \qquad (3)$$

where

r_1 = the radius of the center of the front or steering axle

r_3 = the radius of the center of the rear axle

l_{ko} = the distance of the fifth wheel (also known as the kingpin, the point at which the trailer and tractor are connected) on the tractor to the center of the drive wheels of the tractor,

l = the wheelbase of the tractor

l_2 = the wheelbase from the tractor drive wheels to the rear trailer wheels

If the front-axle turning radius is 41 feet, the tractor wheelbase is 12 feet, the trailer wheelbase is 36 feet, and the fifth-wheel offset is 1.2 feet, the offtrack distance would be approximately 25.4 feet (Fricke 1990, 78-18–78-19). As with the box-truck example, the swept path can be calculated by adding one-half the width of both the front and rear axles to the offtrack distance. If the vehicle comprises a tractor and two trailers, also known as *doubles*, additional data are needed: the rearward overhang of the *pintel hitch* (the hitch between the first and second trailer) location, the length of the *dolly drawbar* (the attachment bar between the first and second trailer), and the wheelbase of the full trailer.

Low-speed offtracking occurs when a combination vehicle makes a low-speed turn—for example a 90-degree turn at an intersection—and the wheels of the rearmost trailer axle follow a path several feet inside the path of the tractor steering axle. Figure 1 illustrates low-speed

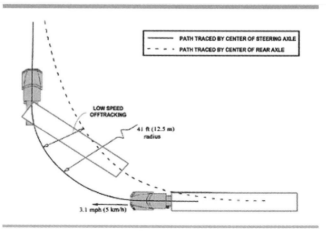

FIGURE 1. Low-Speed Offtracking
(*Source:* FHA 2007)

offtracking in a 90-degree turn for a tractor-semitrailer. Excessive low-speed offtracking makes it necessary for the driver to swing wide into adjacent lanes when making a turn to avoid climbing inside curbs, striking curbside fixed objects or other vehicles. On an exit ramp, excessive offtracking can result in the truck tracking inward onto the shoulder or up over inside curbs. For single trailer combinations, this performance attribute is affected primarily by the distance of the tractor kingpin to the center of the trailer rear axle or axle group. *Kingpin setting* refers to the truck-tractor fifth wheel connection point for the kingpin, which is located to the front of the semitrailer. For multitrailer combinations the effective wheelbase(s) of all the trailers in the combination, along with the tracking characteristics of the converter dollies, dictate low-speed offtracking. In general, longer wheelbases worsen low-speed offtracking.

High-speed offtracking results from the tendency of the rear of the truck to move outward due to the lateral acceleration of the vehicle as it makes a turn at higher speeds. Figure 2 illustrates high-speed offtracking for a standard tractor-semitrailer. The speed-dependent component of offtracking is primarily a function of the spacing between truck axles, the speed of the truck, and the radius of the turn; it is also dependent on the loads carried by the truck axles and the truck suspension characteristics (Fricke 1990).

An Analytical Approach

The Western Uniformity Scenario Analysis (DOT 2004) examines the impact that scenario truck configurations would have on freeway interchanges, at-grade intersections, mainline curves, and lane widths of the current roadway system. It determines what improvements would be needed to accommodate the new trucks, and estimates the costs of these improvements. The focus of this research is to compare the new truck configurations with the current tractor-semitrailers and LCVs operating in the scenario states.

Unlike the analysis for the *Comprehensive Truck Size and Weight (CTS&W) Study*, the base case-vehicle in this analysis varies by state, depending on that state's grandfather laws under the 1991 ISTEA freeze (DOT 2000). The chosen base case-vehicle represents the worst vehicle from an offtracking perspective currently allowed on the analyzed roadway segment. For example, if the worst offtracking vehicle currently allowed on the roadway is a Turnpike Double (TPD), then the TPD is used as the base case-vehicle for that road segment; if the Rocky Mountain Double (RMD) is the worst offtracking vehicle, then it is used as the base case-vehicle; and if the 53-foot tractor semitrailer has the worst offtracking, it is the base case-vehicle. Table 1 shows the base case RMD and TPD for each state. This precise framing of the base case-vehicle is an improvement to the *CTS&W Study*'s analysis that used the 48-foot tractor semitrailer at 80,000 pounds as the base case-vehicle for all roads (FMCSA 2000).

Table 2 shows the low-speed offtracking and swept path for the analyzed configurations. The measure is shown for a standard 90-degree, right-hand turn with a 42-foot radius, negotiated at a speed of 5 kilometers per hour. (Note that the *CTS&W Study* analyzed a 38-foot path radius.) Low-speed offtracking is the one measure where the STAA Double outperforms all the other configurations. The long TPD with twin 48-foot trailers performs the worst of the vehicles.

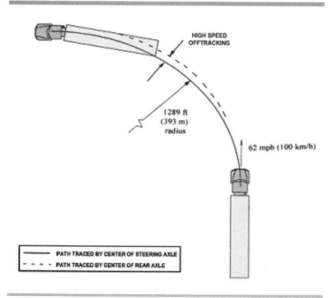

FIGURE 2. High-Speed Offtracking
(*Source:* FHA 2007)

TABLE 1

Base Case-Vehicles for the Scenario States		
State	**Rocky Mountain Double**	**Turnpike Double**
Colorado	43.5 + 31	48 + 48
Idaho	35 + 20	35 + 20
Kansas	48 + 28.5	45 + 45
Montana	38 + 28	45 + 45
Nebraska	38 + 20	38 + 20
Nevada	48 + 28.5	48 + 48
North Dakota	48 + 28.5	48 + 48
Oklahoma	48 + 28.5	48 + 48
Oregon	35 + 20	N/A
South Dakota	48 + 28.5	48 + 48
Utah	48 + 28.5	48 + 48
Washington	35 + 20	N/A
Wyoming	38 + 27	N/A

(DOT 2000)

TABLE 2

Low-Speed Offtracking and Swept Path of Vehicles

Vehicle Description*	Configuration**	Performance Data (ft)	
		Low-Speed Offtracking	Swept Path
Single (53″)	3-S2	16.12	24.12
STAA Double (2@28′)	2-S1-2	13.52	21.52
RMD (38′, 27′)	3-S2-3	18.57	26.57
RMD (38′, 27′)	3-S2-4	22.08	30.08
RMD (38′, 27′)	3-S2-2	21.54	29.54
RMD (35′, 20′)	3-S2-2	15.78	23.78
RMD (38′, 28′)	3-S2-4	20.06	28.06
RMD (38′, 20′)	3-S3-2	18.42	26.42
RMD (38′, 27′)	3-S2-4	21.02	29.02
RMD (43.5′, 31′)	3-S2-4	20.78	28.78
RMD (38′, 27′)	3-S3-4	19.13	27.13
RMD (48′, 28.5′)	3-S2-3	21.87	29.87
Short TPD (2@45′)	3-S2-4	27.98	35.98
Long TPD (2@48′)	3-S2-4	30.63	38.63
Triple A-Train (3@28″)	2-S1-2-2	20.38	28.38
Triple C-Train (3@28″)	2-S1-2-2	20.38	28.38

*Vehicle description shows the vehicle type where RMD is a Rocky Mountain Double and TPD is a Turnpike Double. The numbers in parenthesis give the length of each trailer.

**The first number in the series indicates the number of axles on the power unit, the next set refers to the number of axles supporting the trailing unit ("s" iindicates it is a semitrailer), and the subsequent numbers indicate the number of axles associated with the remaining trailing unit.

(DOT 2000)

Vehicle Power Requirements

Large vehicles, whether articulated or not, need sufficient power to operate safely on highways and streets so they can maintain a safe highway speed and pass safely. *Power* is the time rate of doing work, and the *maximum power* an engine can provide is a measure of its performance capability. The power generated by large vehicles can be determined from the formula (ITE 1990, 60–63):

$$P = RV \div 3600 \qquad (4)$$

where

P = the power used in kilowatts (1 kW = 1.341 horsepower; 1 hp = 550 foot-pounds per second)

R = the total resistance to motion of the truck and trailer

V = the speed of the vehicle in ft/s

3600 = a constant representing the seconds in 1 hr

Newton's laws of physics relating to force, mass, and acceleration scientifically demonstrate the need for additional power to haul heavy loads safely. *Force* is the product of mass and acceleration, and it is necessary to overcome inertia, air resistance, tire and roadway resistance, potential energy loss due to the grade or incline of a roadway, and any other conditions that require acceleration power. More force is needed to pull an 80,000-pound trailer than to pull a 20,000-pound trailer, especially along very steep, hilly streets in cities such as San Francisco, Seattle, and Pittsburgh. The average passenger vehicle requires less force to accelerate than a heavier vehicle on the same roadway.

The mass-to-power ratio is helpful in determining and comparing levels of performance. The ratio can be in watts and kilograms or horsepower and foot-pounds. This ratio is important in determining minimum requirements of a selected power plant for a vehicle with known load-carrying capabilities. When calculating this type of power ratio, consideration should be given to the power source—diesel or gasoline. Diesel engines produce more thrust than gasoline engines since diesel fuel is ignited by compression. For both maintenance and durability, the overwhelming choice for a commercial vehicle power source is a diesel engine rather than a gasoline engine. Diesel engines are much more expensive than gasoline engines due to their heavier construction. Power-requirement considerations should include vehicle operating ranges, locations, and conditions. Driving in a more mountainous terrain requires more horsepower than driving in a typical inner city unless the city has very steep and hilly streets.

The mass-to-power ratio is the measure of a vehicle's ability to accelerate and maintain speed up grades. Mass can be thought of as an indicator of resistance to motion—the higher the mass-to-power ratio, the less the acceleration performance, and the lower the mass-to-power ratio, the greater the acceleration performance. A typical passenger vehicle's mass-to-power ratio is 1550 kg (3425 lbs) to 140 kW (188 hp) of power. A tractor semi-trailer's is approximately 11,000 kg (24,310 lbs) to 240 kW (322 hp) of power (ITE 1990, 57–60). A typical passenger car has approximately 50 percent of the manufacturer's rated engine power available to travel 100 kilometers per hour (approximately 61 miles per hour); a large truck has approximately 94 percent of the manufacturer's rated engine power available. These estimates are useful in determining maximum acceleration rates and maximum speeds on grades for engine power in relation to engine speed and values of acceleration (ITE 1990, 50–54).

Acceleration is determined by the change in velocity over a period of time and is expressed as feet per second per second, or fps2. Since large vehicles have more mass than average passenger cars, large vehicles accelerate more slowly than passenger cars. As a general rule, the range of acceleration for large, loaded trucks is from 0.3 to 1.6 fps2 (see Figure 3).

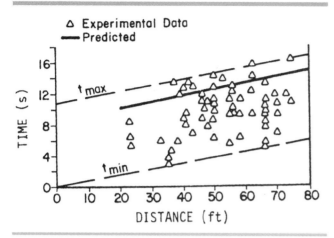

FIGURE 3. Field observations of times for 19.8-m (65-ft) tractor-trailer trucks to clear intersection distances after starting from a stop
(*Source:* Transportation Research Board (TRB) 1997)

Transit Buses

Primary human-factors considerations for public transit buses include the following (Woodson 1992, 85):

1. ***Driver:*** Clear visibility in all directions (360 degrees), ability to visually monitor passengers, lack of interior reflection at night, and a comfortable seat for lengthy occupancy. Figure 4 is a recommended layout for a transit bus-driver station. (Woodson 1992, 296).

2. ***Onboard passengers:*** Level floor with wide aisles, handrails that are easy to grasp, comfortable seating with sufficient room for knees and elbows, good visibility for seeing stops, air conditioning, minimum noise, and a reasonably comfortable ride.

3. ***Boarding passengers:*** Ability to identify oncoming buses from a distance and convenient entry handrails.

4. ***Service personnel:*** Convenient access to all maintenance components, especially those requiring frequent service.

The entry threshold for passengers must be low enough so that passengers do not have to stretch to step onto the first step from the ground or curb. It is recommended that a ramp sufficient to accommodate wheelchairs be considered for the main entrance. Aisles should be level; a grade could create a hazard for walking or standing passengers. Passenger seats are not usually fancy on intracity buses, but comfortable seats are required for buses traveling long distances. Seating on long-distance buses should be roomy so passengers don't find it necessary to stand or walk in the aisle. Arm rests should

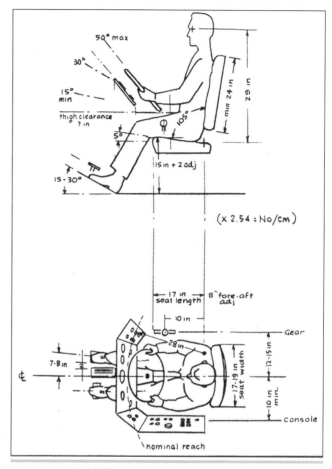

FIGURE 4. Guidelines for bus-driver-station layout
(*Source:* Woodson 1992, p. 296)

be cushioned and ergonomically designed, and reading lamps and footrests should be provided.

The primary consideration in designing intercity buses is the comfort of passengers taking long rides (Woodson 1992, 86). Intercity bus-seat dimensions can be approximately the same as those for city buses, but intercity bus seats must have headrest and reclining backs. A seat that reclines 30 degrees allows a passenger to lean back far enough to prevent his or her head from falling forward. If a seat is able to recline to 45 degrees, it should be adjusted to a horizontal position, which is more comfortable when passengers stretch their legs. The minimum clearance between the seat back in front of a passenger and the forward portion of the passenger's seat is approximately eight inches.

Transit bus companies and those who have the responsibility of locating and posting bus-stop signs must consider and document many issues:

- the safety of passengers entering and exiting the bus

- the impact on parking and adjoining landowners' traffic patterns if the stop is to be located in a business area

- the positioning of stops near intersections (whether to place the stop on the far side or near side of an intersection or midblock) (It is unsafe for a bus to stop at a stop sign, cross through the intersection, and then stop a second time at a bus stop on the opposite corner.)

- crosswalk safety (Onboard signs should direct passengers to wait until the bus departs before crossing streets, and not to cross in front of the bus. At controlled intersections, stops should be placed at a sufficient distance from crosswalks so that pedestrians are not tempted to enter the roadway from behind a stopped bus.)

- the positioning of bus stops with regard to parking areas (They should not be placed within parking areas since normal traffic may have a tendency to park near or within the bus-stop location and create a safety hazard for passengers exiting the bus) (NJ Transit Corp 1998).

- distance from other bus stops

- signage (Bus-stop signs should not be so large that they block regulatory signs or impair the view of the bus driver or other drivers. Usually local townships have regulations about bus-stop-sign locations, and unless there are strong safety objections, signs should be placed accordingly) (Woodson 1992, 87).

All transit companies should have their own procedures and policies regarding the safety of their riders as well as methods of determining bus-stop locations with the safety of both the riding public and driving public in mind. A valuable source of information about bus-stop placement is "TCRP Report 19: Guidelines for the Location and Design of Bus Stops" (TCRP 1996). Companies must review and revise policies and procedures as circumstances change. A written policy is an excellent tool for training employees.

Braking Performance

The efficiency of braking by a vehicle is considered its *braking performance*. How well braking systems perform depends on maintenance, design, and environment. Braking performance (Ma_x) is determined by vehicle weight, linear deceleration, the braking force of the front and rear axles, aerodynamic factors, and the rate of linear elevation of the roadway. The formula for braking performance is (Gillespie 1992, 21–42):

$$Ma_x = -W/g \, D_x = -F_{xf} - F_{xr} - DA - W \sin \theta \quad (5)$$

where

W = the vehicle weight

g = the gravitational acceleration

D_x = the rate of deceleration in feet per second

F_{xf} = the front-axle braking force

F_{xr} = the rear-axle braking force

DA = the aerodynamic drag

q = the uphill or downhill grade

The gravitational acceleration (g) is constant at 32.2 fps². The braking force can be determined through indices (tables) or from testing. Aerodynamic drag, which can be found in wind tunnel tables, varies among vehicles depending upon their configuration (e.g., a Corvette automobile has a lower air drag than a flat-front truck tractor). The angle of rise or fall of a hill can be determined by measurement or by estimating. Most vehicles are equipped with antilock brake systems. Constant pressure during deceleration (rather than pumping the brake pedal) will increase the performance of antilock brakes, allowing the driver to maintain control of the vehicle.

A test bus experienced frontal impact three times with three different speeds (see Tables 3 and 4). The vehicle's dimensions were:

- length: 11,000 mm
- width: 2500 mm
- height: 2940 mm
- axle distance: 5570 mm
- front/rear overhang: 2630/2800 mm

TABLE 3

Frontal Impact on the Test Bus

Measured Values	Bus Frontal Impact onto Rigid Wall 3,6 km/h speed 6,98 km/h speed 29,76 km/h speed		
Maximum impact force at the left longitudinal beam (k/N)	180	220	780
Maximum impact force at the right longitudinal beam (k/N)	160	190	390
Resultant impact force (k/N)	320	390	1100
Maximum acceleration on the floor above the CGV (g)	3	4	12
Maximum resultant acceleration in the Hybrid II head (g)	3	10	60
Measured maximum femur force in the Hybrid II dummy (kN)	1,1	1,3	1,6

(*Source:* FMCSA 2003)

TABLE 4

Buses Involved in Fatal Cashes by Operator Type, 1999–2005

Carrier Type	Number	Percent
School	857	3.18
Transit	731	32.5
Intercity	83	3.7
Charter/Tour	256	11.4
Other:		
Private company	20	0.9
Nonprofit Organization	62	2.8
Government	33	1.5
Personal	3	0.1
Contractor for school district	40	1.8
Other	93	4.1
Other subtotal	*251*	*11.1*
Unknown operator type	74	3.3
Total	**2252**	**100.0**

(*Source:* FMCSA 2003)

As one can see from Figure 5, in a frontal impact the right and left sides of the bus do not have the same force. Also the floor deceleration peaks at about 15 Gs.

Large tractor-trailer combinations have an engine-braking mechanism that uses the engine to retard the forward motion of the vehicle. This is commonly called a "Jake brake" after the company that invented the system—Jacob Manufacturing. The system works by retarding the speed of the vehicle through the use of the engine's exhaust system, which is able to absorb enough energy to stop a 75,000-pound gross combination vehicle without the use of the service brakes at 19 mph on a 10 percent grade (Fitch 1994, 239–254). The system can be adjusted by the vehicle operator.

The two most common types of brake systems are hydraulic and pneumatic. *Hydraulic* systems are used on typical passenger vehicles and use brake fluid to activate the brake shoes or calipers to decelerate the vehicle.

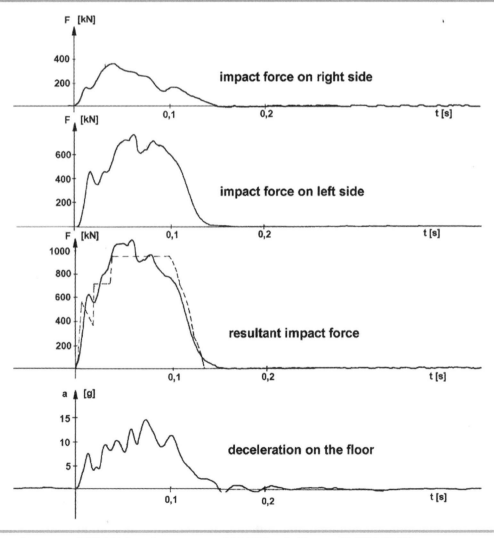

FIGURE 5. Frontal impact of 1K 411 bus; impact speed 29,76 km/h (*Source:* FMCSA 2003)

Typical passenger vehicles have antilock brake systems. Hydraulic brake systems must be checked periodically to ensure that fluid has not leaked or dropped to an unacceptable level due to worn gaskets or hoses. Hydraulic systems must be cleaned (flushed) periodically and new fluid added, since it is very difficult to stop contaminants from entering the system.

Pneumatic brake systems, also known as air brakes, are usually found on large heavy vehicles, such as tractor-trailers (see Figures 6a–d). *Brake lag* is a term used to describe the time it takes for a pneumatic brake system to reach full pressure and begin to lock or retard the wheels. In passenger vehicles with hydraulic systems, the brake lag is negligible—approximately 0.1 second (100 milliseconds). Some experts estimate the brake-lag time for tractor-trailer combinations at 0.5 to 1.0 second, while others estimate it at 0.25 to 0.5 second depending upon the number of trailers.

Another safety component that influences braking performance on tractor-trailer combinations and other vehicles with pneumatic brake systems is the *slack adjuster*. The term *slack adjustment* refers to the distance needed to adjust the actuation arm to fully compress the brake lining and the brake drum. If the slack adjustment is not properly set, braking performance will be greatly reduced. There are usually slack adjusters for each braking wheel.

The specific ranges stated by the manufacturer should be adhered to when adjustment is done. Some pneumatic brakes have automatic adjusters, but those also must be checked for proper adjustment.

Aerodynamics and Tires

The aerodynamics of a vehicle is important for fuel economy and vehicle control. A person traveling down a roadway in a vehicle and with one hand out the window with the narrow part facing forward, will feel little resistance. But if the hand is turned so that the palm is directly forward and into the wind, he will feel greater resistance. This *aerodynamic resistance* decreases vehicle fuel mileage. The geometric design of most vehicles used to carry goods, such as semitrailers, is rectangular. The tractor or cab of a tractor-trailer combination, however, usually has a more aerodynamically efficient shape.

Lift resistance—the downward force on a vehicle due to the motion of air over and around it—varies with the geometric design of the vehicle. Lift resistance can easily be understood by watching a drag race or NASCAR race. Dragsters and NASCAR race vehicles have a wing on the rear to keep them on the road at high speeds. A Corvette has a greater lift-resistance force than an SUV or a tractor-trailer combination since the rear of a Corvette

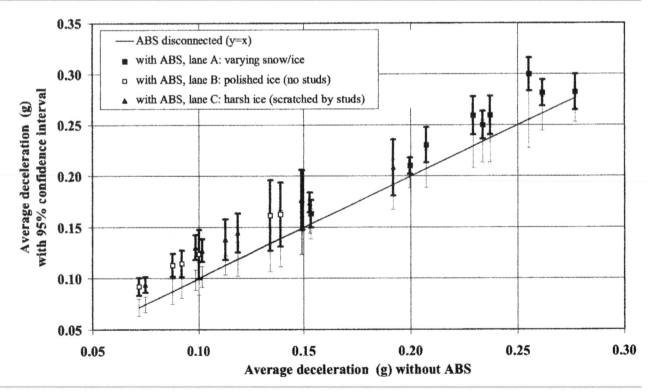

FIGURE 6a. Deceleration capacity on 3 snowy/icy lanes (A, B, C) with ABS in function (y) or disconnected (x). Each value represents one tyre type average over all drivers with 95% confidence interval. Nine tyre types on lanes A and C; 6 unstudded types on lane B (*Source:* Strandberg 1998)

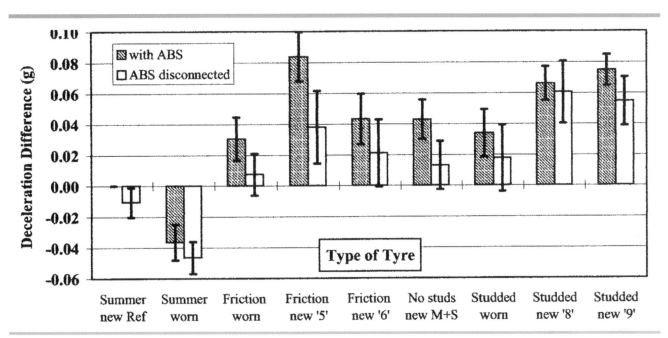

FIGURE 6b. Deceleration difference between certain tyre-ABS configurations and reference summer tyres with ABS. Paired comparisons for each driver on lane A (carrying snow and ice). Average over 24 + 24 + 18 = 66 drivers with 95% confidence interval (*Source:* Strandberg 1998)

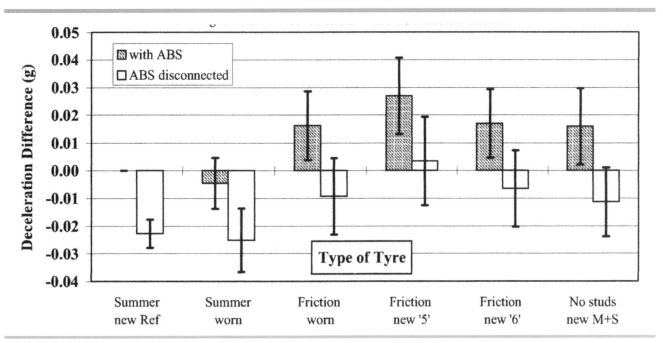

FIGURE 6c. Deceleration differences between certain tyre-ABS configurations and reference summer tyres with ABS. Paired comparisons for each driver on lane B (polished ice surface, no studs allowed). Average over 24 + 24 + 18 = 66 drivers with 95% confidence (*Source:* Strandberg 1998)

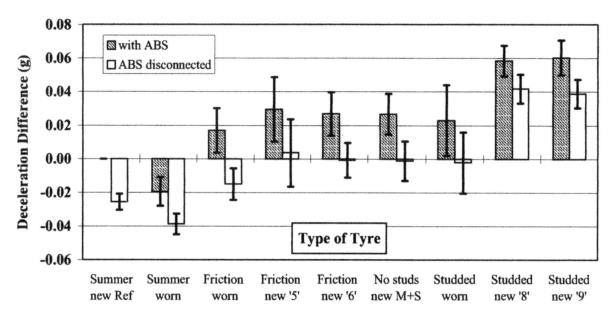

NOTES:

a1) New summer tyres—Reference type (same four-wheel individuals as b1 and c1).

a2) New "friction" tyres. Hysteresis rubber for ice and snow adhesion. Asian makes. ID no. 6.

a3) New unstuddedM+S tyres. Made for studding but without studs.

a4) New studded types. 105 studs per type. Same make and type as a3. ID no.8.

b1) New summer types—Reference type (same four-wheel individuals as a1 and c1).

b2) Worn friction tyres. 5 years old. Tread pattern depth 5 mm.

b3) Worn summer tyres. 5 years old. Tread pattern depth 3-5 mm.

b4) New studded tyres. 110 studs per tyre. Same four-wheel individuals as c4. ID no. 9.

c1) New summer tyres—Reference type (same four-wheel individuals as a1 and b1).

c2) New "friction" tyres. Hysteresis rubber for ice and snow adhesion. European. ID no. 5.

c3) Worn studded tyres. 5 years old. Tread pattern depth 5 mm.

c4) New studded tyres. 110 studs per tyre. Same four-wheel individuals as b4. ID no. 9.

FIGURE 6d. Deceleration differences between certain type-ABS configurations and reference summer tyres with ABS. Paired comparisons for each driver on lane C (harsh ice surface scratched by studs). Average over 24 + 24 + 18 = 66 drivers with 95% confidence interval (*Source:* Strandberg 1998)

is designed to create a downward airflow. Aerodynamics also affects possible loss of control from strong crosswinds. Vehicles are aerodynamically efficient for forward movement and are tested in a wind tunnel for centerline forces, but crosswinds are extremely difficult to counteract (Gillespie 1992, 79–103). Vehicles are not efficiently designed for crosswinds and can be very difficult to control when crosswinds are present. This is especially relevant for tractor-trailers.

Tires are extremely important to safe vehicle movement and also affect fuel efficiency. An underinflated tire creates greater rolling resistance and consequently is less fuel efficient. Overinflated tires cause uneven wear; therefore, the most important factor in tire safety, the depth of tread, is decreased, which may not be noticed until an accident occurs.

Besides inflating tires properly, one must align and balance them in order to maintain safe tire wear and fuel efficiency. Tread depth and wear are very important, since the tread disperses water on roadway surfaces and inhibits hydroplaning and loss of control.

Heavy Vehicle Tire Blowout

Tire blowout of mechanical origin involves the condition of the materials (tire, rim) and the quality of the assembly. While less spectacular than an explosion, the energy released during blowout can lead to significant injuries if people are directly in the projection trajectory of the debris. Four events of a mechanical origin that can cause a tire to blow out are (ASTE 2009):

1. *Overpressurization of the tire:* Possible causes include:
   - poorly adjusted compressor pressure
   - pressure-gauge or valve problem
   - incorrect mounting on the rim and
   - voluntary overpressurization when seating the tire on the rim.

2. *Zipper failure:* A design defect, an overloading, or an impact can cause a weakness, a cracking, or a rupture of the tire carcass (see Figure 7). The result can lead to significant air loss, the projection of tire fragments, and a sudden drop in

FIGURE 7. Zipper failure in heavy truck tire blowout (*Source:* ASTE 2009)

pressure at this location, sometimes accompanied by a mark resembling an unstitched or unzipped fabric. Possible causes include:

- deterioration of the envelope exposing the plys or the belts of the tire to contamination by air or humidity
- mechanical impact that damaged the tire's structure
- driving with an underpressurized tire, below 80% of the recommended pressure
- driving with overpressurized tires
- overloading
- loss of mechanical properties due to heat, pyrolysis, or thermo-oxidation
- significant carcass wear
- design defect in the weave of the tire cord

3. *Tire-demounting:* Tire-demounting occurs when the tire accidentally and suddenly comes off the rim with a violent release of air or other gases from inside the tire. Possible causes include:

- mechanical impact, more or less violent, on the rim or the tire
- abnormal wear of the rim (edge)
- deformation of the rim or one of its components following overheating
- incorrect original mounting of the tire
- incompatible parts of the rim (multipiece rim)
- dimensional or other incompatibilities of the rim and tire

4. *Tire in poor condition or with a structural weakness:* A worn tire or even a new one can have a somewhat noticeable structural defect. It may then be unable to withstand normal inflation pressure.

Steady-State Cornering

Steady-state cornering is a term generally used to describe the handling characteristics of a vehicle. It is important to understand the handling of fleet vehicles since these vehicles operate in all types of environmental conditions. A tractor-trailer's cab has steering in the front axle only; the other axles of the tractor follow. In a turn, the inside front wheel has a greater steering angle than the outside front wheel, and the average of the inside and outside front wheel angles is called the *Ackerman angle.* The angle between the heading of the front wheel and the actual travel path of the wheel is known as the *slip angle.* This angle becomes greater—and the tractor becomes more difficult to control—as the friction value between the tire and the roadway surface becomes smaller (Gillespie 1992, 54–59). The *neutral steering angle* is one in which the steering angle is the same as the Ackerman angle. This occurs when the slip angle is the same for both the front and rear tires. *Understeering* occurs when the front wheels slip to a greater extent laterally than the rear wheels, and *oversteering* occurs when the rear wheels slip to a greater extent than the front wheels.

Suspension, or weight shift, plays a crucial part in cornering because the movement and displacement of the cargo can greatly affect the steering of the vehicle. Trucks that carry liquids have a baffle system within the tank so that movement of the liquid during cornering is generally stabilized. Federal transportation guidelines pertaining to cargo stabilization and securing have been established to address the issue of weight shift, as well as the possibility of personal injury during the unloading process. Suspensions are usually a trade-off between stiffness and the ability to absorb rough roadways. Steering geometry includes the understanding of and proper adjustment relating to the toe-in, caster, and camber of the wheels, especially the wheels on the steering axle.

When wheels are adjusted to have *toe-in*, their front edges are closer together than their back edges. *Caster* is a backward tilting of a wheel in relation to the center of the suspension. *Camber* refers to the amount that the tops of the wheels tilt outward (Gillespie 1992, 60).

Rearward Amplification

When a combination vehicle makes a sudden lateral movement, such as to avoid an obstacle in the road, its various units undergo different lateral accelerations. The front axles and the cab exhibit a certain kind of acceleration, but the following trailer(s) have greater accelerations. This has been experimentally verified and quantified. The lateral acceleration of the first trailer may be twice that of the tractor, and the lateral acceleration of a second trailer may be four times as much.

The factors that contribute to increased lateral accelerations of the trailing units is the phenomenon known as *rearward amplification*:

- number of trailing units
- shortness of trailers (longer ones experience less amplification)
- loose dolly connections
- greater loads in rearmost trailers
- increased vehicle speeds

Quantifying rearward amplification in terms of multiples of lateral acceleration is relevant to vehicle design, but is not generally relevant to highway geometric design. The Transportation Research Board (TRB) recommended that a reasonable performance criterion would be that the physical overshoot that a following trailer exhibits during such a maneuver, relative to its final displaced lateral position, be limited to 0.8 m (2.7 ft) (TRB 1997).

Suspension Characteristics

The suspension of a heavy vehicle affects its dynamic responses in three major ways:

1. determining dynamic loads on tires
2. orienting the tires under dynamic loads
3. controlling vehicle body motions with respect to the axles

Suspension characteristics can be categorized by eight basic mechanical properties (TRB 1997):

1. vertical stiffness
2. damping
3. static load equalization

4. dynamic interaxle load transfer
5. height of roll center
6. roll stiffness
7. roll steer coefficient
8. compliance steer coefficient

Rollover

Rollover is a serious problem in commercial trucks that have a high center of gravity. The propensity for rollover greatly increases with the height of the center of mass above the ground. For example, it is widely known and has been demonstrated that SUVs have a high propensity to roll over—approximately five times that of standard passenger vehicles. The problem is exacerbated when quick movements from side to side are performed. Given the size of the typical commercial fleet vehicle, any quick movements can be hazardous and create a catastrophic event. If vehicles are carrying toxic chemicals, the hazard is multiplied many times.

Rollovers can occur if a vehicle attempts to enter a curve at a speed greater than the design speed of the curve. The cross slope or superelevation is usually a positive bank, which helps the vehicle to maintain an upright position in a curve. The radius of the curve and the cross slope are important factors and affect each other depending upon the grade of the road and the speed of the vehicle. Heavy trucks may have a rollover threshold (stability factor) of 0.4 to 0.6; in contrast, a sports car's threshold is 1.2 to 1.7. These values are unitless since they are ratios based on the height of the center of mass and the track width of the vehicles. The formula to determine the stability factor of a vehicle where there is no superelevation or roadway cross slope is

$$SF = t/2h \tag{6}$$

where

SF = the stability factor,

t = track width

h = the height of the center of mass

If there is a cross slope, the formula is

$$SF = (t/2 + \psi h)/h \tag{7}$$

where

ψ = the roadway's cross-slope angle (Gillespie 1992, 309–317)

Vehicles can also roll over if curbs or other low objects trip them (strike them below the center of mass) as they move laterally. These types of rollovers are generally preventable if the driver uses common sense and safe driving techniques.

The following points (McKnight and Bahouth 2009) apply to rollovers:

- Although they account for about a tenth of all large truck crashes, rollovers result from causes that are relatively unique to the vehicle and where it is driven.
- The majority of rollovers occur in curves, primarily on- and off-ramps where misjudgment and being in a hurry lead to speeds that are excessive to the vehicle's high center of gravity.
- Failure to adjust speed to the load and the stability, height, and weight of the load is a cause relatively unique to rollovers.
- Inattention, dozing, and distraction often necessitate sudden course corrections, leading to rollovers. However, they play a smaller role in crashes involving trucks than other vehicles.
- Three control errors that are relatively unique to truck rollovers are turning too sharply, turning too little to remain on the road, and overcorrecting steering errors.
- A quarter of rollovers result from problems over which drivers have no control. Half of those are the fault of other drivers, far less than is the case in other truck crashes.
- Large truck instructional programs could reduce the incidence of rollover by the use of videos to expose truck drivers to situations leading to rollovers and through simulation to help drivers develop avoidance skills without being exposed to danger.

Data on speed- and control-related rollovers are presented in Tables 5 and 6.

Emergency Fleet Vehicles

Although emergency fire vehicles are not usually thought of as fleet vehicles, they have evolved in their own manner within the transportation system.

Emergency vehicles such as fire trucks may have specialized equipment such as flashing lights and sirens, may be painted special colors, and may have areas of special reflectivity. Flashing lights were invented to bring attention to persons at a distance that an emergency vehicle was approaching. The flashing intensity, duration, and ability to be detected at a distance are of prime importance. Emergency flashing lights primarily convey the message that drivers must give emergency vehicles the right of way. Since they are used among other lights,

TABLE 5

Speed-Related Rollovers

Cause	Number	Description
Speed	108	Speed excessive to circumstances
Curves	77	Curves taken at excessive speed
Misjudgment	67	Misjudged speed at which the curve could be taken
Hurrying	13	In a hurry and disregarded speed limitation
Anger	3	Loss of temper in response to other road users
Oversight	3	Failure to notice speed signs
Loads	26	Not adjusting speed to stability, weight, height
Brakes	15	Not adjusting speed to known poor braking
Road	11	Not adjusting speed to road conditions
Intersect	10	Not adjusting speed to sharp turn at intersection
Vehicles	5	Not adjusting speed to vehicles ahead
Tires	3	Not adjusting speed to worn tread
Sight distance	2	Not adjusting speed to limited sight distance

(*Source:* McKnight and Bahouth 2009)

TABLE 6

Control-Related Rollovers

Cause	Number	Description
Control	46	Errors in controlling motion of the truck
Steering	20	Oversteering or understeering
Overcorrection	19	Overcorrecting after error (off road, out of lane)
Following distance	7	Failing to keep distance from vehicle ahead
Avoidance maneuvers	6	Responding to vehicles/road incorrectly
Downshift	3	Failure to downshift for speed control
Braking	3	Improper braking (e.g., locked brakes)

(*Source:* McKnight and Bahouth 2009)

drivers must be able to identify them and respond quickly in order to avoid an accident.

Color is a key visual component in any emergency vehicle fleet accident-prevention policy. Red may not be the best choice for emergency vehicles because under normal circumstances people have difficulty seeing red objects. During the day, in fact, red is one of the most difficult colors to see, and at night everyone is practically "red blind." A range of yellow colors—from greenish-yellow to yellowish-green—is most easily detected day and night (Southall 1961, 273). School-zone and school-crossing signs are now made with lime or yellowish-green backgrounds. Lime is also seen significantly faster than red in the peripheral (off-central) view, which is important because peripheral vision is most often responsible for early detection.

Colors and shapes that contrast with their back-grounds are essential to use in the design of emergency

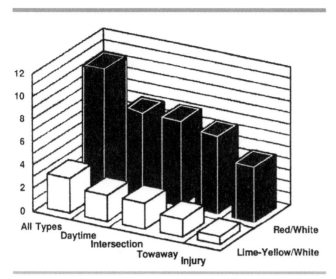

FIGURE 8. Comparison of accident incidents involving fire engines of different colors (*Source:* Solomon 1984)

vehicles. NASA studied this subject and determined that the yellowish-green or greenish-yellow colors, rarely found in nature, attract more attention because they stand out more than other colors. For example, lime-yellow/white fire engines are safer than red/white vehicles. A study by Stephen Solomon published in *Firehouse Magazine* (June 1984) regarding *safety color* reported that red vehicles were involved in twice as many accidents as lime-yellow ones (see Figure 8). To understand this, the article examined the four-part reaction/perception driver-avoidance maneuver.

Use of fluorescent and retroreflective materials for the emergency vehicle fleet is another issue that must be addressed by fleet operators and safety managers.

Fluorescent materials convert the energy from light into different color wavelengths. Fluorescent products are usually brighter and more eye-catching than non-fluorescent products and are used mainly during daylight hours. Fluorescent yellow-green is the most detectable color. Fluorescent signs and warnings are very noticeable when new, but their brightness diminishes over time with exposure to sunlight. Consequently, fluorescent objects must be repainted or have new striping applied. This type of material needs constant maintenance and review to be efficient throughout its lifetime (Southhall 1961, 273). Fluorescent colors do not reflect or radiate light at night.

Retroreflective materials are used for nighttime detection of signs or vehicles. They use microscopic beads, lenses, or prisms embedded in substances or added to paint. Retroreflective materials have the ability to reflect light back to its origin. As light moves away from the center of the axis of the retroreflective material, the brightness or reflectivity diminishes greatly. One of the greatest safety uses for retroreflective materials is on commercial

vehicles such as tractor-trailers, where the materials can assist in reducing underride collisions. One of the problems with outlining the side of a trailer with one line of retroreflective materials is that this does not provide adequate information when the trailer is not viewed in profile. If the rear of the trailer is marked with reflective material in a right-angle pattern, vehicles approaching from the rear have more information about the size and shape of the trailer.

Phosphorescent materials glow in the dark. They absorb light energy and radiate that energy after the light source is removed. This absorption and emission of light does not last long enough to be of value on emergency fleet vehicles.

Emergency vehicles can create a highway hazard even after they have stopped moving, so fleet operation managers must be sure that emergency vehicles have high conspicuity when stopped at a vulnerable location, such as on a highway. Proper lighting and use of warning devices must be understood by emergency vehicle operators so that the vehicle itself does not become part of the emergency scene.

Once an emergency vehicle arrives at a scene, operators should deploy all warning devices—signal arrows, signs, cones, and flares—as soon as possible.

Traffic cones have no nighttime value since they are normally unlit, so they should be used in daytime only. Highway flares are often used in close proximity to emergency scenes, but their sparks make them a hazard near flammable fuel spills. The negative characteristics of flares include not only their sparks but the amounts of smoke and red/orange flickering flames they generate. The flickering flames can detract from the overall attention demanded by emergency lighting because they may reduce or negate the effectiveness of other flashing lights. Smoke and flares contribute to a visually cluttered background and can confuse unsuspecting drivers approaching the scene (Southhall 1961, 276).

As a general rule, the longer emergency vehicles and personnel must be at a scene, the greater the possibility of injury to emergency fleet personnel, hence the more durable the traffic warning controls should be.

Creating a Risk Plan

Responding to emergencies such as fires, police calls, and accidents is a dangerous business. The danger is not limited to transportation to the scene but also at the scene and in dealing with victims. The purpose of a risk-management plan is to control the risk as best as possible to minimize the danger. Risk management is not static; it is a fluid process. At the end of the process, continual review and updating is crucial to maintaining an effective and efficient health and safety program.

Losses have an effect on personnel, property, legal liability, and time. The most important of these is the personnel. Because the responders must enter into or about buildings, crashed vehicles, or dangerous scenes, personnel may be, and at times are, lost through injury or death. While fatalities or injuries are always to be avoided if possible, they do happen and, as a consequence, are costly to the emergency organizations and the team. These costs can be controlled through risk-management planning and recovery planning. Property losses include damage to the emergency organization's property, such as vehicles, which are very expensive since they are usually custom-made equipment. The loss includes cost of a replacement for repair. In recent times, legal liability has become a substantial portion of the insurance premium package and also a large part of the planning. It is no longer to be taken for granted that the victim will feel fortunate to survive; sometimes, the victim and his or her family need someone to blame, and an attorney may be readily available to exploit raw emotions. The time element is the fourth possible loss category and includes the cost of renting equipment or the time damaged equipment cannot be used until it is repaired.

During risk-management planning, there are many choices to be made, some of which are difficult, while others are clear and precise. The best method of making choices is to have as much data and research information as possible about the subject. There are times when the data will be clear, but the choice may not be clear. All choices involve responsibilities and consequences and, since a decision must be made and implemented through training or a written standard operating procedure, all consequences must be thoroughly examined. The personnel or procedure most affected by a new decision or a changing decision must be considered, and discussion with the appropriate personnel should occur so that all sides of the issues and possible circumstances are delineated prior to implementation.

Some of the results obtained from a sound risk-management program include (Andrews 2004):

- The emergency organization may survive a major loss rather than be put out of business.
- The organization achieves a bottom line where the income is still greater than the expenses. Even though most emergency organizations are nonprofit-based, they still need to handle their expenses just as if they were a for-profit organization. Contributions and charity events are usually the main source of income if the local government has problems devoting operating funds through real estate taxes.
- Emergency service organizations must be available 24 hours a day, 7 days a week. Keeping equipment

in good repair means that no emergencies may need to be rerouted to another organization for help until lost or damaged equipment is returned to service.

- The risk-management program is similar to a for-profit corporation's budget. The emergency organization needs to prepare and anticipate any stable expenses for its operating year.
- The management of losses will not impede the growth of the organization, and the organization should maintain good relations with the public it serves.
- As with any process of risk management, all critical areas such as laws, regulations, and standards must be included in the finished program. Compliance is a major factor in any completed and implemented risk-management program.

When starting a risk management plan (RMP), a company must begin by consulting with all applicable parties to obtain their input, such as the legal department, the safety department, and drivers (and the union if warranted). If the business is local or regional, the state's regulations must be considered; if it is national, all appropriate regulations must be included.

TRAFFIC SAFETY PRINCIPLES

Highway Safety and Roadway Geometry

Highway safety is the responsibility of everyone, and safety elements must be reviewed, updated when necessary, and used for training. Management must begin by setting standards, showing employees how to meet the standards, evaluating the safety efforts, and giving recognition or additional training when needed.

Roadway geometry plays an important part in safety and must be considered each time roads are built or improved. Roadway design usually includes the travel portion of the roadway, shoulders or emergency escape path, alignment, and intersecting roadway safety. There are many references on the subject, including the American Association of State Highway and Transportation Officials' "Policy on Geometric Design of Highways and Streets" (AASHTO 1990), the *Manual on Uniform Traffic Control Devices* (DOT 2000), and the *Traffic Engineering Handbook* (ITE 1999). These publications provide detailed standards and best practices relating to roadway geometry. Design guides should also be used as references for driver training.

A railroad-track grade crossing is a special type of highway intersection where three elements converge: the driver, the vehicle, and the physical intersection. At a typical motor-vehicle intersection, drivers take turns yielding to opposing traffic, but at railroad grade crossings, trains are the opposing traffic, and they rarely yield right-of-way to motorists. Motor-vehicle operators can change their path and alter their speed, whereas trains have a fixed path and change speed much more slowly. Fleet-vehicle operators must be aware of the difference between a typical roadway intersection and a railroad grade crossing. At a railroad grade crossing, the vehicle operator bears most of the responsibility for avoiding a collision with a train. The railroad crossing crossbuck is a yield sign, and the motor-vehicle operator must interpret it as such (Southhall 1961, 273).

The Uniform Vehicle Code (NCUTLO 2000) is a model for motor-vehicle laws that indicates actions drivers are required to take at railroad crossings. This code states, in section 11/701, that when a driver of a motor vehicle approaches a rail highway crossing under the following circumstances, he or she shall stop the vehicle within fifty feet of but not less than fifteen feet from the nearest rail and shall not proceed until it is safe to do so (Southhall 1961, 275):

- A clearly visible electric or mechanical signal indicates the approach of a train.

- A crossing gate is lowered or the presence of a human flagman gives or continues to give the signal of an approaching train.

- A train approaching within 1500 feet of the highway crossing gives an audible signal.

- The approaching train is clearly visible and presents a hazardous condition.

Fleet drivers must also be aware of the various decision zones relating to railroad crossing hazards:

- The *approach zone* is an area in which drivers must begin to formulate their actions in order to avoid a collision. In this zone drivers look ahead and determine whether a train is nearby or present.

- The *nonrecovery zone* is the area in which drivers begin to stop if a train is crossing or approaching as well as being cautious and looking left and right for additional information if a train is not immediately perceived.

- The final zone is the *hazard zone*. In this zone, drivers must stop if a train is crossing or approaching and also must decide whether or not to go across the tracks. If there is no train present, drivers must look both ways before crossing the tracks.

Vehicle type is another component of decisions made at railroad crossings. A passenger vehicle that has acceleration and deceleration superior to that of a truck can cross railroad tracks much more quickly than a truck. The length of the truck, its braking ability, and its acceleration are important in determining whether a truck driver can cross tracks safely. Longer and heavier trucks must be considered when designing railroad crossings with respect to these factors:

- *Sight distance* (A longer sight distance is needed for trucks due to their slower deceleration and handling compared to passenger vehicles.)

- *Placement of advanced warning signs* (They must be far enough away that trucks have time to stop.)

- *Train warning whistles* (Whistles must be sounded in time for trucks to hear them and stop.)

- *Sight lines of approach and departure grates* (Truck drivers must be able to see them in time to react and stop.)

When approaching railroad crossings, truck operators must consider the type of road, the traffic volume, the angles and geometry of the crossing, the presence of nearby intersecting roadways, and the illumination. They must never be impatient or attempt to cross in front of an oncoming train.

Passing Sight Distance

Greater sight distance is required for one vehicle to pass another in the lane normally reserved for opposing traffic on a two-lane highway than is required simply to bring a vehicle to a stop before reaching an object in the road. Table 7 presents the passing sight-distance criteria used

TABLE 7

Design Criteria for Stopping Sight Distance	
Design Speed (mi/h)	**Minimum Stopping Sight Distance Used in Design (ft)**
15	80
20	115
25	155
30	200
35	250
40	305
45	360
50	425
55	495
60	570
65	645
70	730
75	820
80	910

Note: Brake reaction distance predicated on a time of 2.5 s; deceleration rate of 11.2 ft/s² used to determine calculated sight distance

(*Source:* TRB 1997)

in geometric design, and the criteria used in marking of passing and no-passing zones on two-lane highwaysis shown in Table 8. The geometric design criteria are more conservative than the marking criteria, but neither is based on a completely consistent set of assumptions.

The current passing sight-distance criteria shown in Table 7 were derived on the basis of passenger-car behavior and do not explicitly consider heavy vehicles. Using a new sight-distance model with more consistent assumptions, Harwood et al. derived sight-distance requirements for various passing scenarios involving passenger cars and trucks, as shown in Figure 9 (TRB 2008). The figure indicates that all passing scenarios are accommodated within the current geometric design criteria. Furthermore, Harwood et al. also found that a

truck can safely pass a passenger car on any crest vertical curve on which a passenger car can safely pass a truck (see Figure 10). The current marking criteria for passing and no-passing zones do not necessarily accommodate all passing maneuvers that truck drivers might wish to make (TRB 2008).

However, there is currently no indication that the passing and no-passing zone markings lead truck drivers to make poor passing decisions, or that trucks are over-involved in passing-related accidents. Thus, there is no indication that a change in marking criteria to better accommodate trucks would have safety benefits. There is concern that such a change could eliminate some passing zones that are currently used effectively by passenger cars. Further research on this issue is needed.

TABLE 8

Design and Marking Criteria for Passing Sight Distance		
Design or Prevailing Speed (mi/h)	Highway Design[a]	Marking of Passing and No-Passing Zones[b]
25	900	450
30	1090	500
35	1280	550
40	1470	600
45	1625	700
50	1835	800
55	1985	900
60	1985	900
65	2285	1100
70	2480	1200

[a]*Based on AASHTOGreen Book.*
[b]*Based on MUTCD.*

(*Source:* TRB 1997)

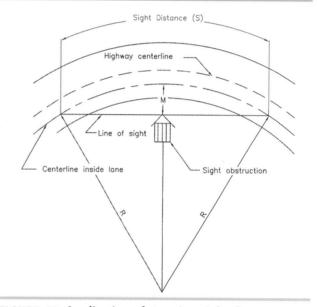

FIGURE 10. Application of stopping sight distance to horizontal curves (*Source:* TRB 1997)

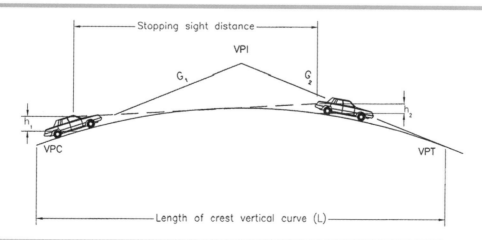

FIGURE 9. Application of stopping sight distance to crest vertical curves (*Source:* TRB 2008)

Fleet Statistics

It is important for fleet managers to keep statistics because they can demonstrate the proficiency of fleet drivers with regard to avoidable and unavoidable accidents. Statistics also assist the maintenance department in creating vehicle maintenance schedules. Accident and injury statistics such as data compiled for large trucks and buses in the State of New Jersey for 2001–2005 (Tables 9 and 10) can also demonstrate the effects of efforts toward safety; but, in and of themselves, they cannot achieve a reduction in injuries. Statistics are a snapshot taken at one point in time that can guide safety managers in continuing or developing fleet safety programs. These programs can include regular driver-safety updates as well as safety

at loading and unloading docks and warehouse facilities. According to the National Highway Traffic Safety Administration, motor vehicle crashes and fatalities increased in 2012 after six consecutive years of declining fatalities on our nation's highways (NHTSA November 2013). Statistical graphs of the type shown in Figures 11–16 for large trucks and buses are a valuable asset for review and are especially useful in determining whether a company is keeping up with or doing better than its state or the nation in controlling injuries and deaths. These statistics are for New Jersey, but statistics for each state and the nation are available online at www.ai.volpe.dot.gov/crashprofile/crashprofilemainnew.asp. [*NOTE:* For Tables 9 and 10 and Figures 11 through 16, Fatality Analysis Reporting

TABLE 9

Summary of Large Trucks Involved in Crashes
(New Jersey)

Number of Large Trucks Involved in:	Year				
	2001	**2002**	**2003**	**2004**	**2005**
Fatal and nonfatal crashes (FARS & MCMIS)	7735	6928	7741	7893	NA
Fatal crashes (FARS)	76	69	85	87	NA
Fatal crashes (MCMIS)	73	39	61	87	66
Nonfatal crashes (MCMIS)	7659	6859	7656	7806	6680
Injury crashes (MCMIS)	3653	3176	3547	3500	2851
Towaway crashes (MCMIS)	4006	3683	4109	4306	3829
HM placard crashes (FARS & MCMIS)	0	0	2	3	NA
Fatalities (FARS)	77	72	75	79	NA
Injuries (MCMIS)	5358	4694	5171	4979	4154

The MCMIS crash file is intended to be a census of trucks and buses involved in fatal, injury and towaway crashes; however, some states do not report all FMCSA-eligible crashes. FMCSA continues to work with the states to improve data quality and reporting of all eligible truck and bus crashes to the MCMIS crash file.

(*Source*: FMCSA Analysis and Information Online 2006)

TABLE 10

Summary of Buses Involved in Crashes
(New Jersey)

Number of Buses Involved in:	Year				
	2001	**2002**	**2003**	**2004**	**2005**
Fatal and nonfatal crashes (FARS & MCMIS)	1282	1024	1182	1197	NA
Fatal crashes (FARS)	10	13	10	10	NA
Fatal crashes (MCMIS)	7	8	6	8	8
Nonfatal crashes (MCMIS)	1272	1011	1172	1187	1034
Injury crashes (MCMIS)	713	574	624	656	554
Towaway crashes (MCMIS)	559	437	548	531	480
HM placard crashes (FARS & MCMIS)	0	0	0	0	NA
Fatalities (FARS)	12	14	11	11	NA
Injuries (MCMIS)	1379	1149	1223	1309	990

The MCMIS crash file is intended to be a census of trucks and buses involved in fatal, injury and towaway crashes; however, some states do not report all FMCSA-eligible crashes. FMCSA continues to work with the states to improve data quality and reporting of all eligible truck and bus crashes to the MCMIS crash file.

(*Source*: FMCSA Analysis and Information Online 2006)

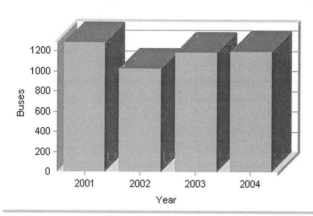

FIGURE 11. Number of buses involved in fatal and nonfatal crashes (FARS and MCMIS) in New Jersey (*Source:* FMCSA Analysis and Information Online 2006)

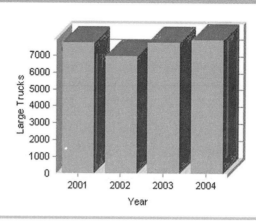

FIGURE 12. Number of large trucks involved in fatal and nonfatal crashes (FARS and MCMIS) in New Jersey (*Source:* FMCSA Analysis and Information Online 2006)

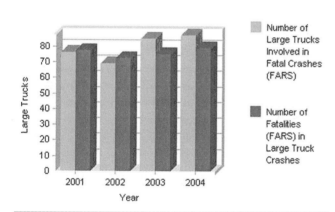

FIGURE 13. Number of large trucks involved in fatal crashes in New Jersey (*Source:* FMCSA Analysis and Information Online 2006)

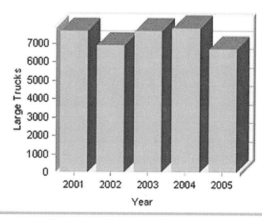

FIGURE 15. Number of large trucks involved in nonfatal crashes in New Jersey (MCMIS) (*Source:* FMCSA Analysis and Information Online 2006)

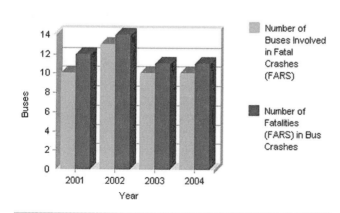

FIGURE 14. Number of buses involved in fatal crashes in New Jersey (*Source:* FMCSA Analysis and Information Online 2006)

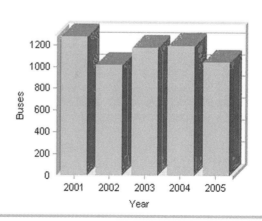

FIGURE 16. Number of buses involved in nonfatal crashes in New Jersey (MCMIS) (*Source:* FMCSA Analysis and Information Online 2006)

System (FARS) and Motor Carrier Management Information System (MCMIS) data are from March 2006. FARS data from 2005 are not available.]

Injury Crashes

From 2007 to 2011, the number of large trucks involved in injury crashes per 100 million vehicle miles traveled declined by six percent, while the rate for passenger vehicles dropped by eight percent (see Figure 17).[1]

One notable statistic shows that passenger vehicles far surpass large trucks in injuries per million miles

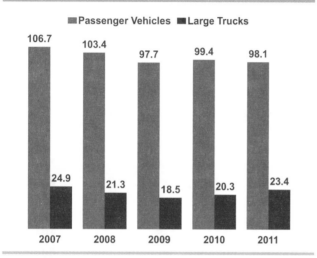

FIGURE 17. Vehicles involved in injury crashes per 100 million vehicle-miles traveled (*Source:* FMCSA 2013)

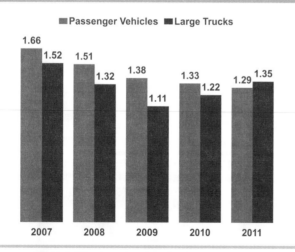

FIGURE 18. Vehicles involved in fatal crashes per 100 million vehicle-miles traveled
(*Source:* FMCSA 2013)

---

[1] The downward trend continues with the FHA reporting a vehicle involvement rate of 35.67 for large trucks in 2012 (NHTSA 2014).

traveled, but large trucks outnumber passenger cars in deaths (Figure 18). It is no surprise that large-truck death figures surpass those of passenger vehicles since the results of an impact between a large truck and a passenger vehicle normally are weighted against the passenger vehicle. Statistics such as these are of great importance to a safety analysis, and statistics generated regarding a company's own fleet are even more meaningful. Committees that decide whether accidents are preventable or not can use statistical information such as this along with specific facts surrounding the accidents.

Work-related roadway accidents kill more employees each year than any other occupational cause of death. In addition to the devastating human toll to employees, communities, and families, companies face massive productivity losses and soaring medical and workers' compensation costs. Michael Deak, safety director at DuPont in Wilmington, Delaware, stated, "If a worker is injured driving their own vehicle or driving a fleet vehicle, the cost is the same to us." In an attempt to counter the high productivity cost as a result of accidents, OSHA is bringing more agency resources to bear on the problem of occupational driving fatalities (Deak 2004, 44–48).

Increasingly, employers are instituting their own internal driving standards, procedures, and regulations covering subjects from seatbelts to fleet vehicle selection and use of personal vehicles on company business. DuPont has outlined driving standards for vehicle safety which include procedures for driver training as well as for auditing and measuring the results (Deak 2004, 44–48). Some believe that statistically, the more moving violations or preventable crashes a driver has, the greater the chance he or she will be involved in a catastrophic crash (Deak 2004, 44–48). It is believed that people with no moving violations on their driving record have been careful. Some insurance carriers check driving records of those who drive company-owned vehicles quarterly and assign a point system for moving violations and preventable crashes. When a driver reaches a certain level of points, action is taken to improve his or her performance.

A study completed by the National Institute of Occupational Safety and Health (NIOSH) in 2004 determined that 28 percent of workers fatally injured while driving a vehicle were wearing seatbelts, and 56 percent were unbelted or had no seatbelt available. OSHA, in its movement toward creating driving standards, indicates that in 2001 approximately 4.2 million workers drove a motor vehicle on the job. They ranged from long-haul truckers to pizza deliverers and from school bus drivers to salespersons. Between 1992 and 2001 over 13,000 workers died in crashes. The statistics bear out the need for fleet training as well as constant monitoring of drivers and driver records (see Tables 11 and 12 and Figures 19 through 24).

TABLE 11

National Summary of Large Trucks Involved in Crashes

Number of Large Trucks Involved in:	Year				
	2004	2005	2006	2007	2008
Fatal and nonfatal crashes (FARS & MCMIS)	139,345	147,202	147,149	147,697	132.,791
Fatal crashes (FARS)	4902	4951	4766	4633	4066
Fatal crashes (MCMIS)	4848	5240	4967	4808	4169
Nonfatal crashes (MCMIS)	134,433	142,251	142.,383	143,064	128,725
Injury crashes (MCMIS)	60,796	61,777	60,248	58,089	51,147
Towaway crashes (MCMIS)	73,647	80,474	82,135	84,975	77,578
HM placard crashes (MCMIS)	2453	2574	2278	2296	2630
Number of:					
Fatalities (FARS)	5235	5240	5027	4822	4229
Injuries (MCMIS)	85,023	86,642	84,199	80,098	70,567

The MCMIS Crash File is intended to be a census of trucks and buses involved in fatal, injury and towaway crashes; however, some States do not report all FMCSA-eligible crashes. FMCSA continues to work with the States to improve data quality and reporting of all eligible truck and bus crashes to the MCMIS crash file.

(*Source*: FMCSA Analysis and Information Online 2009)

TABLE 12

National Summary of Buses Involved in Crashes

Number of Large Trucks Involved in:	Year				
	2004	2005	2006	2007	2008
Fatal and nonfatal crashes (FARS & MCMIS)	9181	11,148	12,514	13,529	14,089
Fatal crashes (FARS)	279	280	305	281	247
Fatal crashes (MCMIS)	210	5240	273	260	257
Nonfatal crashes (MCMIS)	8902	249	12,209	13,248	13,842
Injury crashes (MCMIS)	5224	10,868	6912	7143	7491
Towaway crashes (MCMIS)	3678	6140	5297	6105	6351
HM placard crashes (MCMIS)	0	8	10	11	11
Number of:					
Fatalities (FARS)	315	340	337	325	307
Injuries (MCMIS)	12,368	14,426	15,466	15,633	16,935

The MCMIS Crash File is intended to be a census of trucks and buses involved in fatal, injury and towaway crashes; however, some States do not report all FMCSA-eligible crashes. FMCSA continues to work with the States to improve data quality and reporting of all eligible truck and bus crashes to the MCMIS crash file.

(*Source*: FMCSA Analysis and Information Online 2009)

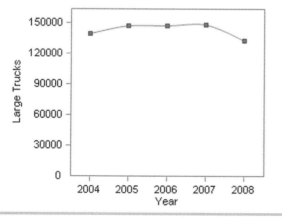

FIGURE 19. Number of large trucks involved in fatal and nonfatal crashes (*Source:* FARS and MCMIS 2009)

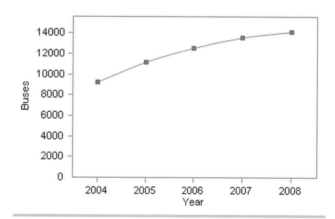

FIGURE 20. Number of buses involved in fatal and nonfatal crashes (*Source:* FARS and MCMIS 2009)

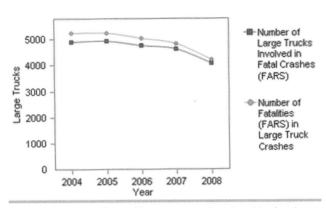

FIGURE 21. Number of large trucks involved in fatal crashes (*Source:* FARS and MCMIS 2009)

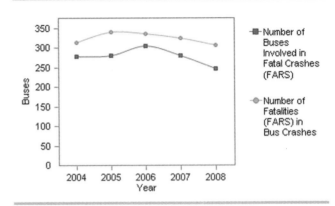

FIGURE 22. Number of buses involved in fatal crashes (*Source:* FARS and MCMIS 2009)

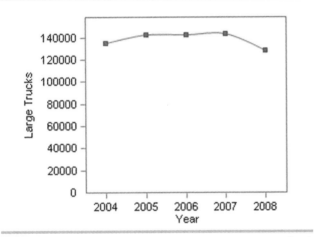

FIGURE 23. Number of large trucks involved in nonfatal crashes (*Source:* FARS and MCMIS 2009)

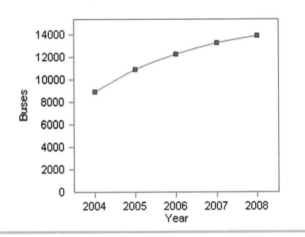

FIGURE 24. Number of buses involved in nonfatal crashes (*Source:* FARS and MCMIS 2009)

Note: Although efforts have been made to provide the most accurate and complete MCMIS crash data possible, data quality can vary from state to state. Please use caution when interpreting MCMIS crash data.

Nighttime Driving and Vision

Safety issues when it is dark involving nighttime driving require special evaluation and action since the visibility and acuity is are critical to safe driving. Reaction time is considerably slower at night than during the day (Allen 1996, 201–238). The human eye sees using rods and cones. *Rod* vision is known as *scotopic* vision, while *cone* vision is *photopic* vision. Scotopic vision is the vision a driver uses during nighttime driving. Photopic vision is used for acuity and to distinguish between colors. The level of nighttime lighting on roadways is below what is necessary for photopic vision. At night the human eye relies on the more sensitive 125 million rod cells, usually seeing shades of gray or black, which explains why it is difficult for someone to see an object that is not fully illuminated. Daytime vision is performed with cones, which comprise approximately 5.5 million cells. They allow for quicker identification of colors and possible hazards than rods, which do not distinguish between colors except for shades of gray and black.

State traffic regulations require visibility at certain distances when using illuminated headlamps: 250 feet on low beam and 500 feet on high beam. Therefore, on low beam a driver needs to know what is ahead within the next 250 feet, and in order not to overdrive the headlights he or she must consider the vehicle's speed, the road conditions, and his or her own acuity. Perception and reaction times are believed by some to be a minimum of 1.5 seconds for a single emergency maneuver. This 1.5-second perception-reaction time is controversial because some perception-reaction studies allow drivers to know that they will be expected to react to an object, and consequently their attention is high—usually higher than that of a typical driver with no idea a hazard may lie ahead. The 1.5 seconds may be accurate for one reaction, such as braking, to an expected emergency, but it does not include more complicated perception, evaluation, and reaction sequences in reaction to different types of unexpected hazards, so nighttime perception and reaction times could be much greater than this value.

The *Manual on Uniform Traffic Control Devices* (DOT 2000, 2A-19) uses a standard of 2.5 seconds for simple reaction and perception times. Of course all drivers are different, and to use an exact figure would be inconsistent with good engineering judgment. It would be best to use a range for perception and reaction times depending upon the specific accident issues being investigated. For example, one would not use the same time for a simple emergency braking maneuver for a driver who requires more information to make an appropriate safety maneuver and is traveling closer to the hazard while acquiring the information.

Nighttime visibility involves many factors, including brightness and contrast. *Brightness* is the reflection off an object from light falling on the object, and *contrast* is the difference in brightness between an object and its background. At night, if pedestrians wear dark clothing and there is no backlighting, even an alert driver will find it difficult to spot them soon enough to avoid impact. There are many other reasons for poor nighttime visibility, including dirt on the inside and outside of the windshield, dirty headlamps, inattention, and so on.

Research has been a valuable tool in alerting drivers to the problems of nighttime driving. It has found that light clothing is preferable to dark clothing and that visibility is better if some portion of the clothing is made of reflective material. Tests have also shown that fog creates a substantial driving hazard because light reflects off the water droplets and returns directly to the eye of the driver. The driver's level of expectancy or attention also plays a critical part in detection of hazards during nighttime driving (Shinar 1985, 243–245).

The driver's limit of vision varies outside of the accurate vision area (one degree on either side of the centerline of the eyes). The word recognition limit for signs occurs between 5 and 10 degrees, and the symbol recognition limit is between 5 and 30 degrees from the centerline of the driver's eyes while facing forward. Limits for locating emergency controls within the truck cab are between 30 and 60 degrees. Cleaning the cab interior, especially the lens caps of instruments, as well as a routine maintenance program for replacing instrument bulbs, adds to the safety of the driver (Marshall 2000, 376–380).

Sensitivity to contrast is the ability of the human eye to perceive a small difference in luminance. Visual acuity—the ability to detect small details and small objects—decreases with age: the visual acuity of an 80-year-old is approximately 50 percent that of a 20-year-old. Contrast sensitivity is more important than visual acuity for many jobs such as inspection and product control. Speed of perception and contrast sensitivity are closely connected to each other and must be maintained for safe driving at night (Kroemer 1999, 275–282).

On December 10, 1992, the National Highway Traffic Safety Administration (NHTSA) published a final rule requiring that trailers manufactured on or after December 1, 1993, which have an overall width of 2032 mm (80 inches) or more and a gross vehicle weight rating (GVWR) of more than 4536 kg (10,000 pounds), except pole trailers and trailers designed exclusively for living or office use, be equipped on the sides and rear with a means for making them more visible on the road.

The NHTSA rule allows trailer manufacturers to install either red and white retroreflective sheeting or reflex reflectors. Manufacturers of retroreflective sheeting or reflectors are required to certify compliance of their product with Federal Motor Vehicle Safety Standard (FMVSS) No. 108 (49 CFR 571.108), whether the product is for use as original or replacement equipment. The manufacturer's certification will consist of one of the following markings, depending on the type of conspicuity material:

- DOT-C: Rectangular reflex reflectors certified as meeting the standard.
- DOT-C2: 50 millimeter (mm) wide retroreflective sheeting material certified as meeting the standard.
- DOT-C3: 75 mm wide retroreflective sheeting certified as meeting the standard.
- DOT-C4: 100 mm wide retroreflective sheeting certified as meeting the standard.

Currently, Section 393.11 requires that all lamps and reflective devices on motor vehicles placed in operation after March 7, 1989, meet the requirements of FMVSS No. 108 in effect on the date of manufacture. Therefore, trailers manufactured on or after December 1, 1993, must have reflective devices of the type and in the locations specified by FMVSS No. 108, including the conspicuity treatments.

If you plan on driving after the sun goes down, it is important to remember that driving at night presents different challenges than driving during the day. Traffic death rates are three times greater at night, yet many of us are unaware of the hazards that night driving poses or of effective ways to handle them.

At night, vision is severely limited. Drivers lose the advantage of color and contrast that are available during the day, and depth perception and peripheral vision are also diminished.

To improve night vision and driving ability after sunset, the Motor Vehicle Lighting Council (MVLC) offer drivers these tips (MVLC 2009):

1. *Use your lights courteously.* Turn your headlights on one hour before sunset to make it easier for other drivers to see you in early twilight. Keep your headlights on at least one hour after sunrise. Refrain from flashing your high beams at a vehicle with its high beams on; this will only increase the chance that drivers will not be able to see. In fog, use low-beam headlights; high beams reduce your own ability to see and may temporarily blind other drivers. If your vehicle is equipped with fog lamps, use them with your low beams only when there is fog or inclement weather.

2. *Make it easy for others to see you.* Be sure that all exterior vehicle lights work properly. In case of a vehicle breakdown, pull completely off the road beyond the end of the guardrail, if possible, and turn on the emergency flashers.

3. *Avoid glare.* Instead of looking at oncoming headlights, look toward the right side of the road and watch the white line marking the outside edge of the traffic lane. When headlights from vehicles following you reflect in your rearview mirror, use the "day-night" feature on the mirror or adjust your mirror to cut out as much of the light as possible.

4. *Adjust your vehicle's interior lighting.* If streetlights cause a lot of glare, dim your dashboard lights and use your sun visor. Avoid using any other light inside your vehicle.

5. *Keep all windows and headlights clean.* Dirty windows can increase glare, making it more difficult to see, while dirty headlights can reduce efficiency by as much as 90 percent. Be sure to clean the inside and outside of your windshield as well as your headlights.

6. *Keep your eyes moving.* Look for flashes of light at hilltops, curves, and intersections that may indicate the headlights of other vehicles.

7. *Increase your following distance.* Increasing your distance by four to five seconds can make it easier to spot potential problems on the roadway and gives you more time to respond. In addition, proper lighting will enable you to react quicker and stop at a safe distance from the vehicle in front of you.

8. *Regulate speed.* Driving too fast is more dangerous after dark than during the day because of decreased visibility. Traveling at high speeds does not allow you enough time or distance to stop when you see something dangerous on the road ahead.

9. *Prevent fatigue.* Night driving can be tiring, so ensure good ventilation inside the vehicle and take frequent refreshment breaks to give your eyes a chance to recover. Take a short nap or a brisk walk, or have some caffeine to help you stay alert.

10. *Use vehicle mirrors to your advantage.* Exterior mirrors that are properly aligned not only reduce blind spots, they also reduce glare from vehicles behind you. The outside rearview mirrors should be adjusted so that the bodywork of the vehicle is just outside of the driver's view. In addition, the rearview mirror can be flipped to its "day-night" setting, which changes the angle of the reflective surface and appears to dim the mirror.

In addition, there are also some general practices one can follow to help ensure safe night driving:

1. *Align your headlights correctly.* Properly aligned headlights will help you see the road better and will help other drivers avoid glare. If you live in a state that requires regular safety inspections, ask the service technician to check and correct the aim of your headlights. If your state does not require such an inspection, take your vehicle to a dealer or repair shop at least once a year for a headlight checkup.

2. *Have your vision checked regularly.* The American Optometric Association recommends that everyone under the age of 40 have a thorough eye exam at least every three years; drivers 41–60, every two years; and drivers over 60, every year. Age can make eyes more sensitive to glare. In addition, certain medical conditions, such as encroaching cataracts, will increase eye sensitivity.

3. *Look into antireflective eyeglass coating.* Many eye-care professionals strongly recommend eyeglasses that have an antireflective (AR) coating. This ultra-thin film reduces internal reflections in the lenses. AR-coated glasses actually transmit more light than regular lenses, which improves vision at night and helps distinguish fine details during the day.

Work Zone Safety

Good safety professionals are acutely aware of safety in roadwork zones. Safety is also an important consideration when the work involves closing lanes or complete roadways due to emergency events. Safety in work zones is and has been crucial to the protection of public employees and emergency responders. Work-zone setup or design is based on the regulations found in the *Manual on Uniform Traffic Control Devices* (DOT 2000, ch. 6) and 29 CFR 1926.21 and .200. These regulations define and guide the proper placement of signs, markings, barriers, flaggers, and so on.

Safety professionals should be cognizant of three terms used throughout these manuals and regulations:

- *Shall* means that use of a device or practice is mandatory.
- *Should* means the device or practice is recommended but not mandatory.
- *May* means the device or practice is not required by regulation.

Work zones are planned and designed according to the type of work to be done, the location, characteristics of the roadway, and the length of time the work will take. For example, if a work zone requires closing one lane of a multilane roadway, signs of different kinds are installed at various distances before and after the actual work area. Regulations are specific regarding the use of the devices mentioned earlier, and the placement of warning devices is also dictated by regulation. The purpose of the warnings is to allow drivers to pass work areas safely and without incident. In some locations, such as on interstate highways, the first notice of the impending work area is a sign approximately one mile from the traffic cones that taper the traffic into other lanes if one lane is closed.

Typical equipment used at a work zone includes standard orange cones, lighted and flashing signs, crash-cushion trucks, and human flaggers. Flaggers are normally used on single-lane roadways where traffic is stopped in one direction to allow traffic from the opposite direction to pass through the work area. Alternating traffic through this work area is the prime concern of the flagger. The placement of traffic-control devices such as signs is important, since they can create hazards within the roadway and can be hazards themselves. Signs must be temporary in work zones of short duration or be made to break away in more permanent installations. Traffic-control devices used in work zones are different from those used for standard traffic control, but the goal is the same: safety of the traveling public and pedestrians.

Several principles and procedures must be considered when designing a safe work zone. If the work is to continue for a number of days or weeks, traffic-control devices are more permanent in nature, especially if the roadway remains in repair over this period of time! Many accidents that occur in work zones are contributed to by inattentive drivers. Work zones must be planned well in advance so that proper notice and guides for drivers are in place. One of the most common violations of work-zone design is the lack of appropriate advanced notice to drivers of the impending work area. Work-zone design for nighttime driving must include more highly visible warnings, such as lighted signs, so the attention of nighttime drivers will be drawn to the warnings.

The following factors are important for work-zone safety:

- Traffic safety is a high priority in every emergency or work zone. Every element regarding planning and design must be thoroughly analyzed and a sound and safe plan properly implemented.
- Traffic movement is the main element to consider when designing a work zone since the traffic that must pass through the work zone is the number one hazard to both workers and other traffic.
- *Traffic guidance* is the method whereby motorists are guided on a safe travel path through and around a work zone. The guidance must include daytime and nighttime traffic-control devices and must consider the human factors of the majority of drivers.
- Inspection of the work zone is imperative for continuous safe operation. Once a work zone is designed and the design is implemented, the traffic-control devices must be constantly monitored for consistent expectancy and safe operation. The work zone must be inspected during both daytime and nighttime operation.
- Maintenance of the work zone needs constant attention during the period the work zone is active because hazards may change from time to time.

Work zones must be analyzed by considering the type and location of work being performed, the expected life of the work zone, the type of roadway, and the traffic speed and volume. The location of the work zone is important because the design for a highway is not applicable to all situations, especially inner-city work zones. Shoulders and lane widths must be considered in the design of new traffic patterns as well as traffic volume during various times of day.

Signs and other control devices should be consistent for all work-zone areas so that drivers know what to expect. The colors and sizes of signs specified by regulation must be adhered to since drivers expect certain types of signs to be a certain size and color. Various types of tubular markers and barricades are designed to alert drivers at various stages as traffic flows through a work zone. Flaggers should be used when traffic is compressed into a single lane so that traffic congestion and accidents are reduced or eliminated.

The training of flaggers must be consistent with regulations, and any deviation from the standards and expectancies of the traveling public should be eliminated. Flashing traffic-control devices that alter traffic patterns must be set up at the minimum distance required. If the warning distance is insufficient for drivers to alter their travel pattern in time, accidents and congestion can develop. During any traffic-pattern change, traffic signs, especially route signs and detour signs, become crucial.

DEFENSIVE DRIVING TACTICS

Weather-Related Safety

In addition to darkness, weather (high winds, snow and rain, dust storms, and so on) is a key factor contributing to accidents and injuries. Under the best dry conditions, posted speed limits can be used to regulate speed, but when weather conditions are adverse, speed limits no longer should be used as a guideline. Large tractor-trailers are especially vulnerable to poor weather conditions; they may jackknife under slippery surface conditions or be blown off the road during high winds. During long hauls, driver fatigue sets in, and if this is coupled with adverse weather, the driver's attention and precision are drastically reduced. Frequent stops will help with fatigue, and drivers should stop and sleep when necessary.

Weather can affect the mechanics of vehicles too:

- Moisture in air-brake bleed-off tanks (drain moisture) can freeze and lock the brakes if not drained properly.

- Antifreeze must be appropriate for anticipated temperatures; it should be adequate for a lower temperature range than anticipated in case there is an extreme cold snap.

- During winter months when snow or slush is on the roadway, windshield wipers and washers must work properly, and washer fluid must be antifreeze protected. Dirty windshields may cause vision problems and accidents.

- Headlamps must be kept clear during nighttime use, and if the roadway is covered with rain or snow, they must be cleaned periodically during a long trip.

- On slippery surfaces, it is easy to lose traction, so drivers must accelerate slowly and with light foot pressure.

- Most commercial vehicles, state regulations permitting, may use chains or studded tires on their drive axle. They work well on snowy roadways, but on dry roadways, they produce less friction (stability) than standard tires do.

- During adverse weather conditions, stopping and braking efficiency are reduced. Adjusting speed will improve these problems, but increasing the following distance behind other vehicles is also critical in order to stop safely.

- During turns in poor weather, a gentler and slightly wider turn, if possible, should be made since cutting a turn sharply in adverse weather will exacerbate poor handling and possibly cause accidents and injuries.

- Drivers must not drive through water above the vehicle's brake lining, since wet brakes will dramatically reduce stopping distance.

Pretrip Vehicle Examination

A pretrip inspection should be performed each time a driver begins a trip. A thorough pretrip inspection to catch operational problems is a defensive driving practice since it is an active step compared to waiting until a problem arises. Drivers doing pretrip inspections may identify defective safety devices or worn parts prior to driving on the road, thereby avoiding an accident or injury. Inspections are designed so that the operator can spot system problems prior to an actual failure. Specifically, the following items should be checked to make sure they are working properly prior to starting out on a trip (ATA 1996, 46):

1. Service brakes, including couplings between tractors and trailers, should be inspected for cracks or holes. The hoses can rupture or crack because of changes between one climate and another, and the ensuing loss of brake fluid or air pressure could be critical.

2. The parking brake should be inspected to determine whether it is working properly. If the service brakes do not function, this is the driver's last line of defense.

3. The steering mechanisms must be examined for unusual noise or friction, and if there is a problem, a determination must be made regarding its seriousness. An examination of the steering mechanism by a garage mechanic is not warranted at the start of each trip; this type of detailed inspection is done during regular maintenance.

4. The horn, windshield wipers, and rearview mirrors must all be in proper working order prior to the start of a trip. If any of these devices are not working or are damaged, they must be replaced prior to the start of the trip.
5. Wheels, rims, and emergency equipment (flares, reflective triangles, communication radio, and so on) must be inspected for damage and defects. Wheels and rims, if damaged, must be replaced, because they can cause loss of control and accidents. Emergency equipment must be carried and maintained on every commercial vehicle. The required number of flares, reflective triangles, and radios must be present, and they must be in proper working order and have working batteries. It is prudent to carry extra batteries. Emergency equipment may include extreme cold-weather clothing in case of a breakdown or being stranded.

During inspections, the cargo must be examined to be sure tie-downs or other securing methods have not become loose. The cargo must be thoroughly inspected for shifting that could cause a loss of cargo and possibly cause the truck to overturn on a curve. If cargo has shifted and the driver cannot correct the problem, the truck must be taken out of service until the load can be secured properly. When trailers are security sealed and the driver cannot inspect the cargo for shifting, unusual noises could indicate shifted cargo, and the driver should warn unloading personnel of a possible hazard as they open the trailer door.

Figure 25 is an example of an inspection record. It can be modified to accommodate different fleet vehicle types and other information needed. The author suggests that vehicle trip sheets be kept for approximately one year and reviewed to determine whether retraining is necessary.

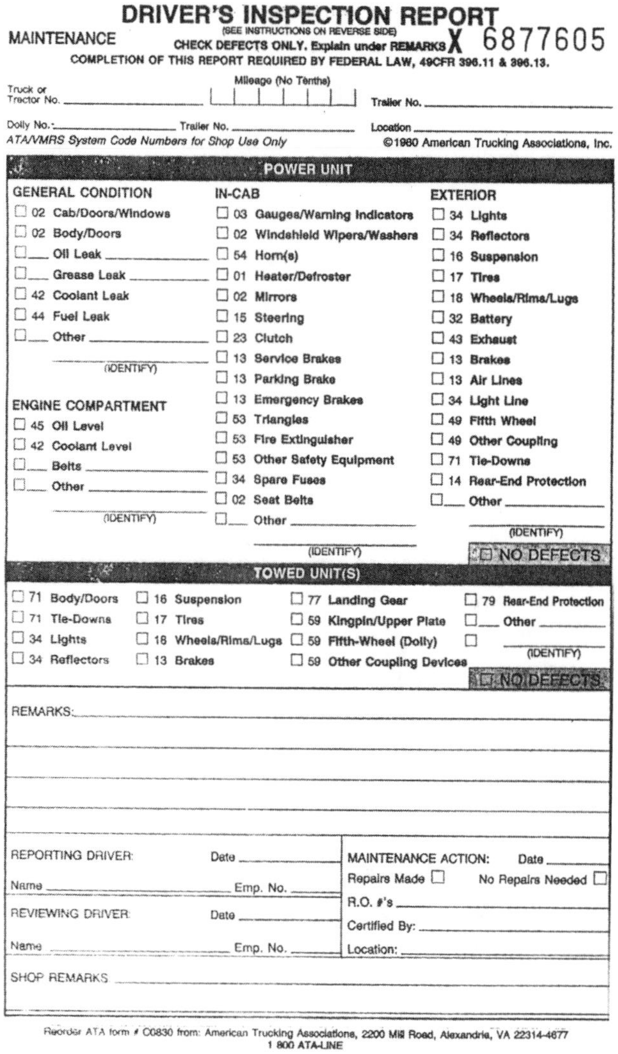

DRIVER'S INSPECTION REPORT
(SEE INSTRUCTIONS ON REVERSE SIDE)
MAINTENANCE
CHECK DEFECTS ONLY. Explain under REMARKS X 6877605
COMPLETION OF THIS REPORT REQUIRED BY FEDERAL LAW, 49CFR 396.11 & 396.13.

Truck or Tractor No. ______ Mileage (No Tenths) ______ Trailer No. ______
Dolly No.: ______ Trailer No. ______ Location ______
ATA/VMRS System Code Numbers for Shop Use Only
©1980 American Trucking Associations, Inc.

POWER UNIT

GENERAL CONDITION
- ☐ 02 Cab/Doors/Windows
- ☐ 02 Body/Doors
- ☐ __ Oil Leak ______
- ☐ __ Grease Leak ______
- ☐ 42 Coolant Leak
- ☐ 44 Fuel Leak
- ☐ __ Other ______ (IDENTIFY)

ENGINE COMPARTMENT
- ☐ 45 Oil Level
- ☐ 42 Coolant Level
- ☐ __ Belts ______
- ☐ __ Other ______ (IDENTIFY)

IN-CAB
- ☐ 03 Gauges/Warning Indicators
- ☐ 02 Windshield Wipers/Washers
- ☐ 54 Horn(s)
- ☐ 01 Heater/Defroster
- ☐ 02 Mirrors
- ☐ 15 Steering
- ☐ 23 Clutch
- ☐ 13 Service Brakes
- ☐ 13 Parking Brake
- ☐ 13 Emergency Brakes
- ☐ 53 Triangles
- ☐ 53 Fire Extinguisher
- ☐ 53 Other Safety Equipment
- ☐ 34 Spare Fuses
- ☐ 02 Seat Belts
- ☐ __ Other ______ (IDENTIFY)

EXTERIOR
- ☐ 34 Lights
- ☐ 34 Reflectors
- ☐ 16 Suspension
- ☐ 17 Tires
- ☐ 18 Wheels/Rims/Lugs
- ☐ 32 Battery
- ☐ 43 Exhaust
- ☐ 13 Brakes
- ☐ 13 Air Lines
- ☐ 34 Light Line
- ☐ 49 Fifth Wheel
- ☐ 49 Other Coupling
- ☐ 71 Tie-Downs
- ☐ 14 Rear-End Protection
- ☐ __ Other ______ (IDENTIFY)

☐ NO DEFECTS

TOWED UNIT(S)
- ☐ 71 Body/Doors
- ☐ 71 Tie-Downs
- ☐ 34 Lights
- ☐ 34 Reflectors
- ☐ 16 Suspension
- ☐ 17 Tires
- ☐ 18 Wheels/Rims/Lugs
- ☐ 13 Brakes
- ☐ 77 Landing Gear
- ☐ 59 Kingpin/Upper Plate
- ☐ 59 Fifth-Wheel (Dolly)
- ☐ 59 Other Coupling Devices
- ☐ 79 Rear-End Protection
- ☐ __ Other ______ (IDENTIFY)

☐ NO DEFECTS

REMARKS: ______

REPORTING DRIVER: Date ______
Name ______ Emp. No. ______
REVIEWING DRIVER: Date ______
Name ______ Emp. No. ______

MAINTENANCE ACTION: Date ______
Repairs Made ☐ No Repairs Needed ☐
R.O. #'s ______
Certified By: ______
Location: ______

SHOP REMARKS ______

Reorder ATA form # C0830 from: American Trucking Associations, 2200 Mill Road, Alexandria, VA 22314-4677
1 800 ATA-LINE

FIGURE 25. Example of an inspection record
(*Source:* ATA 1996, 19-1–19-12)

Driver Distraction

The specific sources of distraction among distracted drivers are listed in Table 13.

Percentages for the different types of distractions should be viewed as preliminary estimates that are likely biased by differential underreporting. These are research results that will be useful in building a broader understanding of driver distraction. The percentages for the different types of distractions should not be used to guide policy development.

Young drivers (under 20 years of age) were most likely to be involved in distraction-related crashes. In addition, certain types of distractions were more prominent

TABLE 13

Specific Driver Distractions

Specific Distraction	% of Drivers
Outside person, object, or event	29.4
Adjusting radio, cassette, CD	11.4
Other occupant in vehicle	10.9
Moving object in vehicle	4.3
Other device/object brought into vehicle	2.9
Adjusting vehicle/climate controls	2.8
Eating or drinking	1.7
Using/dialing cell phone	1.5
Smoking related	0.9
Other distrction	25.6
Unknown distraction	8.6
	100.0

(AAA Foundation 2001)

in certain age groups: adjusting the radio, CD, or MP3 player among the under 20-year-olds; other occupants (e.g., young children) among 20–29 year-olds; and outside objects and events, among those age 65 and older. Variations by the gender of the driver were less pronounced, although males were slightly more likely than females to be categorized as distracted at the time of their crash (AA Foundation 2001).

Drivers see more poorly at night, and pedestrians overestimate how visible they are to motorists, according to Richard Tyrell, a Clemson University psychology professor and researcher who has been studying night driving for 20 years. Tyrrell has conducted more than 30 experiments to find ways to keep both drivers and pedestrians safer after dark (Tyrrell et al. 2009).

Over the weekend, two pedestrians in Aiken County died after being hit by cars while trying to cross a highway at night, and a Walhalla man died after he was struck by a Greenville County sheriff deputy's car while crossing a street early in the morning.

Each year about 5000 pedestrians are hit and killed in traffic accidents. "Most of those incidents happen at night even though there are fewer drivers," Tyrrell said. Tyrrell's research has found that drivers steer pretty well at night, which may lead to not slowing down. Most drivers also rely too heavily on low-beam headlights (Tyrrell 2006).

Most pedestrians wear dark clothing, making them harder to see and when they do wear reflective material, it usually consists of a vest. Reflective material would be better if people wore it on their joints so it would move more. "Humans are good at seeing humans in motion" (Tyrell 2006).

Tyrrell and another Clemson psychology professor, Johnell Brooks, use a driving simulator to study how drivers of different ages perform at night. They have found that while drivers stay in their lanes well, they overestimate how well they see in the dark. Older drivers have more difficulty seeing at night but then also tend to be more aware of the problem. The simulator allows researchers to put people into what might be dangerous situations and record how they react (Balk et al. 2008).

In another experiment, a volunteer pedestrian walks in place in a low-traffic area in a Clemson neighborhood. Sometimes the volunteer wears only dark clothing, other times reflective material. Student volunteers then are driven through the area and push a button when they first see the pedestrian. The study found that if people are going to wear reflective material, the best place is on the ankles because they move as you walk and the low beams will shine on the ankles first. Tyrrell said people need to be educated about the hazards of night driving and hopes pedestrians will wear more reflective

clothing and stay away from busy traffic areas. If such warnings "can get into their heads before they decide to step into an intersection, I've succeeded," he said (Balk et al. 2008).

Driver Training

Driver training begins with a driver's application for a commercial driver's license and should never stop. The interviewing, hiring, and training of transit bus drivers in particular should be taken very seriously, since dozens of passengers will be exposed to unsafe situations if the bus driver is not properly evaluated and trained. Even when drivers have commercial driver's licenses (CDLs), a safety-conscious transportation organization will continually provide them with updated training and critique their driving records. At the time drivers are being considered for hiring, transit companies should order a motor-vehicle driving license abstract to determine whether any moving violations appear on their record. With constant monitoring and continuing driver education, insurance carriers may reduce premiums if companies demonstrate a serious commitment to employing safe drivers and maintaining driving safety. If fleet operators are not able to teach defensive driving in-house, there are trucking associations [such as the American Trucking Association (ATA) and regional or state trucking associations] that offer defensive driving courses. Drivers should be instructed about stopping distances and following distances and participate in emergency warning-device exercises. Transit companies should have written policies on conducting accident analyses and thoroughly review accidents to determine whether they were unavoidable or avoidable. This type of analysis can help to determine whether drivers need refresher courses.

During driver training, issues relating to vehicle size should be discussed thoroughly, including methods of performing emergency maneuvers. Safe driving requires qualified drivers, and professional drivers should have as their objectives the desire and pride to improve professional driving knowledge and awareness, good driving judgment, foresight, and skill. Driver training must encompass pretrip inspections, fatigue and stress, handling emotions, and having a good attitude, as well as the effects of age on a driver's vision, hearing, and mobility. Driver retraining is a good time to spot bad habits and correct them. People who drive more than one type of vehicle must also be instructed on the unusual aspects of safe operation for each type of vehicle they will be expected to operate.

Buses must be driven with a high degree of safety because they carry a very precious commodity: human passengers. Specific considerations must be incorporated into the decisions bus drivers make regarding where to stop buses in relation to parked vehicles, high curbs, pedestrian hazards, crosswalks, and so on. Safely picking up passengers is also crucial, since passengers boarding buses can be seriously injured. Bus drivers should be instructed that they are authorized to pick up and drop off passengers only at designated bus stops.

Bus drivers must constantly evaluate their surroundings. They must be sure the bus is safe to operate in the existing environment given the bus's width, length, and height. They must be sure there are no overhead hazards that can hit the top of the bus and jolt the occupants. One way to prevent this type of incident is for drivers to know the height of the bus. Choosing appropriate locations for bus stops is extremely important and is usually done by transit companies in cooperation with local towns and law enforcement. Locations have good points and bad points and must be evaluated in total context for the good of the overall ridership.

Accident Avoidance and Anticipation

The motor fleet industry must consider and create a system to control accidents and injuries. The core aspects of an efficient system include record keeping, analysis, prevention activities, and evaluation. Records that reveal what types of accidents typically occur must be kept so that avoiding them can become part of a teaching program. Records also indicate injuries sustained by employees and can be a means to analyze the cost of injuries to the fleet company. A simple accident register can be prepared using the Department of Transportation (DOT) Federal Highway Administration (FHWA) requirements in 49 CFR Part 390.15. This information can be found online at the U.S. Department of Transportation's Web site (www.dot.gov). Two important aspects of accident analysis are specifics of the cause of the accident and recommendations for what can be done to eliminate the same type of accident in the future. An accident review should include the following data (ATA 1996, 56–59):

- the *employee's name* (Repeated problems involving the same individual will come to the surface, and appropriate action can be taken.)
- the *time of day, lighting conditions, and other conditions* that may or may not have contributed to the accident.
- the *day of the week* (Patterns may emerge that indicate solutions. For example, if records show that accidents occur more frequently on the first and last day of the week, this could be an indication of preoccupation by employees.)

- *hours driver had been on duty at the time of the accident* (This information must be recorded by regulation, but can also be critical in evaluating driver fatigue.)
- *weather and road conditions* (They can indicate the conditions that most often cause accidents, and steps can be taken to work around them.)
- the *type of vehicle*, including handling characteristics and whether the vehicle was being loaded or unloaded
- the *speed and condition of the vehicle* (These are usually looked at first as primary accident causes.)
- the *type of accident* (For example, if the driver's back was turned when the accident occurred, this may indicate that the driver needs additional training.)
- *what the employee was doing at the moment of injury, body part(s) injured, and other pertinent information that will help to analyze the accident*

Accident avoidance and anticipation are major factors in safe driving. Avoiding an accident requires anticipation and the proper choice of an evasive action. In order to anticipate a possible hazard in the roadway ahead, the driver must be attentive—not distracted. Accident avoidance is a learned process—not an inborn one. For example, many drivers, when confronted with a vehicle entering their travel path from the right, steer to the left in an effort to avoid impact. If, under these circumstances, the driver steers to the right, the encroaching vehicle will usually pass through the driver's original travel path and an impact will be avoided. This is a quick response that can be learned.

Anticipation requires more than attention; it requires training and a conscious desire to understand what constitutes a developing hazard. A hazard could develop when another vehicle slows to a stop from either the left or right or when traffic ahead becomes congested. Drivers should always enter intersections with their foot off the accelerator and hovering over the brake so that their reaction time is cut to a minimum. An accident has been said to be an unfortunate event resulting from unavoidable causes. While some may think this definition is true, others question the term *unavoidable*. Accidents can be unfortunate, but they should never be accepted as the cost of doing business. Many can be avoided, depending upon the circumstances and the drivers involved. A term used by many, *preventable collision*, is defined as a collision in which the driver failed to do every reasonable thing. While litigators may latch onto this terminology, there is much more to the term preventable. Drivers should be aware of some preventable causes of collisions:

- slowing down too late
- failing to scan the road
- failing to check blind spots
- not driving at the appropriate speed given an adverse condition, regardless of the posted speed limit
- following too closely
- not focusing on the driving task

Other factors contribute to accidents, such as the condition of the roadway, work-zone traffic, and heavy vehicle loads. Factors can generally be categorized into three areas: driver factors, vehicle factors, and condition factors. Avoiding accidents requires training in recognizing hazards, understanding proper defensive maneuvers, and deciding and acting correctly in time to prevent an impact. One anticipation training tip is for drivers to ask themselves "What if?" To plan ahead, drivers can be driving down a roadway, looking for an escape route. A constant "what if" strategy can help drivers predetermine accurate evasive maneuvers when faced with specific hazards.

Turning and Maneuvering

Drivers of large trucks must use extreme care when turning and maneuvering. The large mass and length of commercial and fleet vehicles demand vigilance and caution that is referred to as managing space—in other words, operating, parking, and maneuvering fleet vehicles. If drivers are not thoroughly familiar with the space and rear vision limitations of the vehicles they operate, they will be at a disadvantage and may become involved in avoidable incidents. Understanding the length and turning ability of large vehicles is crucial when learning how to drive them. Space is limited on highways and must be preserved during parking and limited-space maneuvering. Braking maneuvers require drivers to be familiar with the weight of their vehicles, their cargo, and the distance needed to safely brake and come to a complete stop. Drivers also must be aware of the spacing between their vehicle and the one in front of them—the *following distance*. This is a crucial factor in avoiding rear-impact accidents. Some transportation engineers the author has spoken with understand and acknowledge that roadways in the United States are built and designed mainly for passenger vehicles, not for fleet or commercial vehicles. Lanes are normally eleven to twelve feet wide. Although curves are designed for speeds greater than the posted speed limit, drivers of commercial trucks must be aware of design limitations and know that speed limits on curves should not be exceeded.

Overhead space is another factor drivers must consider when operating large vehicles in close spaces or on open roadways. Overpasses are generally fourteen feet high. It is important for drivers of closed-end trailers to know their trailer's height and for drivers of flatbed trailers to know the height to the top of their cargo in relation to the height of each overpass they drive under (ATA 1996, 85-87) so that overpass collisions can be avoided. Drivers must also be aware that strong winds can force trailers out of travel lanes and that vehicles could hit overpass abutments or other vehicles passing in adjacent lanes.

Making right turns in urban areas may be very difficult since vehicles in the right lane of the intersection may not give trucks sufficient turning space. Signaling long before starting the turn is crucial. Attempts to squeeze by in limited roadway spaces, especially in city driving, can cause impacts with other vehicles and pedestrians. To make a proper turn, a driver must keep the vehicle in its own lane and make a wide turn into the two lanes of the street he or she is turning onto (NJDOT 1988, 2-22–2-25). All turns must be approached with caution. Before starting a left turn, drivers should keep the vehicle in the center of the intersection and not cut the corner.

When backing into a dock, drivers must be prepared to use a spotter. Sometimes—usually at loading or unloading docks, not on roadways—the trailer will be parked and the tractor will be in a jackknifed position.

Tanker trucks and their cargo are constantly moving during transit. Tanker trucks are designed with a baffle system that slows displacement of the liquids in the tank compartment. These trucks are especially susceptible to rollover since the baffles are sometimes lateral and liquids shift to the outside during a turn. The suspension of tanker trucks is usually stiffer than that of other trucks to allow for very little compression during turns so that liquid cargo remains stable.

ERGONOMIC AND INJURY BIOMECHANICAL ISSUES

Investigating Employee Injuries

The musculoskeletal system is quite complicated and is very vulnerable at times. The *musculoskeletal system* includes tendons, ligaments, fascia, cartilage, bone, and muscle. Soft-tissue injuries usually relate to tendons, ligaments, fascia, and muscle. Soft-tissue injuries can occur in an occupational environment as well as a nonoccupational environment, such as motor-vehicle impact and so on. Functional units or joints are a necessary connecting point that allows linear body segments to move and interact.

Ligaments connect bone to bones, which provide stability through the joints, and tendons attach muscle to bone, which transmits force. The *fascia* is also a connective tissue that covers organs or parts of organs and keeps them separate within the body cavity. The fibers run parallel in tendons, nonparallel in ligaments, and irregularly in the skin. Each group of fibers creates strength of its own, which is based upon the structure of the fibers. Collagen fibers, while under tension, first stretch slightly and then become stiffer until failure. The fibers have a wavy pattern, which accounts for the initial slight stretching until the wavy pattern is eliminated. Elastic fibers are weakened and become brittle as they stretch greater than collagen fibers and can deform more than at higher degrees. As the elastic fibers stretch, they reach a point where they stiffen, and failure occurs with little warning. Connective tissue as one conceding gets its strength, depending upon the number of collagen or elastic fibers contained in the tissue.

Bone can be molded or change in size and shape based upon the stress and the duration of the stress. The relationship between change and stress is still unknown but could be described mathematically. The skeletal system reaches its maximum mass (strength) at about age 30, after which bone loss occurs continuously. Gradual aging changes normal bone into osteoporotic bone at an accelerating rate. In the early 30s, there is little change in bone loss between men and women, but it sharply increases for women after menopause. Changes relating to aging produce the following results:

- continuing decrease in mineral content
- cortical bone becomes thinner
- increasing diameter of long bones, which increase the moment arm
- decreasing trabeculae (inner core of cancellous bone) in cancellous bone

For these reasons, the bones are weaker and fracture more often after trivial trauma in older people, especially women.

Disc compression studies have shown the discs are flexible at low loads and resistance increases at higher loads (Backaitis 1993a). This study also indicates the discs are particularly at risk from lateral bending and rotation, and portion is especially harmful to the disc and responsible for failure when combined with compression. Compressive loads to the lumbar-supplied failure occur in the end plates, then in the vertebrae bodies and, lastly, in the discs proper. There is great variation among individuals and age groups in equating moment rotation and force deformation of the motion disc segments.

Muscle strength is of great importance, since many jobs in industry require workers to exceed their strength or at least approach their limit. Muscular strength is defined as the strength muscles can produce during maximum exertion. *Muscular strength* is separate from *muscular endurance*. The latter is a measurement of the amount of muscular strength over time intervals. Naturally, the initial exertion of muscular strength is greater for a short time but, over a longer time, the measured muscular strength is reduced. This correlation is important when creating jobs requiring muscular strength over a worker's shift. *Isokinetic strength* is determined by controlling the movement of the joints. *Isotonic strength* requires continuing muscle activity while the velocity of the muscle changes. *Static strength* involves fixed postures (holding an object) and is usually associated with isometric contractions or exercises. Isokinetic, isotonic, and isoinertial are considered dynamic muscular movement, such as lifting or pushing. Strength and force curves can be developed and analyzed upon obtaining data from subjects. This information is valuable for matching the worker with the required task.

Sitting while performing tasks saves energy and is generally best for close and precise work. The lumbar curve is *lordotic* (backward curve), since the vertebrae and discs are thicker in front than in the back. This is the posture that creates the upright torso, which is what all of our mothers meant when they said "sit up straight." The lumbar spine articulates, or moves, while the sacrum is fused with the pelvis. This feature creates a rotation about the pelvis and shapes the lumbar spine. In a sitting posture, the pelvis rotates forward, which creates lordosis in the lumbar. When a person is sitting in a relaxed posture, the lumbar may be either straight or in a slight *kyphosis* (forward curve) position. The spine is comprised of four segments: (1) the cervical with seven vertebrae; (2) the thoracic, with twelve vertebrae; (3) the lumbar, with five vertebrae; and (4) the sacrum, also with five vertebrae that are not articulated. The posture shape of a seatback can influence the curvature of the spine. Normally, the cervical is in slight lordosis, along with the lumbar, and the thoracic is in slight kyphosis when a person is standing.

There are times when an injury claimed by an employee is investigated; either in response to a workers' compensation claim or civil or criminal litigation. The claimed injury can occur while driving a fleet truck or fleet passenger vehicle. Your attorney will usually take the lead in this scenario but you will still be expected to assist in the claim defense and process.

Injury biomechanics includes the analysis, research, and calculations relating to a specific accident (motor vehicle, slip, trip, fall, etc.). The conclusion of injury biomechanics is to determine from the evidence if there exists a mechanism of injury to support the claim. The mechanism is crucial in determining the probability of injury. Biomechanics does not conclude an injury could or could not have occurred, only that a mechanism is present or not. Studies are used to quantify forces of an impact of an accident to help evaluate the probability of the claimed injury. The accuracy of the injury biomechanical analysis is directly dependant on the evidence, testimony, and available replicate research.

Injuries to employees may include upper and lower extremities, neck, back, and so on. All claimed injuries have a mechanism of injury and must be accurately analyzed using the appropriate scientific principals (Rivers 2001, 53–57).

Occupants in vehicles are subject to injuries and fatalities if safety is not of prime importance, and of course, occupants must actually use seatbelts in order for them to prevent injury or death. It is easy to understand that, in a collision between a large commercial truck and a typical passenger vehicle, the truck occupants will probably be injured less seriously than those in the passenger vehicle.

Seatbelts use two types of mechanical systems: (1) *gravity* or (2) a *pretensioner.* In the gravity-operated seatbelt, a mechanism in the spooling portion simply rotates upon emergency braking. When the front of the vehicle dips, the mechanism locks the seatbelt in place. The disadvantage of this type of seatbelt is that unless the occupant has the seatbelt properly positioned and tight against his or her body, the slack in the seatbelt remains on impact. The pretensioner system resolves this problem: the pretensioner automatically takes up the slack and usually presses the occupant against the back of the seat.

Occupant protection in motor fleet and commercial vehicles is usually more of a concern with passenger vehicle fleets or small vans than with large tractor-trailers. Usually during impacts, drivers of tractor-trailers or large trucks do not sustain serious injury due to the large mass of the vehicle. If the vehicle rolls over, however, drivers of such vehicles could be severely injured or killed if they did not use a seatbelt.

While today it may be difficult to believe, until the 1950s seatbelts were not even considered an option on most vehicles, apparently because the public was not demanding safety items on vehicles they purchased. Research into the safety of seatbelts was not widely understood or demanded. However, occupant protection in standard passenger vehicles requires understanding and proper use of seatbelts. seatbelts should be adjusted so that the shoulder portion passes between the middle of the shoulder and the neck. The belt must be snug so that the wearer cannot move forward or side to side upon impact. Figure 26 is a diagram of a side view of a typical seat-belt locking mechanism without a pretensioner. Diagram B-2 is the position of the locking mechanism upon impact. If occupants move out of position during an impact while an

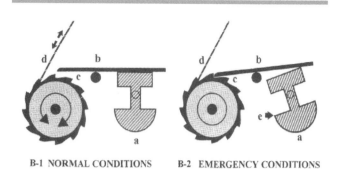

FIGURE 26. Side view of a typical seatbelt locking mechanism without a pretensioner (*Source:* Rivers 2001, 53–57)

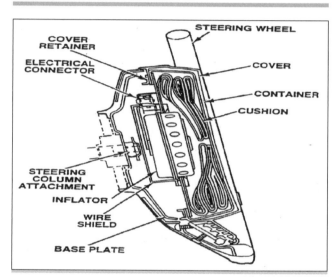

FIGURE 27. A cutaway showing the manner in which an airbag is folded inside the steering wheel (*Source:* Rivers 2000, 55–60)

airbag deploys, more severe injuries could occur. Figure 27 shows a folded airbag ready to be deployed.

One of the most prevalent types of injury in motor-vehicle impacts is the whiplash (cervical spine) injury, which is a severe problem in the United States. Even though most people survive this type of injury, the cost from lost work and medical treatment is a burden on the U.S. economy and on productivity. Accurate prediction of this type of injury is crucial if prevention devices are to be invented and proper medical diagnosis and treatment is to be effective through the understanding of the mechanisms of the injury.

Statistics concerning whiplash (Croft 1995, 86–98) include:

- Most injuries occur at crash speeds below 12 mph.
- Most cars withstand 8–12-mph impacts without vehicle damage.

- More than half of all low-speed, rear-impact collision (LOSRIC) injuries occur without vehicle damage.

- There is no correlation between vehicle damage and injury outcome.

- During impact, the peak acceleration of the occupant's head is much greater than the peak acceleration of the vehicle.

- In a 5-mph crash the occupant's head typically experiences 10–12 g of acceleration.

- More than three million Americans sustain whiplash injuries every year.

- The reported risk (probability) of injury in a LOSRIC is 35 percent to 68 percent. The Japanese Auto Insurance Rating Association reports a 50 percent risk of injury.

- About 10 percent of those injured become permanently disabled.

- *Minor* neck injuries account for up to 60 percent of all permanent impairment claims.

- For every 6 million occupants in LOSRICs,
  - about three million will be injured (approximately the population size of South Carolina)
  - about 1.5 million will have chronic pain (approximately the population size of Nebraska)
  - about 400,000 of those with chronic pain will become disabled, usually due to pain (approximately the population size of Wyoming) (Microsoft Encarta 2006).

- Nearly half of all chronic neck pain in America is due to car crashes—mostly LOSRICs.

- About 9 percent of all Americans suffer from chronic neck pain due to LOSRICs.

- Children are two to three times more likely to suffer whiplash injuries than adults.

A conservative estimate of the cost of spinal cord injuries to the health and insurance industries due to medical costs and lost productivity is $97 million annually (Nahum 2002, 324–330).

The number of spinal cord injuries, including whiplash, in the United States continues to climb and is a major concern of the automobile, insurance, and health industries as evidenced by the following data (Shands 1993, 75–79):

- The number of new injuries in the United States in 2007 was about 10,000.

- The gender breakdown for whiplash is 82 percent male, 18 percent female.

- The highest per-capita rate of injury occurs between the ages of 16 and 30.

- The leading causes of spinal cord injury are
  - motor-vehicle accidents: 44 percent
  - acts of violence: 24 percent
  - falls: 22 percent
  - sports: 8 percent (two-thirds from diving)
  - other: 2 percent.

Whiplash analysis does not seem to be consistently accurate, and the true mechanisms are still not fully understood. The mechanisms and their predictability must be thoroughly understood by the medical community and automobile manufacturers in order for proper treatment to be given and prevention methods instituted. See "Important Terms" at the end of this chapter for definitions of biomechanical injury anatomy terms.

As previously noted, the mechanisms that cause whiplash are not fully understood. Kornhauser of EM Systems Inc., concluded "it is apparent that the injury threshold, the approximate level of trauma to cause injury, is above 8 kph, or 5 mph, *even for subjects with mild preexisting spinal degeneration*" [author's emphasis] (Kornhauser 1993, 1–14). Further uncertainty is evidenced by Nielsen, et al., who tried to accurately predict the human response to delta-v (severity of impact) using mathematical modeling. They concluded "further work is required to explore the validity of the model used to calculate delta-v" (Nielsen et al. 1997, 23–28). Delta-v is a widely used measurement for determining the probability of injury. It is a measurement of the change of velocity over time. For example, decelerating from 50 mph to 0 mph in 0.1 second is more severe than decelerating from 50 mph to 0 mph in 0.5 second. The probability of injury depends on both the change of force and the amount of time over which the change of force takes place. Astronauts, for example, are not injured when accelerating from zero to approximately 18,000 mph because of the length of time it takes for this change to occur. It is the opinion of the author that, while the mechanisms of whiplash injury are controversial and not totally understood, diagnosis of whiplash without a full understanding of the mechanisms involved is often given.

Whiplash injury has a great potential for insurance fraud and can greatly increase the cost of insurance for all consumers. This problem is worldwide, as evidenced by Cupid's research, which concluded that "there is urgent need to introduce accident reconstruction in the Caribbean [to counter insurance fraud]. Insurance companies continue to receive a level of practice that needs to be brought up to international standards" (Cupid 2002, 1–16). The research associated with this type of problem is of paramount importance. Millions of dollars in health-care and insurance costs could be saved and devoted to designing better and more efficient safety equipment to reduce the problem and costs. The United States is not the only country with widespread insurance fraud, and we may be able to learn from other countries how to prevent or at least greatly reduce insurance fraud.

Pintar states a need for "further research to better understand the biomechanics and mechanisms of [motor-vehicle injuries]" (Cupid 2002, 1–26). Learning how to accurately and reliably diagnose whiplash and understanding the mechanisms that cause it, can aid in the fight against insurance fraud. The research of Lawrence et al. concluded that "it is not known if the conclusions drawn from [research] testing can be applied to higher severity collisions" (Kornhauser 2002, 1–15).

It is the opinion of the author that future studies should focus on determining how to accurately predict the occurrence of whiplash injuries, beginning with a review of present research in assessing whiplash probability. In order to fight whiplash fraud, determining injury thresholds for the general population is critical. Fraud from rear-end motor-vehicle accidents, according to insurance advertising, has increased dramatically over the past few years. Research can assist in preventing fraud by developing a more accurate understanding of the mechanism of injury and the probability of injury.

Driver Work Space and Vision

The interior of a truck's cab can be considered a closed environment, and as such must be controlled for the driver's comfort. Air temperature, temperature of surrounding surfaces, humidity, air movement or ventilation, and air quality must all be controlled. The temperature of the human body is not a constant 98.6°F throughout. This temperature, also known as *core temperature*, is found only in the interior of the brain and other organs. There is great temperature variation in the muscles, the limbs, and the skin—called the *shell temperature*. The body automatically attempts to regulate body heat by either conserving or dissipating it. The rule of thermodynamics states that energy always flows from a warm location to a cold location. As a driver's body begins to suffer from excessive heat or cold, his or her safety and the safety of passengers and other motorists becomes jeopardized (Kroemer 1999, 355–369).

The temperature of adjacent surfaces within a truck's cab should not fluctuate more than two to three degrees. Humidity does not affect temperature substantially, but air begins to feel stuffy within the range of 80 percent humidity at 18°C (64.4°F) and 60 percent humidity at 24°C (75.2°F). Conditions also become unpleasant when

air movement is below 0.5 meters per second (m/s), even when the air is warm. Air currents from behind are more unpleasant than frontal currents, and the neck and feet are especially sensitive to drafts; a cool draft is less welcome than a warm one. Seat occupants have reported finding air movement unpleasant at more than 0.2 m/s. Recommended temperatures for comfort are 20–21°C in the winter and 20–24°C in the summer for sedentary work such as driving (Kroemer 1999, 370–377).

The driver's environment is important for both comfort and safety. The ergonomics of the various dials and switches contributes to driver comfort by reducing fatigue and to driver safety by reducing unnecessary movement or distraction. When drivers take over-the-road trips in large trucks with large trailers, sleeping accommodations must be considered as well as aspects of driver comfort in all climates. It is also important to consider ease and safety of entering and exiting the cab. The number and placement of footholds and handholds and the distance between each pair are important because some tractors are high enough above the ground that a slip could cause a serious injury (Woodson 1992, 82-85).

Driver limitations must be considered during interviewing for, hiring for, and operation of motor-vehicle fleets. The ability of operators to drive in inclement weather should be strongly analyzed since they will be expected to drive in all types of environments and with different types of cargo. Important assets for professional truck drivers are good judgment and not taking chances. Drivers limit themselves by using poor safety practices and having avoidable accidents. Vision is one of the most important factors of safety since it is mandatory for the safe operation of fleet vehicles. Poor visibility, whether due to poor roadway design, weather, an obstructed windshield, or a poor driving position, must be dealt with immediately.

Limitations placed upon drivers also come from the type of truck being driven and the cargo being carried. If the truck is a tractor with two trailers, it will be more difficult to drive and have more limitations than a tractor with one trailer. Drivers must understand, realize, and consider these limitations when making maneuvers.

Visibility, both front and rear, is important, since without good, clear visibility the operation of fleet vehicles is extremely compromised. Visibility is directly affected by seating placement and window size and shape. Visibility is also affected by the placement of dashboard dials and switches; if they are placed incorrectly, viewing them could take the driver out of safe visibility range for operating the vehicle. If the numbers on the dials are too small or the lighting within the dials is too dim, the driver will have difficulty instantly determining the position of the hands. Dials should be placed so that they are not partially or totally blocked by the steering wheel or another fixed object in the tractor's cab. Dials should be designed and installed so that drivers do not have to move their head or torso to read them. Drivers should also be able to read any dial on the dashboard without staring or removing their eyes from the roadway for an unsafe period of time, usually more than one second. Visibility to the back of the trailer must be unrestricted, because the cargo may become loose and the driver must stop when he sees that the cargo needs to be tightened.

The interior of the tractor must be an ergonomically friendly environment, since over-the-road or other long trips can easily fatigue drivers and create unsafe situations. Special attention should be paid to temperature, ventilation, noise, and vibration. Over time, vibration—the oscillating motion of the body and its limbs and organs—will cause fatigue and produce an unsafe driving situation. *Free vibration* is caused by internal forces, and *forced vibration* is caused by external forces. Truck drivers are constantly subjected to vibration forces since they sit on a relatively stiff seat in a vehicle with a relatively stiff suspension. Harmful vibration usually occurs at the lower end of the vibration frequency scale (Chaffin 1999, 463–473).

The vibration and frequency of noise is harmful to the human ear. Humans are sensitive to vibration of the *vestibular* (hearing) system at low frequencies—1 to 2 hertz (Hz), such as vibrations generated by ships, cranes, or aircraft. Humans are also sensitive to vibration of the body at frequencies of 2 to 20–30 Hz, the middle frequency range, which is generated by vehicles and aircraft. At high frequencies—greater than 20 Hz, the receptors in muscles, tendons, and skin are highly sensitive. This high-frequency vibration is generated by tools or machines (Chaffin 1999, 485–488).

Designing driver and passenger spaces in buses requires special consideration. Drivers must be able to see nearby hazards or objects as well as necessary gauges and dials. They must also be able to see onboard passengers in case one falls or needs assistance. Seeing passengers is very important during the operation of the bus as well as during stopping and starting. Boarding passengers must also be visible to drivers since injuries can occur when drivers prematurely close access doors or pull away when all passengers are not properly seated.

Material Handling

Commercial fleet operators must be concerned with material-handling injuries when loading and unloading their vehicles. Forklifts, cranes, and hoists are used regularly at truck depots, and rules for operating these types of equipment can be found in OSHA regulations 29 CFR parts 1910.179 and 1926.550. Any time large machines are used, space is at a premium. Minimum width of warehouse aisles is 36 inches when small hand trucks are used and 10 feet if forklifts are used (Marshall 2000, 372–375). NIOSH offers the following statistics:

- Over 60 percent of lower back pain is caused from overexertion.
- Overexertion injuries of the lower back account for a significant loss of work time, and less than one-third of injured employees return to work.
- Overexertion injuries account for one-fourth of all reported occupational injuries in the United States, with some industries reporting that over 50 percent of their total injuries are due to overexertion.

Many characteristics of containers affect material-handling systems, including the load dimensions, distribution of the load, handling the load, and stability of the load. There are physiological limits to lifting based upon size and weight of the load and the frequency of lifting. The more often a load is lifted, the less weight a worker can safely handle. People who lift should consider the following NIOSH recommendations (Marshall 2000, 376–386):

- Lifting should be smooth, with no sudden acceleration.
- Objects lifted should be of moderate width—less than approximately 75 centimeters.
- The lifting path should be unrestricted, with no need to brace the torso with a hand.
- Handles should be secure and in good shape, and temperatures should be favorable to lifting (not too cold or too hot).

NIOSH uses the following formula to determine the recommended weight limit (RWL) for lifting:

$$RWL = LC \times HM \times VM \times DM \times AM \times FM \times CM \quad (8)$$

where

LC = the load constant,

HM = the horizontal multiplier,

VM = the vertical multiplier,

DM = the distance multiplier,

AM = the asymmetric multiplier,

FM = the frequency multiplier, and

CM = the coupling multiplier

These values can be obtained from D. Chaffin's *Occupational Biomechanics* (1999, 315–324).

When material handling is done with equipment such as a forklift or lift truck, the forklift/lift truck operators must be trained, and if they are involved in an accident or near-miss, they must be retrained. Forklift operators must pay special attention to moving in and out of open trailers from a dock since there may not be a smooth transition between the two and there may be a gap that could cause an accident. Usually a large metal sheet is placed over the gap for safety. Forklift operators must also never go around corners without sounding the horn to alert possible pedestrians (NSC 1999, 22–25).

A maintenance schedule must be kept so that fleet vehicle maintenance is performed regularly. If items need to be replaced, they should be replaced promptly even if they are approaching the end of their useful life. If safety items are not replaced but allowed to be used beyond their useful life expectancy, they could fail and cause an accident. Fleet vehicles should be equipped with all necessary parts and equipment that will assist drivers to safely reach a location for permanent repairs.

Loading and unloading should be done in a safe and efficient manner. The shifting of cargo on an open trailer is easy to spot, but on a closed trailer the cargo may shift without the driver knowing it. On a closed trailer, if the cargo has shifted it may fall when the trailer doors are opened, or the cargo may have been jostled to the point that it is unsafe to begin removing packages or boxes for fear that the rest of the cargo will fall. Loading is not only labor-intensive and time-consuming, but is also an art and must be thoroughly thought through prior to the start of the loading process. When cargo is organized by stops, it is convenient for the driver to check it for possible shifting prior to leaving each stop.

Determining the proper method for performing tasks requires planning and forethought. A preferred method, standard practice, and a time standard should be considered when attempting any job function. Training the worker is of utmost importance, since the worker must not only be trained in what the job function is but also how to safely complete the daily tasks. Several methods must be used to determine the safest way to perform a task, which include using accepted practice and safety scientific data for the subject task at hand. During the interview for the job position, the best worker in relation to experience, knowledge, safety, and physical criteria should be selected. A spirit of cooperation between management and the worker must exist so that the worker does not feel safety is only his responsibility or that management does not care about injuries. It has been clearly shown that a low number of injuries usually provide a higher profit. Another aspect of safety is dividing the workload as equally as possible, so that one worker does not have to perform his task faster and, consequently, in a less safe manner.

Biomechanical safety begins with knowledge of unsafe stress factors, which should be identified by the worker along with his or her supervisor. Trained persons who either perform the task or supervise the task performance can easily identify these stress factors. To analyze safe performance of tasks, one must be able to separate and evaluate each movement of a particular task. Each task has a minimum, median, and maximum time limit for performing the task safely. The evaluation of the worker and the subject task is required to set safe time limits for a particular job function. This motion can be predetermined for a specific task. Some of the movements include reach, position for most efficient movement, the release factor after the motion is completed, rebound as when pulling pieces apart on an assembly line, grasping or controlling an object, eye movement and focus, turning or manipulation of tools as parts, body segment motion, and motion of all or some of these movements simultaneously.

During lifting, the load should be kept as close to the body, lumbar spine, as possible, which results in a much smaller moment arm than if the weight was held outward. Figure 28 demonstrates the compression on the male back at various stages of the distance that the horizontal load (constant 650 kg) is from the spine at L5/S1. The spine must be supported by its own structure, along with the specific muscles; if it is not, it becomes unstable and can buckle under a very low compression force of

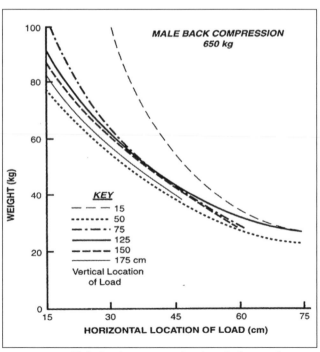

FIGURE 28. Male back compression in relation to the distance of a horizontal load from the spine at L5/S1 (*Source:* Chaffin et al. 1999)

approximately 20 newtons. The individual muscles exert lateral or front to back forces on the spine to prevent injury from bending and compression buckling. Loading on the disc is less during pushing than pulling, which is why material handlers are usually told to push instead of pull. Minimizing internal disc pressure can be achieved by having the backrest recline at approximately 120 degrees, and the lumbar support at approximately 5 cm. The greatest disc pressure was observed when the backrest was at 90 degrees with no lumbar support. Lumbar support affected lordosis, or backward banding, when the angle of the backrest affected disc loads (Andrews 2005).

There are a number of techniques for lifting. Many are described in other literature; the following are some of the more common techniques (Andrews 2005):

- Select strong people, based on testing, for heavy lifting.
- Bend the knees when in a squat in position, leaving the back straight.
- Do not slip, jerk, or twist during the strongest part while lifting.
- Use machines when possible.
- Divide the weight into smaller, more manageable parts.
- Use a good grip rather than a less secure one.
- If the load consists of smaller pieces, find a container, which will place the load in a more compact state, making sure that the weight is not excessive.
- Keep the load close to the body, since that will greatly reduced the moment arm and reduce the force on the spine.
- If possible, work at knuckle height; avoid lifting loads below the knees and above the shoulders.

Vehicle Design and Driving in the Future

In the author's opinion, about every three to four years there is usually a major design change for family passenger vehicles, and the change is usually based on customers' wants and safety regulations. The future of fleet vehicle design is one in which efficiency, economy, and safety are paramount. Current roadways limit the size of fleet vehicles and consequently limit the size of their cargo. Fuel is one of the main expenses for large truck fleets. The price of fuel may continue to rise, if history is any reference, and a more efficient combustion engine will be required to hold down or at least mitigate the high cost of fuel. Reduction in wind resistance, the rolling resistance of tires, and friction of mechanical parts will be of increasing importance since they directly relate to fuel savings.

Various inventions, such as forward-looking radar, self-parking, and so on, called intelligent transportation systems (ITS), are currently being researched. Another useful system of the future uses infrared to spot pedestrians or animals on roadways long before the driver can see them, especially in adverse weather conditions. Some fleet systems currently use the global positioning system (GPS) to track the speed and location of their tractors and trailers so that it is more difficult for drivers to be off schedule or speeding.

Ride and Vibration

Seating plays an important function in riding performance and vibration dampening. Seat design should be ergonomically correct. The seat's back should be flat vertically and somewhat concave horizontally. Sling-type seats should be avoided because they could cause the weight of the torso and upper legs to be pinched, and the resulting decrease in blood flow could create numbness. Very soft or thickly cushioned seats should also be avoided, since they may cause drivers to become too relaxed when fatigued, compromising safety. The seat back must be inclined so that drivers will be comfortable yet able to keep safety uppermost in their minds (Woodson 1992, 82–85). The seat material should be breathable for air circulation and comfort and have a pattern that will help the driver avoid slipping. It should also be nonflammable, highly resistant to friction and wear, and easy to clean. Foam used in seats should be sufficient to maintain comfort yet not impede visibility or cause *submarining* (sliding forward toward the dashboard) in a frontal collision. Seatbelts must be made of standard materials and must be kept clean and functioning. The seat position must be appropriate for clear and unobstructed vision yet maintain comfort.

It is important to reduce vibration not only for safe vehicle operation but also to avoid driver injury. Usually vibration injuries are subtle at first and become increasingly severe until the source of vibration is eliminated. The smoothness of the vehicle's ride and the construction of the driver's seat play important roles in dampening harmful vibration. The dynamics of vibration begin with an excitation source such as road roughness, tires and wheels, or the engine. The response of the vehicle to this stimulus is the severity of the vibration. A rough road would normally be of short duration while subtler but higher cycles of vibration would usually be over a longer period. Tires can create vibration when their shape is elongated during high-velocity operation. The more misshapen the tire is, the more intense the vibration will be, and the greater the probability of injury is (Kumar 1999, 233–237).

The smoothness of the ride depends on the equilibrium and center of the mass as the mass is rotated.

A vehicle's suspension is the main factor in dampening harmful vibration and creating a smooth ride. Dampening consists of both compression and extension of the vehicles' suspension system. Suspension includes the shock-absorber system, which reduces harmful rebounding and extends the time between cycles, effectively dampening or softening vibration. Evidence of *wheel hopping* are bumps on the tread surfaces of tires. It is caused when the dampening effect of the suspension is not operating properly but allows wheels to rise and fall very quickly and with great force. Since compression and extension usually are not equal, the spatial frequency of this type of dynamic is best when the frequency is further apart rather than close together.

Vibrations can be injurious to the human body, especially if it is exposed to them over a period of time. *Vibration* is the movement back and forth of a body or mass. Any body that is elastic is subject to vibration. *Free vibration* occurs from internal forces only, such as the vibration of an electric hand tool. *Forced vibration* is a result of external forces, such as motor vehicles riding over bumps. Forced vibration is considered to be more harmful. Regular repetition is referred to as *periodic motion*, and the repetition rate is called *frequency*. Normal frequency is determined using a time value, such as per second. Oscillating movements can be repeated regularly or irregularly. A simple periodic or regular repetition is what is known as a *sine wave* or *harmonic wave*. These types of vibrations, which are regular, can be easily determined in a given period of time. Stochastic or random vibrations cannot be so easily determined, except by means of averaging over time. Vibrations can be small or large; the large vibrations are usually considered *peak*. These vibrations can be considered strong or a weak by their displacement, velocity, or acceleration. The displacement is the movement over time; the velocity is the speed over time, while the acceleration is the change of velocity over distinctive periods of time.

Acceleration is usually determined in metric terms as meters per second per second or in standard units, such as feet per second. The easiest way to describe oscillations is by the terms *peak* and *average*. This can be easily seen on an oscilloscope. An oscilloscope is similar to a television screen, but rather than entertaining pictures, harmonic vibration is seen as wavy lines of different displacement over time. Vibration can be measured in various ways; the most accurate method is the root mean square value, which is between the average and peak values. The human response to vibration is dependent upon the frequency of such vibration. The greater the cycle of peaks and average is over time (i.e., one second), the more harmful the vibration. The greater occurrence of vibration that applies to a human body is a random motion, as opposed to a regular or periodic motion.

This motion, when analyzed, is split into spectrums, and the most used spectrum for human analysis is the third octave bandwidth. *Accelerometers* are used to measure human exposure to vibration. The data from the accelerometers is broken down into displacement and velocity, which are more easily understood and analyzed. Vibration is a vector quantity, and the human body has mechanical properties that vary with the direction of the vibration. Vibration is usually measured along three directors, which are classified as the x, y, and z axes. The specific direction of the vibration depends upon the hand tool or other source of vibration such that any harmful vibration effects followed the vector and access of the tool and body region.

The human body does allow absorption of certain amounts of vibration; however, beyond this threshold, vibrations become mechanisms of injury and, in extreme cases, may cause death. We have all become familiar with vibrators that, when used on the back of the neck, have a calming and soothing effect. If this same vibration is kept on the skeletal system for any duration, injury could occur. Injury vibrations depend mainly on their frequency, amplitude, or direction, as well as exposure time (Chaffin et al. 1999).

Occupational Stress

Occupational stress is the reaction of an individual to a threatening or pressing situation (Kroemer 1999, 211–215). Stress comes from many sources and could lead to injury or death depending upon the work being performed. Humans are better than machines at (Kroemer 1999, 157–160):

- detecting low levels of light and sound
- detecting a wide variety of stimuli
- perceiving patterns and the formulation of their general makeup
- detecting signals when the noise level is high
- storing large amounts of information for long periods of time and recalling the appropriate information at the right moment
- using judgment when all of the necessary facts or information are not available
- being flexible when inflexibility is a hazard
- reacting to sudden or unexpected problems and hazards
- solving problems when ingenuity and new methods must be employed
- learning from experience and mistakes
- performing human reasoning

To overcome boredom and fatigue, workers need to be satisfied and challenged. They should be challenged to use their skills—not just be human machines assembling parts. Workers must also feel that the work they perform is meaningful and that they are responsible for the outcome.

Stress may mean different things for different people even within the same field. Stress generally refers to physiological and emotional effects that come with job performance, worry and pressures of the job, and family problems. Stress may include physical problems such as ulcers and cardiovascular problems as well as emotional ones such as fear, jealousy, and moodiness. Stress can also be caused by an overload of work activities acting upon the sensory organs of the body. One well-known, overloaded, computer-like organ is the brain. If workers' brains become overloaded from stress, their training or skill becomes secondary to the handling of the stress or problem. There are times when a human brain receives or perceives one billion bits of information per second, but it is estimated that only about three billion bits can actually be transmitted to the nervous system for action. Of these, approximately sixteen per second become conscious thought in the brain and an even smaller number, one bit per second, is retained by memory.

When the brain becomes overloaded due to a massive influx of information, it is said to be under stress. If it is overloaded with data bits that cannot be processed, the bits are held until the brain can absorb them. If they cannot be absorbed within a relatively short period, the information is no longer accurate and will be distorted, and a possible harmful action could result. Everyone at one time or another exhibits mental fatigue—burnout—when he or she can no longer think clearly or absorb the information necessary to safely perform a task (Kroemer 1999, 191–194).

As with physical fatigue, human movement can also become stressed from mental fatigue, which is complex and has different elements that must be dealt with. A feeling of tiredness when sufficient rest has been received is a sign of mental fatigue, and with the tiredness comes slowed reactions and a slow thought process. It is thought that tiredness is a warning sign. Yawning appears to be a mechanism that increases oxygen intake to the lungs. Oxygen is a crucial element in worker performance, since the brain needs it to survive, and when muscle exertion occurs, oxygen is needed to replenish necessary chemicals. Blood carries oxygen to muscles and also takes waste products such as carbon dioxide and water from the system. Normal basal metabolism is usually sufficient during light physical activities, but when strenuous work is necessary it soon becomes insufficient. To improve the situation, breathing and heart rate increase, and physiological changes in the body can occur since the mind controls body functions. A reduction in output or reduced efficiency of work performance is a sign of mental fatigue, but it can also represent other areas that must be investigated and improved.

Mental fatigue is caused by brain overload, and this overload is more difficult to recover from than physical overload. Mental fatigue appears to be correlated with psychological and emotional stress, while physical overload is caused by work exertion. A factor that may help to increase resistance to mental fatigue is a good mental attitude toward the work performed. Education, experience, good working conditions, and contact with other workers are crucial ways to hold off mental fatigue. A worker's ability to perform a task varies based upon mental stress, fatigue, and distractions. Given the fact that the work function also varies, a combination of mental stress, physical fatigue, distractions, and varying work functions can be a recipe for injury. A worker's ability to perform a specific task should exceed the demand of that task. Boredom is said to be a reaction to a situation where there are too few stimuli, causing a decrease in baseline activity in the human central nervous system and can degrade efficiency and safety. Different people react differently when faced with a monotonous, prolonged task. Monotonous tasks breed boredom and should be interspersed with numerous short breaks and, if possible, a slight change of pace from usual activities.

There are many stressors in the work environment, some of which include the following (Kroemer 1999, 219–225):

- *Lack of job control.* If workers cannot participate in determining their own work routines, boredom and stress can occur.

- *Lack of supervisor support.* Support of supervisors appears to reduce the effects of stress on workers and should be encouraged whenever possible.

- *Heavy workload.* Job distress can be caused by a heavy workload. Too much stress and a heavy workload results in job dissatisfaction and possible loss of employees. If a job has a high rate of turnover, this is usually the reason.

- *Tasks and demands of the job such as deadlines, efficiency ratings, and so on.* These play a very important part as stressors and can reduce efficiency.

- *Lack of job security.* Lack of job security itself is not usually a problem, but when combined with other stress factors, it becomes a very highly important issue and consequently a high source of job stress.

Fatigue and Shift Work

Stress and fatigue are recipes for disaster, or at least injury. Mental stress and fatigue are as dangerous as their physical partners. Mental activity occurs in any job where incoming information must be processed by the brain. Some brain work, such as thinking, does not involve physical movement. Sometimes brain work can involve a link between a human and a machine. Brain work includes the ability to formulate ideas without acting on them. Humans require perception, interpretation, and the processing of information transmitted by the body's organs. Workers or commercial drivers have an obligation to maintain the highest level of alertness over long periods and to be responsible for making decisions involving the safety of people and equipment while fighting off occasional monotony. The mind may become stressed when more than two bits of information need to be classified and sequenced simultaneously. Fleet drivers run into this type of information overload every time they take the wheel and enter the roadway (Kroemer 1999, 219–225). Bits of information constantly bombard drivers' minds and compete for time. Over a long period this can become quite exhausting. Mental fatigue may take over and, consequently, safety is compromised.

The phases of the human cycle fall into daytime (*ergotropic*) and nighttime (*trophotropic*) categories. A *circadian rhythm* (24-hour cycle) is necessary in order for humans to recycle and regenerate for the next working and relaxation cycles. The cycles are triggered by changes from light to dark, social contacts, work and its associated events, and changes in time as shown on clocks. These events occur on a routine basis, and, consequently, circadian periods are considered routine.

The human body changes during different periods of the circadian cycle:

- Body temperature, heart rate, and blood pressure may fluctuate.
- Respiratory volume and adrenaline production vary.
- Mental ability changes.

During daytime activities all bodily functions and organs are ready for activity and the mind is rested. During nighttime activities, most of these functions are dampened, but they can be regenerated with recuperation and renewal of energy for the next cycle. It is believed that humans are oriented toward daytime performance and nighttime rest. Organizations can perform their own research on this by plotting the number of injuries or near-misses during various time periods and noting whether they occur near the beginning or the end of a shift. Some shift-work studies have found that workers report illnesses 2.5 times more often on evening and night shifts than on day shifts. These illnesses include stomach problems, ulcers, nervous disorders, and intestinal problems. Some can be directly correlated with the type of food ingested during the second or third shift. These problems occur because of disturbances in the sleeping and eating habits of the worker. There is a correlation between chronic fatigue and unhealthy eating habits and increased nervous disorders and stomach ailments. The symptoms of chronic fatigue are loss of appetite, disturbed sleeping, and digestive problems (Kroemer 1999, 191–201).

Younger workers may not sustain illness or injury as often as older workers and may be able to handle disturbance of their circadian rhythm better than older workers. Older workers already have higher probabilities of injury or illness and, coupled with the circadian periods, usually suffer stress more often than younger workers.

Effect of Noise and Vibration

Vibration is the rapid oscillation of waves and can cause injuries to the auditory system as well as to the rest of the body. Vibrations experienced when working with hand power tools can injure the nervous and skeletal systems; the seriousness of the injury depends upon the severity of the vibration and the length of exposure. Vibration is the motion or oscillation of bodies containing mass and elasticity that can move short distances at very fast velocities. *Free vibration* is caused by internal forces of the system, while *forced vibration* is caused by external forces. An example of free vibration is the ear receiving sound waves and the eardrum and the inner ear reacting. There is a limit to the decibels (dB) human ears can withstand over a period of time without permanent injury. Sound waves react with the natural frequency (HZ), resonance occurs and creates *motion amplitude*. Large amplitude within a system is harmful—for example, crystal can be shattered in the presence of very loud sound waves (Kroemer 1997, 320–324).

Motion during vibration can be *harmonic*, meaning that it can be represented by a simple sine wave and is predictable. These predictable motions or frequencies are called *deterministic* if they can be calculated mathematically. *Stochastic* or random vibration is the opposite of deterministic. Random vibration can be determined by averaging the waves. *Oscillation* has magnitude, displacement velocity, and acceleration. For this reason vibration is usually measured with accelerometers. Accelerometers are used to determine the value of the magnitude and are measured in meters per second squared (m/s^2). The quantifying value is so small that it is usually signified by thousands or millions or even greater values of a second squared. Gravity provides an example; at the earth's surface it is approximately 32.2 feet per second squared.

Frequency is the repetitive rate or oscillations per second. These wavelengths of vibration have peak values and average values, which indicate stress relationships. *Peak values* indicate maximum stress but do not consider the time duration, and consequently they are used to determine short-term motion such as shock or impact loading. Average acceleration is mathematically determined by considering cycle time and instantaneous amplitude. *Root mean square* (RMS) is the square root of the mean squared values of the motion of the body. RMS is proportional to the energy of the vibration and is usually between the peak and average values.

How the human body reacts to vibration depends on its frequency. Normally vibrations are applied to the human body randomly. Vibrations act as vectors, and the biomechanical properties of the human body are different depending on the direction of vibration. Therefore, measurement of vibrations must be along the three whole-body axes—z-axis (top to bottom), y-axis (side to side), and x-axis (front to back). These axes must be carefully determined so that the correct threshold of injury can be determined. It should be remembered that vibration is rarely unidirectional and consequently may cause confusion during an analysis if not properly understood.

Injury is caused from the frequency, amplitude, and direction of the vibration over time. If any one of these changes, the probability of injury can decrease or increase. Sensitivity of the human body is as follows:

- A low frequency—1 to 2 Hz—creates sensitivity in the vestibular system—the sensory receptors of the inner ear. This type of vibration may come from ships, cranes, or aircraft.

- A medium frequency—2 to 20–30 Hz—creates sensitivity from a biomechanical standpoint of body resonance. This resonance takes place in body tissues. This type of vibration is caused by vehicles or aircrafts.

- A high frequency—above 20 Hz—creates sensitivity in receptors of the muscles, tendons, and skin. This type of vibration is seen in tools and machinery.

Individual injuries and effects of vibration are based not only on the strength of the vibration and length of time someone is exposed to it but also on the physical condition of the individual. All individuals do not have the same susceptibility to injury, and consequently healthy individuals should adhere to safety guidelines regarding vibration. Vibration in and of itself may not produce injury, but in combination with noise,

temperature, posture, or exertion of force, it can create a hazard or injury. Everyone is familiar with motion sickness, either in a motor vehicle or on a ship. Motion sickness is caused by low-frequency vibration and affects the vestibule or receptors of the ear. There are two receptors, the semicircular canal, which is sensitive to angular accelerations, and the otolith organs, which have linear acceleration sensitivity. Motion sickness is believed to occur when these two sensors conflict with each other in relation to head motion.

The human body is said to be a dynamic biomechanical system, but it also models as a linear system within specific ranges of spine oscillations, up to approximately 100 Hz when body tissues have small deformations. The body can be considered a nonlinear model and is said to be better for predicting effects of random and shock vibrations. Vertical vibrations from 5 to 10 Hz cause resonance in the thoracic or abdomen area; vibrations from 20 to 30 Hz affect the head, neck, and shoulders, and vibrations from 30 to 60 Hz affect the eyeballs. Generally, there is less motion in body segments as the frequency increases above 10 Hz.

It is well known that spinal fractures can be caused by compression from large vertical accelerations. Vibrations at lower acceleration levels may cause fatigue fractures in different spinal components. These vibrations also interfere with the nutrition of spinal discs and predispose them to degenerative changes. Normally, degenerative changes are not one-time events but occur over a long period of time, which is one reason older people are more likely to suffer from degenerative discs than younger people. The physiological effects when people are exposed to vibrations include changes in heart rate, blood pressure, ventilation rate, oxygen intake, and so on. The vibrations necessary to produce simple effects are moderate to high in magnitude and in the middle of the frequency range. Vibration applied to a seated person increases the activity of back muscles from the lumbar, thoracic, and cervical regions.

Noise and vibration are harmful over a long period of time and can be harmful even over a short period, depending upon the frequency and level. Vibration affects different areas based upon different frequencies. Various peak-to-peak accelerations affect arm and hand steadiness, which could create a significant hazard. Vibration tolerance limits are classified in vertical or horizontal planes and the following tolerance limits for vertical vibration demonstrate the effects:

- Eight hours can be tolerated for a frequency of 1 Hz to maintain levels of proficiency with an acceleration of 0.6 Gs.

- Four hours can be tolerated for the same frequency with an acceleration of 1.

IMPORTANT TERMS

Basic Definitions of Biomechanical Injury Anatomy Terms (*Stedman's Medical Dictionary* 1997)

Cervical: referring to a segment of the spine, C1 through C7 (vertebrae beginning at the occipital bone and ending at thoracic vertebra T1)

Disc: a jellylike substance between each pair of vertebrae of the spine

delta-v: the change of velocity over time

herniated disc: a disc that protrudes either anteriorly or posteriorly from the vertebrae

LOSRIC: low-speed rear-impact collision

lumbar: referring to a segment of the spine having five vertebrae, L1–L5, between T12 and S1

occipital bone: the bone at the rear base of the skull just above C1

sacrum: an area of the spine with five vertebrae, S1 through S5, between T12 and the coccyx; the buttocks area

thoracic: referring to twelve vertebrae, T1 through T12, between C7 and S1; the upper trunk section

vertebra: a segment of the spinal column. There are seven cervical vertebrae, twelve thoracic, five lumbar, and five sacral.

The following terms and their positions are accepted and used consistently (Andrews 2001, Nahum and Melvin 2002):

- Anterior—Ventral—Forward
- Posterior—Dorsal—Back
- Flexion—Bend forward
- Extension—Bend rearward
- Mid Sagittal Plane—The right and left halves of the body
- Superior—Cranial—Toward the head
- Inferior—Caudal—Toward the feet
- Coronal Plane—The front and rear halves of the body
- Medial—Lateral—Side
- Palmar—Palm side of the hand
- Dorsal—Back of the hand
- Abduction—Movement away from the center of the body
- Adduction—Movement toward the center of the body

Terminology for body position:

- Sagittal—Divides the body into right and left
- Medial sagittal—Close to the center; lateral away from medial
- Corona—Divides the body into the front and back
- Anterior front or ventral side—Posterior back or dorsal side
- Transverse—Divides the body into top and bottom
- Superior—Closest to the head
- Posterior—Closest to the feet
- Limbs, proximal—Closer to the torso
- Limbs, distal—Farther from the torso

Wrist and hand motions:

- Flexion—Bend down
- Extension—Bend up
- Radial deviation—Bend the hand horizontal towards the thumb
- Ulnar deviation—Bend the hand horizontal towards the little finger
- Pronation—Rotation toward palm down
- Supination—Rotation toward palm up

REFERENCES

Allen, Merrill. 1996. *Forensic Aspects of Vision and Highway Safety.* Tucson, AZ: Lawyers & Judges Pub. Co.

American Association of State Highway and Transportation Officials (AASHTO). 1990. *Policy on Geometric Design of Highways and Streets.* Washington DC: AASHOC.

American Trucking Association (ATA). 1996. *Motor Fleet Safety Supervision: Principles and Practices.* 5th ed. Alexandria, VA: ATA.

ASTE. 2009. "Heavy Truck Tire Blowout." France: ASTE.

Backaitis, Stanley H., ed. *Biomechanics of Impact Injury and Injury Tolerances of the Extremities.* Warrendale, PA: SAE International, 1993.

Backaitis, Stanley H., ed. *Biomechanics of Impact Injury and Injury Tolerances of the Thorax and Shoulder Complex.* Warrendale, PA: SAE International, 1993.

Balk, S. A., R. A. Tyrrell, J. O. Brooks, and T. L. Carpenter. 2008. "Highlighting Human Form and Motion Information Enhances the Conspicuity of Pedestrians at Night." *Perception* 37, pp. 1276–1284.

Chaffin, D. 1999. *Occupational Biomechanics.* 3d ed. New York: Wiley-Interscience Publication.

Croft, Art. 1995. "Mechanisms." Whiplash Biomechanics Seminar. Spine Research Institute of San Diego. March 13–17. www.srisd.com

Cupid, Carl. 2002. "Application of Collision Deformation Classification to Compute a Numerical Value Called 'Extent of Collision Damage' (ECD) for Motor Vehicles Involved in Accidents." SAE Technical Paper 2002-01-2133. Warrendale, PA: Society of Automotive Engineers (SAE) International.

Deak, Mike. 2004. "Fleet Injuries." *Safety and Health Magazine* (June 2004), pp. 44–48.

Department of Transportation (DOT), Federal Highway Administration (FHWA). 2000. *Manual on Uniform Traffic Control Devices*. www.mutcd.fhwa.dot.gov/kno_millenium_12.08.01.htm

Federal Motor Carrier Safety Administration (FMCSA). 2003. *Commercial Truck and Bus Safety*. Washington, D.C.: FMCSA.

_____. Information and Analysis Online. www.fmcsa.dot.gov

_____. 2013. "Large Truck Crash Overview 2011." Publication No. FMCSA-RRA-13-002 . www.fmcsa.dot.gov

Fitch, James. 1994. *Motor Truck Engineering Handbook*. 4th ed. Warrendale, PA: SAE.

Fricke, Lynn B. 1990. *Traffic Accident Reconstruction*. Evanston, IL: Northwestern University Traffic Institute.

Gillespie, Thomas T. 1992. *Fundamentals of Vehicle Dynamics*. 4th ed. Warrendale, PA: SAE.

Institute of Transportation Engineers (ITE). 1999. *Traffic Engineering Handbook*. 5th ed. Washington, DC: ITE.

Kornhauser, Murray. 1993. "Delta-V Thresholds for Cervical Spine Injury." SAE Technical Paper 960093. Warrendale, PA: SAE International.

Kroemer, K.H.E. 1997. *Engineering Physiology: Bases of Human Factors/Ergonomics*. 3d ed. New York: Van Nostrand Reinhold.

_____. 1999. *Fitting the Task to the Human: A Textbook of Occupational Ergonomics*. 5th ed. London; Bristol, PA: Taylor & Francis.

Kumar, Shrawan, ed. 1999. *Biomechanics in Ergonomics*. London; Philadelphia, PA: Taylor & Francis.

Lawrence, J. 2002. "The Accuracy and Sensitivity of Event Data Recorders in Low-Speed Collisions." SAE Technical Paper 2002-01-0679. Warrendale, PA: SAE International.

Marshall, Gilbert. 2000. *Safety Engineering*. 3rd ed. Des Plaines, IL: American Society of Safety Engineers.

McKnight, A. James, and George T. Bahouth. "Analysis of Large Truck Rollover Crashes." *Traffic Injury Prevention*, 2009.

Microsoft Encarta. 2006. MS XP Software. "State Populations."

Nahum, Alan, and John W. Melvin, eds. 2002. *Accidental Injury: Biomechanics and Prevention*. 2nd ed. New York: Springer.

National Committee on Uniform Traffic Laws and Ordinances (NCUTLO). 2000. *Uniform Vehicle Code*. Alexandria, VA: National Committee on Uniform Traffic Laws and Ordinances. www.ncutlo.org

National Highway Traffic Safety Administration (NHTSA). 2013. "Traffic Safety Facts" (November) http://www-nrd.nhtsa.dot.gov/Pubs/811856.pdf.

National Safety Council (NSC). 1999. *Coaching the Lift Truck Operator*. Itasca, IL: NSC.

New Jersey Department of Transportation (NJDOT). 1998. *Commercial Driver Manual*. Trenton, NJ: State of New Jersey.

Nielsen, G., et al. 1997. "Repeated Low Speed Impacts with Utility Vehicles and Humans." *Accident Reconstruction Journal* (Jan.-Feb. 1997), pp. 23–28.

Pintar, Frank. 2002. "Biomechanics of Inertial Head-Neck Trauma: Role of Cervical Components." SAE Technical Paper 2002-01-1445. Warrendale, PA: SAE International.

Pike, J. 2008. *Forensic Biomechanics*. Warrendale, PA: SAE.

_____. 2002. *Neck Injury*. Warrendale, PA: SAE.

Rivers, R. 2001. *Seat Belt and Air Bag Systems Manual for Traffic Crash Investigation and Reconstruction*. Jacksonville, FL: Institute of Police Technology and Management.

Shands, 1993. "Health Care Spinal Cord Injuries." *Spine* (October 1993).

Shinar, David. 1985. "Effects of Expectancy, Clothing Reflectance, and Detection Criterion on Nighttime Pedestrian Visibility." *Human Factors and Ergonomics Society* (HFES) (June) 27:327–333.

Solomon, Stephen.1984. "The Safety Color." *Firehouse Magazine*. (June 1984) 9:106.

Southhall, J. P. 1961. *Introduction to Psychological Optics*. New York: Dover Publications.

Stedman's Medical Dictionary for Health Professionals. 3d ed.1997. Philadelphia: Lippincott Williams & Wilkins.

Strandberg, L. 1998. *Winter Brake Tests 1998*. Tokyo, Japan: National Research Institute of Police Science.

Transit Cooperative Research Board (TCRP). 1996. "TCRP Report 19, Guidelines for the Location and Design of Bus Stops." Washington, D.C.: National Academy Press. www.trb.org/onlinepubs/trcp/trcp_rpt_19a.pdf

Transportation Research Board (TRB). 1997. *Physical and Performance Characteristics of Heavy Vehicles*. Washington, D.C.: TRB.

Tyrrell, R. A., J. M. Wood., A. Chaparro, T. P. Carberry, B. S. Chu, and R. P. Marszalek. 2009. "Seeing Pedestrians at Night: Visual Clutter Does Not Mask Biological Motion." *Accident Analysis & Prevention*, 41, pp. 506–512.

U.S. Department of Transportation, Federal Highway Administration (FHWA). 2007. Roadway Geometry VI. Washington, D.C.: DOT.

Woodson, Wesley E. 1992. *Human Factors Design Handbook: Information and Guidelines for the Design of Systems, Facilities, Equipment, and Products for Human Use*. 2nd ed. New York: McGraw Hill.

RECOMMENDED RESOURCES

Backaitis, Stanley H., ed. *Biomechanics of Impact Injury and Injury Tolerances of the Head-Neck Complex.* Warrendale, PA: SAE International, 1993.

Commercial Vehicle Safety Alliance (CVSA). 1996. "Out of Service Criteria." www.regscan.com

Hyde, Alvin S. 1992. *Crash Injuries: How and Why They Happen: A Primer for Anyone Who Cares about People in Cars.* Key Biscayne, FL: Hyde Associates.

International Traffic Medicine Association (ITMA). *Traffic Injury Prevention.* London: Taylor & Francis. www.traffic medicine.org

International Society of Biomechanics. *Journal of Applied Biomechanics.* www.humankinetics.org/JAB/journal/About.htm

New Jersey Transit Corp. 1998. *Manual for Locating Bus Stops, Bus Stop Sign Installation and Shelter Installation.* Trenton New Jersey: New Jersey Transit Corp.

Ozkaya, Nihat, and Margareta Nordin. *Fundamentals of Biomechanics: Equilibrium, Motion, and Deformation.* 2d ed. New York: Springer, 1999.

Spine Research Institute of San Diego. 1999. *Whiplash Injury Statistics.* www.srisd.com

Watts, Alan J., Dale R. Atkinson, and Corey J. Hennessy. *Low Speed Automobile Accidents: Accident Reconstruction and Occupant Kinematics, Dynamics, and Biomechanics.* Tucson, AZ: Lawyers & Judges Pub. Co., 1999.

Whiplash Associated Disorders Conference. World Congress Convention. Vancouver Canada, 1999.

ADDITIONAL READING

ERGONOMICS AND THE MOBILE ENVIRONMENT*

Tina Minter, MS, CSP, ARM, ALCM
Property & Casualty Risk Specialist
Chubb & Son, a division of Federal Insurance Company
Milwaukee, WI

Introduction

In today's society, working in a mobile environment has become almost as common as working in a traditional office environment. In 2010, 26.2 million people worked from home or remotely for an entire day at least once a month—a figure a representing nearly 20 percent of the U.S. working adult population of 139 million.[1] Over the past several years, mobile work environments and interaction with mobile devices such as laptops, tablets, notebooks and smartphones have increased substantially. In 2010, experts estimated that 17.6 million tablets were sold—a number that was expected to increase more than three-fold in 2011.[2] Market projections predict that there could be more than 300 million tablets sold worldwide in 2015, with more than 80 million tablet users in the United States alone.[2,3]

Not only do workers interact with increasing numbers of mobile devices, but they now use their car, van or home as a work area in which to routinely carry out tasks that would previously have been done at a desk in the office. Evidence shows that this trend is probably here to stay. According to a recent survey from Staples Advantage, the business-to-business division of Staples, Inc., employees who telecommute say they feel and work better from home. In fact, 86 percent of telecommuters say they are more productive in their home office.[4]

While working on mobile devices allows workers to be more productive, there are downsides to consider. Mobile and telecommuting computing environments have introduced new areas of ergonomic concern that may threaten workers' well being and lead to increased health costs in the workplace. For example, there are a variety of injuries they may experience as a result of working with the technology in a mobile or home office environment.

Postural Demands

Though the use of mobile devices has increased dramatically, few employers have considered the postural demands on their workers who use laptops, tablets and other mobile devices. Instead, the user ergonomic focus has primarily been on stationary computer use. In theory, a mobile work environment and home office should meet the same health and safety standards as those available at the traditional office. For example, the work surface, chair and accessories should be of comparable quality to that found in the traditional office. The desk should be the appropriate height and sturdy enough to handle the weight of any peripheral equipment placed on it (e.g., computers, printers, fax machines, scanners, etc.). Unfortunately, many home-based workers use the kitchen table, which is not an ideal work surface since it is too high and doesn't allow for proper positioning of the wrists in relation to the keyboard. In addition, workers have little control over ergonomic factors in their mobile work environment while conducting business at other locations outside the home such as the library, Starbucks or even the airport. To address this problem, businesses and managers should monitor the use of mobile devices from an ergonomic perspective to reduce potential injury.

Injuries

Laptop Burn

Laptops can generate a lot of heat since they tend to run fast microprocessors. When the laptop is placed on a solid surface or on a lap, ventilation is greatly reduced because the heat that mainly vents out of the bottom of the device isn't dispersed. As a result, a hot laptop can suffer from reliability problems, and a system that overheats can fail.[5] In addition, a hot laptop can be uncomfortable to use since the heat it generates can be enough to cause superficial skin burns, even through clothing. *The Lancet* medical journal reports the case of a healthy 50-year-old scientist, fully dressed in trousers, who burned his genital area after using a laptop for an hour. Though he did occasionally feel the heat and a burning feeling on his lap and thigh while using the device, he was surprised to find two days later that he had blisters that burst and developed into infected wounds.[6]

Ways to prevent such burns include using a laptop stand that elevates the device for better cooling as well as decluttering the workplace to increase airflow around it. Users could also consider using laptops with built-in fans that generate airflow to keep them cool. Users should also refrain from placing a laptop on the lap for long periods. Those who must use a laptop for a long time should take it off their lap periodically and allow the laptop to cool down.

Mobile Device Neck

The posture adopted by many laptops users even more by tablet and smartphone users puts them at risk of chronic neck and shoulder pain. The tendency is to stand or sit overlooking the device while bending the neck and back to view the screen. Any activity where you hold your head/neck forward in a flexed or bent position for a prolonged period e will cause neck injuries.[7] Because of this injury trend, tablet and laptop users should receive the same ergonomic attention from their employers as desktop computer users did a decade ago. One solution is a laptop stand. Many laptop stands allow for multilevel positioning that improves the ergonomic sight line to the monitor, thus reducing strain on users' shoulders and necks when they view the laptop.

Repetitive Strain Injuries

Repetitive strain injuries are also occurring from overuse of handheld communication devices. These injuries range from "BlackBerry® thumb" and "iPod finger" to "Wiinjuries" and "Nintendinitis," which are more formally known as carpal tunnel syndrome, De Quarvain's tenosynovitis and trigger thumb. Symptoms range from pain and weakness to disability, with the effects being greater in older users who may be more susceptible to inflammation and pain.[8]

When people use laptops, they usually focus on the laptop screen while using the supplied keyboard. As a result, individuals are more likely to tilt their head forward, hunch their backs and use the front portion of their chair. The reasons for this positioning may include reading small character sizes, performing difficult/complicated tasks, working with glare on the screen, or viewing the screen from far away.

To reduce the chance of developing injuries, ergonomic experts advise users to take breaks from electronic devices especially when they notice strain or pain. They can also try to use the auto-text feature or to writer shorter/fewer messages. Those who have pre-existing joint problems should avoid overuse of electronic devices and seek medical assistance if swelling occurs or if symptoms don't go away.

Breaks

In an office environment, there may be many natural breaks, such as discussions with co-workers or a quick walk to the printer, that offer opportunities for a change in body position. But, for those who use mobile devices or work in a home office, there are few, if any, natural breaks that occur throughout the day to help reduce the potential for injury. Extended hours in the same body position or use of repeated motions can lead to various musculoskeletal injuries. Mobile workers should be conscious of taking occasional breaks throughout the day if no natural breaks occur. They can use mobile apps and computer programs that remind them to take breaks or to stretch throughout the day. These apps and programs help breaks up tasks and offer employees a chance to move about, infuse oxygen within the muscles, and lessen body fatigue.

Mobile Equipment Solutions

Laptops

Society's challenge is to start using laptops ergonomically; the good news is that the solutions are relatively simple. For those with a laptop at a desk area, experts recommend using a docking station or port replicator with a peripheral keyboard and mouse along with a separate monitor. A laptop stand or a separate monitor will allow the worker to raise the screen to avoid neck bending. Using a cordless keyboard and mouse will allow the user more flexibility to place the screen appropriately so it is comfortable for the eyes. Using a separate mouse gives the user the opportunity to work with the shoulders relaxed and elbows by the body, thus greatly reducing muscle fatigue.

iPads/Tablets

Currently, the iPad/tablet is not a true substitute for a laptop. Extended typing on-screen can be rather cumbersome, and fingertips may get sore or tender from repeatedly tapping against solid glass as opposed to energy-absorbing keys that allow an added tactile feel not matched by typing on glass. Ergonomic experts recommend that users writing for long periods on a tablet obtain and use a Bluetooth keyboard. Although adding a keyboard increases the bulk and clutter of using a tablet and may ruin the dynamic of working on a lightweight and portable system, it can help mitigate muscle fatigue.

In addition to concerns about typing on a tablet, it can be uncomfortable to hold an iPad for long periods. Tablet and smartphone users are similar to laptop users in that they are very likely to tilt their head forward and hunch their backs while using their devices, although they are usually standing rather than sitting. The many reasons tablet/smartphone users assume this awkward body position include trying to read small character sizes, performing complicated tasks, working with glare on the screen, or viewing the screen from far away. One solution is to use a tablet stand that props up the device so the user can view the screen at eye level. Another suggestion is to use an external keyboard to facilitate easier and more comfortable typing over long periods.

Mobile Computing

Advances in wireless communications and mobile computing have turned today's car into a fully functional office on wheels. While those using their vehicles to perform work may enjoy the benefits of mobility, it may be at the expense of comfort, performance and sometimes even health and safety. In general, vehicles are not ergonomically suitable for working on a laptop. For the mobile worker, ergonomic solutions primarily take the form of devices designed to properly position computers, peripherals and other equipment to avoid problems such as eyestrain, back strain and wrist strain.

The equipment necessary to create an ergonomic workplace in a vehicle includes a keyboard, monitor and storage area. Critical for data entry, keyboards must tilt to provide wrist relief during data entry. While using a laptop mount, the entire laptop will need to tilt, allowing the user to position it at an ideal angle. If a separate keyboard is used, it too should utilize a tilt mechanism. In addition, users should never allow an external keyboard to be loosely stowed in the cab, as it could become a projectile during an accident. Workers should position their monitor to reduce neck strain. Brighter screens are better, but users need to know how to dim the screen for nighttime use. Many times, employees forget creature comforts in the mobile world. A good storage console for a laptop and peripherals will also offer cup holders and a place to store tissues, pencils and paper. Employers should not underestimate the impacts these items can have on worker comfort and job satisfaction.

Telecommuting

With advances in technology (e-mail, Wi-Fi, tablets, smartphones, etc.), more and more employees are opting to work from their private residences on a regular basis (once a week, twice a week or more).

The Benefits

The benefits of telecommuting include savings of over $100 billion in commercial real estate, electricity, employee turnover and absentee costs.[9] In addition, companies increase productivity since employees are allowed to work at their own pace and in an environment with fewer interruptions. There are also several environmental benefits resulting from fewer vehicles on the road: less fuel consumed, less pollution and shorter commute times for those who still go to offices. Telecommuting also allows for "flexing" time for family commitments, which results in increased employee satisfaction. However, it is important that organizations committed to providing employees with telecommuting options also provide work-at-home employees with the same safe environment given to office employees.

The Drawbacks

Because employees are working in the "course and duty" of their employer while working at home or another location, the costs of an injury would be covered under their employer's workers compensation coverage. Thus, when a home office is set up, it should be done with safety in mind, making sure the work area has ergonomically suitable equipment and furniture to help mitigate the risk of a workers compensation claim. Documentation of employers' efforts to provide a safe and ergonomically designed work area will help prove they did their part to ensure their workers' safety.

Summary

Generally, ergonomic risk factors are identified in the office workplace. However, as mobile electronic devices help many workers cut the cords with the traditional workplace, ergonomics are now an important factor for those who telecommute or work in a mobile environment such as their car. These risk factors, left uncontrolled, will result in an increase in ergonomic injuries over time. Uncontrolled ergonomic risks can mean potential liability for those corporations that support telecommuting and a mobile workforce. In fact, many companies may find that the cost of workplace injuries can mean the difference between being competitive or not.

To maintain the health of employees and reduce potential corporate liability, risk and safety professionals must address ergonomic risk factors faced by the telecommuters and a mobile workforce. One approach to mitigating this risk is to develop telecommuting processes, standards and program elements using employee input from a number of corporate disciplines (facilities, HR and other departments). This collective planning process ensures that employees have the proper equipment, workstation setup and other tools to work more productively and safely in their home, a coffee shop or the airport.

Endnotes

[1] Ozias, Andrea. 2011. Telework 2011: A World at Work Special Report. World at Work, June.

[2] Gartner, Inc., 2011. "Gartner says Apple will have a free run in tablet market holiday season as competitors continue to lag." http://www.gartner.com/it/page.jsp?id=1800514.

[3] Pepitone, Julianne. CNN Money, 2011. "Tablet sales may hit $75 billion by 2015." http://money.cnn.com/2011/04/19/technology/tablet_forecasts/index.htm.

[4] TelecommuteNews Staff, 2011. "There's No Place Like a Home Office: Staples Survey Shows Telecommuters are Happier and Healthier, With 25% Less Stress When Working from Home." TelecommuteNews, July 21, 2011. http://www.telecommutenews.com/telecommute_friendly_companies/there%E2%80%99.

[5] "Portable Power (Laptop Computers) (Product Service Evaluation)," Consumer Reports, March 2003, 44–47.

[6] Ostenson, Claes-Goran, 2002. "Lap Burn Due to Laptop Computer," The Lancet, 360 (9346), 1704.

[7] "iPad Neck – Ergonomics Experts Warn of Tablet Injury," Herald Sun, April 11, 2011.

[8] Avitzur, Orly. 2009. "Rx for Blackberry Thumb." Consumer Reports, January 2009. http://www.consumerreports.org/health/conditions-and-treatments/rx-for-blackberry thumb/overview/blackberry-thumb-ov.htm

[9] Bram, Thursday, 2012. "Telecommuting Means Billions in Savings." GigaOM, March 12. http://gigaom.com/collaboration/telecommuting-means-billions-in-savings

Chapter 5

Basic Economic Analysis and Engineering Economics

Anthony Veltri and James D. Ramsay

LEARNING OBJECTIVES

- Describe the main motivation for applying economic analysis to occupational safety, health, and environmental affairs.

- Articulate the rationale that supports and the logic that is behind incorporating economic analysis findings into safety, health, and environmental investment proposals.

- Describe the safety, health, and environmental investment strategies available to firms and currently being practiced by firms.

- Characterize what is needed to construct a safety, health, and environmental economic analysis model.

- Describe what will be needed for economic analysis to become an on-going practice within the occupational safety and health profession.

The economic aspects of occupational safety, health, and environmental (OS&H) issues and practices are a timely subject to explore, study, and comprehend. Today, OS&H needs are affecting how business decisions are made, and the needs of business are affecting how OS&H decisions are made. This perspective is expected to dramatically change how proposals for investment in OS&H practices will be put together and presented within an organization's overall investment-allocation process. The primary motivation for applying economic analysis to OS&H investment proposals is to become more competitive when the firm makes decisions about which projects to fund. This indicates that investment allocators will make OS&H investments for the same reasons they make other strategic investments within a firm—because they expect those investments to contribute to economic performance. The desire to understand and use OS&H financial analysis has been attracting increasing attention. There are various descriptions of what an OS&H financial accounting system looks like, but essentially all definitions describe the system as a way of enhancing OS&H financial performance.

Economic analysis was defined by Friedman (1987) as the study of trends, phenomena, and information that are economic in nature. While it is understood that the principles of economic analysis will not change much over time, many aspects of how they are applied and under what context they are applied do occur. For example, developments in SHE economic analysis have moved to making the business case covering the social/community/people component of sustainability, supply-chain management, and the lean operation movement. Economic analysis has been used extensively by other internal organizational specialists (i.e., research and development, purchasing, design and process engineering, quality assurance, facility maintenance, operations management, transportation/distribution, and information management). So far, however, OS&H professionals have lagged behind in this effort. The significance of incorporating OS&H elements in the economic analysis of investment proposals was first recognized over a quarter century ago by Professor C. Everett Marcum, founder and curriculum designer of the West Virginia University graduate degree in OS&H Management Studies. Mar-cum reasoned in his course lectures that "The design intent (i.e., functionality and form) of a firm's products and technologies, and its operational processes and services, are first expressed by their economic attractiveness; and foremost judged from an economic point of view; and any other features are secondary to the initial economic review."

Bird (1996), in his book entitled *Safety and the Bottom Line*, expressed a similar reasoning in his concept concerning the Axiom of Economic Association. Bird stated that "A manager will usually pay more attention to information when expressed or associated with cost terminology."

These crucial lines of reasoning have generally evaded the practitioners, professors, and students in OS&H management. While they may be well read in the strategic management practices, technical principles, and regulatory aspects that guide decision making and operating actions for the field, practitioners seldom have studied and used the concepts and methods that underlie their economic logic and attractiveness. Most commonly, books, journal articles, and lectures merely mention these in passing.

Concern about analyzing the economic aspects of OS&H issues and practices initially surfaced in the early 1990s and continues today (Henn 1993, Cohan and Gess 1994, Warren and Weitz 1994, Cobas et al. 1995, Brouwers and Stevels 1995, Mizuki et al. 1996, Van Mier et al. 1996, Lashbrook et al. 1997, Hart et al. 1998, Timmons 1999, Nagel 2000, Warburg 2001, Adams 2002, Behm et al. 2004, Asche and Aven 2004, Oxen-burgh and Merlin 2004, Markku Aaltonen et al. 2006, Santos et al. 2007, Marelli and Vitali 2009). During the last fifteen years, there has been a growing need to understand the economic impact that OS&H issues and practices have on competitive performance. Yet the economics of those issues is one of the least-understood subjects in the industry (Tipnis 1994). Increasingly, U.S. firms have taken steps toward better understanding their competitive impact. This trend is evidenced by the development of OS&H sections of national technology roadmaps (Semiconductor Industry Association 1997–1999, The Microelectronics and Computer Technology Industry Environmental Roadmap 1996, and The United States Green Building Council 2003) that incorporate initiatives to reform the way costs linked to OS&H issues and practices are profiled and by the construction and use of various cost-of-ownership (CoO) models (Venkatesh and Phillips 1992, Dance and Jimenez 1995) that have been developed.

The next chapter will go into detail about cost analysis and budgeting. Therefore, this chapter was developed to present economic analysis as a useful tool for changing how proposals for investment in practices to confront and manage OS&H issues are put together and presented

within a firm's overall investment decision-making process. Specifically, this chapter provides (1) a rationale that supports economic analysis and the logic behind incorporating its findings into OS&H affairs and investments, (2) a catalog of OS&H investment strategies available to firms and some currently being used by firms, (3) a blueprint recommended for constructing and using an OS&H economic analysis model, and (4) a summary of elements necessary for economic analysis to become a regular practice in the safety, health, and environmental management profession.

A RATIONALE FOR INCORPORATING ECONOMIC ANALYSIS FINDINGS INTO SAFETY, HEALTH, AND ENVIRONMENTAL INVESTMENT PROPOSALS

Showing a relationship between investments in OS&H practices and economic performance can be an elusive undertaking (Behm et al. 2004). The question that continues to challenge internal organizational stakeholders is "Do investments in practices intended to confront and manage OS&H issues contribute to economic performance?" Many OS&H field practitioners and academics have answered yes (Goetzel 2005, The European Agency for Safety and Health at Work 2004, American Society of Safety Engineers 2002, Jervis and Collins 2001, Smallman and John 2001); however, there is no compelling research that provides a *definitive* financial answer. Many internal stakeholders say no (Asche and Aven 2004, Dorman 2000, Shapiro 1998). They are very skeptical about how OS&H economic analyses are conducted; specifically, they question how cost and potential profitability data are collected, calculated, analyzed, interpreted, and reported. The reality may be that OS&H investments do not routinely set up opportunities to make money. At the same time, the opposite stance that OS&H investments seldom provide a financial payoff is also inaccurate. There should be no denying that investing in practices to confront and manage OS&H issues has always been a complicated proposition with very real methodological issues and economic implications. Even so, most firms invest in OS&H practices despite their economic impact, but they should do so knowingly.

Typically, concern for OS&H performance and economic performance have been viewed as separate lines of attack operating independent of and usually in opposition to one another. However, the actual *interdependence* between these concerns increasingly highlights the need for showing some type of an economic relationship. Generally, OS&H professionals have not incorporated economic analysis as a way of showing how investments in these practices contribute to economic performance

(Behm et al. 2004). As a result, left out of the firm's competitive business strategy and excused from internal stakeholder expectations that this function justify its internal and external affairs with an economic perspective, OS&H practices tend to be looked at as a necessary cost of doing business, with little economic payback expected (Veltri et al. 2003a). To say the least, this is not a viable perception for internal stakeholders to bring and hold onto during the investment-allocation process. Only a focus on the results of economic analysis can provide internal stakeholders with the necessary information to set investment-allocation priorities. The emphasis on the results of economic analysis should not be interpreted to mean there is any intention to deemphasize the importance of ensuring compliance with regulatory mandates. Concern for compliance surely exists, as it rightly should, and employing economic analysis is not intended to replace compliance applications. However, to focus *only* on maintaining compliance with OS&H regulations should not be expected to yield positive financial returns. Alternatively, what one attempts to accomplish with economic analysis is to go beyond compliance in ways that provide pertinent quantitative and qualitative economic information about how a firm's organizational activities (i.e., products, technologies, processes, services) tend to create OS&H issues and how strategic investments in innovative practices to confront and manage these issues might offer financial opportunities and reduce liability.

As a rule, the investment decision-making process hinges on a firm's competitive strategy, its research and development capability, its technology wherewithal, and the human means to productively use and protect organizational resources. The analysis used to reach investment-allocation decisions tends to be heavily slanted toward economic aspects. How well economic analyses are conducted and how well analysis findings support a firm's competitive strategy will usually affect how investments are allocated within a firm. During the last 25 years, existing and emerging OS&H issues (e.g., occupational injuries and illnesses, environmental incidents, natural and man-made hazardous exposures, tough government regulatory requirements, pressure from nongovernment interest groups concerning sustainable resource development and use, and long-term contingent liabilities as a result of past operations) are also increasingly affecting how decisions to fund projects are made within a firm. The real dilemma facing financial decision makers is how investment choices to confront and manage OS&H issues can be made in the absence of sound quantitative economic information. Without economic analysis results that detail the estimated cost and potential profitability of investments, even the most zealous OS&H internal stakeholders are left without a means to objectively make fiscally prudent investment-allocation decisions.

The following are beneficial outcomes that should be expected and leveraged when OS&H economic analyses are effectively conducted (Veltri 1997):

1. A refined understanding of the products, technologies, processes, and services that tend to drive OS&H life-cycle costs.

2. A more complete and objective data set on life-cycle costs and profitability potential of OS&H investments, enabling improvements to product, technology, process, and service designs.

3. An enhanced way of determining which OS&H management strategies and technical tactics to pursue and what level of investment will be required.

4. A new investment analysis structure in which fashioning OS&H issues and practices affects how business decisions are made, and in which business needs affect how OS&H decisions are made.

Despite these leveraging opportunities, usually there are internal organizational barriers to overcome when applying economic analysis to OS&H investments. The following are a sample of internal perceptions that OS&H professionals should be expected to confront:

1. An operations-level perspective that OS&H issues linked to the firm's processes are primarily regulatory-compliance-based and play a very small part in the investment-allocation process of the firm.

2. A design engineering-level perspective that sees the existing strategy and methodology for performing economic analysis of OS&H issues and practices that affect new product, technology, and process designs as qualitatively and quantitatively immaterial for enhancing design changes.

3. A senior-level executive perspective that proposals for investments in practices to counteract OS&H issues affecting the firm are not financially structured and reported in a manner that allows them to compete with other investment-allocation alternatives.

Such internal organizational barriers can be significant and must be overcome so that OS&H proposals can compete for the firm's investment dollars. The strategy considered most effective in overcoming these barriers is to employ economic analysis in a manner that discloses both the internal and external OS&H-related costs throughout the productive/economic life cycle of a firm's existing, new, and upgraded organizational activities and reveals the financial impact that investments in OS&H practices have on these organizational activity designs.

AVAILABLE OS&H INVESTMENT STRATEGIES

OS&H professionals who wanted to better understand how investment allocation decisions are made have had to satisfy themselves with professional literature that is nonobjective and fragmented with piecemeal approaches, causing them to be disadvantaged during the investment-allocation process. It is imperative that the forward-thinking OS&H specialist, who is interested in making his/her firm more competitive and in advancing his/her own career, understand how the firm makes strategic investment decisions and how it views investment utilization. However, to accomplish this, the OS&H specialist has to first understand the type of investment strategy being used by his/her firm. Figure 1 offers such a framework by providing a catalog of typical OS&H investment strategies that are available to firms or that are already being practiced by firms. The framework is a derivative work and borrows heavily from other strategy typologies (Miles and Snow 1978, Porter 1980, Adler et al. 1992, Roome 1992, Schot and Fischer 1993, Welford 1994, Chatterji 1995, Ward and Bickford 1996, Epstein 1995, Day 1998, Brockhoff et al. 1999, Stead and Stead 2000, and Coglianese and Nash 2001).

Each of these levels represents a distinct strategy for how a firm typically makes strategic OS&H investment decisions and how they tend to view investment utilization. Together they represent a way of thinking about OS&H investments that goes beyond existing investment strategies, which are at a distinct disadvantage when competing with the firm's other investment options. Investment allocators are usually reluctant to accept qualitative estimates (i.e., compliance audits performed, behavior-based training provided, perception surveys) when deciding to invest in OS&H investment proposals. They prefer quantitative estimates (i.e., cost and profitability potential).

Internal organizational stakeholders constantly face investment choices among alternatives that are linked specifically to changes in the firm's organizational activities. They may have to decide whether to continue or drop a product or service, acquire certain technologies, or reengineer a process. Generally, making these decisions requires conducting economic analyses that provide cost and profitability comparisons among mutually exclusive alternatives (i.e., accepting one alternative means not accepting others). Likewise, investment decisions about OS&H practices require choosing among alternatives that are mutually exclusive and linked to the changes in the firm's organizational activities (e.g., products—substituting regulated occupational safety and health resource inputs with unregulated and perhaps less harmful ones, technologies—employing new environmental toxicity monitoring and detection systems, processes—reengineering to eliminate process waste

from resource outputs, or services—modifying supply-chain relationships related to OS&H practices). This results in investment-allocation decisions that are usually based on the direct result of the projected economic impact of the mutually exclusive alternatives under analysis. Economic analysis, then, provides a recommended approach to how one might best present proposals for OS&H investments where economic aspects dominate and drive decision making and where economic effectiveness and efficiency are the criteria for choosing which OS&H issues to confront and manage and in which alternative solutions to make selected investments.

An abridged life-cycle costing method, which features net-present-value financial analysis, is the recommended tool for constructing a OS&H economic analysis model. The rationale for this abridged approach is that internal stakeholders have questioned both the relevance of the full life-cycle costing methodology for the actual business decisions they must make and the efficacy of the full methodology for making business decisions in real time. As a result, most firms are encouraging their OS&H professionals to develop and use a more streamlined method that focuses on internal private costs (i.e., costs incurred from organizational activities that result in product-yield quality and process logistical performance problems, injury/illness and environmental incidents, and liability) rather than on external societal costs (i.e., costs incurred as a result of organizational activities that cause pollution of air, water, or soil; natural resource depletion or degradation; chronic or acute health effects; alteration of environmental habitats; and social/economic welfare effects) to make the economic analysis more relevant and useful for business decision making.

Several abridged life-cycle assessment methods have been described in the literature (Graedel et al. 1995), ranging from primarily qualitative approaches to quantitative ones in which expert judgment, a limited scope, and a system boundary keep the life-cycle assessment effort manageable. Experience demonstrates that life-cycle assessment for a complex manufactured product or an industrial manufacturing process works most effectively when it is done semiquantitatively and in modest depth. Unlike the full life-cycle assessment method, an abridged method is less quantifiable and less thorough. It is also quicker and more practical to implement. An abridged assessment will identify approximately 80 percent of the useful OS&H actions that could be taken in connection with corporate activities, and the amounts of time and money consumed will be small enough that the assessment has a good chance of being carried out and its recommendations implemented. The foundation for the abridged architecture was based on the unabridged life-cycle framework developed by the Society of Environmental Toxicology and Chemistry (SETAC 1991).

Levels of Investment Strategy	
Level 1 Reactive:	Posture is to invest only when required, with attention to responding to government directives or insurance carrier mandates
Level 2 Static:	Posture is to invest cautiously, with specific attention on preventing occupational injuries, illnesses, and environmental incidents from occurring
Level 3 Active:	Posture is to invest assertively, with major emphasis on reducing risk to existing operations, and to lower contingent liability resulting from past operations
Level 4 Dynamic:	Posture is to invest strategically, with major emphasis on counteracting the life-cycle risk and cost burdens linked to the firm's organizational activities carrier mandates

Level 1 Reactive

Strategy for financing the firm's OS&H investments at this level can be characterized as a reactive and resistive arrangement. Access to financial resources is based solely on correcting violations cited by government regulatory agencies and mandates from insurance carriers. Additional financial resources needed for providing technical day-to-day OS&H services are provided when it financially suits the company. Tools for performing economic analysis of OS&H issues do not exist because the firm does not want to, does not think it needs to, or is not aware of the potential cost impact of failing to counteract these issues.

Level 2 Static

Strategy for financing the firm's OS&H investments at this level can be characterized as an informal arrangement. A mentality of funding only as much as others in their industry sector is strongly adhered to. An informal pay-as-you-go funding mentality exists; invest to counteract issues only when trying to reduce the outlays associated with injury/illness and environmental incidents. Investments undertaken for preventing occupational injuries, illnesses, and environmental incidents and to meet compliance with regulations generally do not compete for access to financial resources. However, access to financial resources needed to confront and manage more technically discriminating OS&H issues depends upon the capabilities of the firm's OS&H professionals to assemble internal coalitions of support in order to compete for funding. These technically discriminating prevention initiatives tend to have no clear criteria and pattern of funding, thus subjecting them to unpredictable funding outcomes. Tools for performing economic analysis of OS&H investments are considered by internal organizational stakeholders to be qualitatively and quantitatively immaterial for competing with other investment allocation decision alternatives. OS&H cost accounting practices focus on aggregating cost data, causing costs to be hidden in general overhead accounts rather than included throughout the life cycle of the product, service, technology, or process responsible for their generation. As a result, integrated and concurrent design engineering decision-making capabilities required for aggressively controlling OS&H costs are limited and incomplete.

Level 3 Active

Strategy for financing the firm's OS&H investments at this level can be characterized as an applied arrangement. Access to financial resources tends to be allocated when investment requests are intended to reduce risk to products, technologies, processes, and services; enhance compliance with regulatory standards; reduce contingent liability caused by past operations; and minimize outlays associated with accidents, environmental incidents, lawsuits, and boycotts. The funding level tends to be above others in their industry sector and included in the overall budget of the core business units obtaining the services. Tools for performing economic analysis of OS&H investments are chiefly focused on cost-benefit analysis and payback, and sometimes internal rate of return. Costs are accumulated either through the use of cost accounting systems or through the use of cost-finding techniques and are reported on a regular basis for management information purposes. The cost of incidents are charted and charged back to core business units and incorporated into the firm's budget process. However, profiling the cost and profitability of OS&H issues affecting the organizations products, technologies, processes, and services, and integrating cost information into decision-making, does not occur. This condition results in senior-level executives looking at OS&H issues as nonbusiness issues.

Level 4 Dynamic

Strategy for financing the firm's OS&H investments at this level can be characterized as being self-sustaining and a down-to-business arrangement. A strategically opportunistic funding position is taken; this means having sufficient funding for the long-term, while having the financial wherewithal to remain flexible enough to solve new issues and support research and development and other opportunities for innovation that, over time, will lead to significant OS&H performance gains while advancing measurable business goals. Business strategies and OS&H changes are tightly interwoven; changes in products, technologies, processes, and services affect OS&H, and changes in OS&H issues and practices in turn force product, technology, process, and service changes. Access to financial resources and capital is approved for 3 years (typically related to potential business contribution over the long and short term) and is based on factors and circumstances that are causing the firm to fail in its efforts to protect and use resources productively and on conditions/circumstances under which OS&H pays. Senior-level financial executives desire OS&H strategy and activities to become financially self-sustaining and contribute measurably to company competitiveness. Tools for performing economic analysis of OS&H investments provide reliable and timely information on the full cost burdens associated with the firm's products, technologies, processes, and services over their productive and economic life cycle. Major thinking is performed on how to enhance the efficiency and effectiveness of OS&H spending.

FIGURE 1. Available safety, health, and environmental investment strategies (*Source:* Veltri and Maxwell 2008)

Present-value financial analysis provides the final link in the architecture. As a dollar today is always preferable to a dollar tomorrow, the sheer nature of OS&H initiatives at the work site often take multiple fiscal years to become fully realized. That is, dollars spent today on OS&H programs and activities may not reap or return benefits to the firm for several years. Hence, present-value financial analysis provides the most reliable means of comparing the financial performance of mutually exclusive alternatives when said alternatives fully mature in subsequent fiscal years (Newman 1983). In this way, present-value financial analysis helps to delineate the long-term financial impact of OS&H investments by presenting the after-tax cash flow and the present-cost value of the investment over a sufficient time horizon. The rationale for using net-present-value financial analysis is that many of the traditional financial analysis techniques employed by OS&H professionals, such as payback and

rate of return on investment, fail to take the time value of money into consideration. Although useful tools in the financial analysis of investment decisions, exclusive use of these methods can result in making incorrect decisions, such as accepting OS&H project proposals that lose money, or, conversely, rejecting OS&H project proposals that may represent financial opportunities and may reduce contingent liability.

Figure 2 provides an architecture for the OS&H economic analysis model. This architecture is built around three stages: (1) defining and setting all the boundaries necessary for managing the economic analysis; (2) conducting an abridged life-cycle inventory analysis and impact assessment of existing OS&H issues and proposed alternatives, from upfront analyses and the acquisition of capital and the permits through resource and material use, disposal, and closure; and (3) conducting postimplementation reviews that will ensure that the

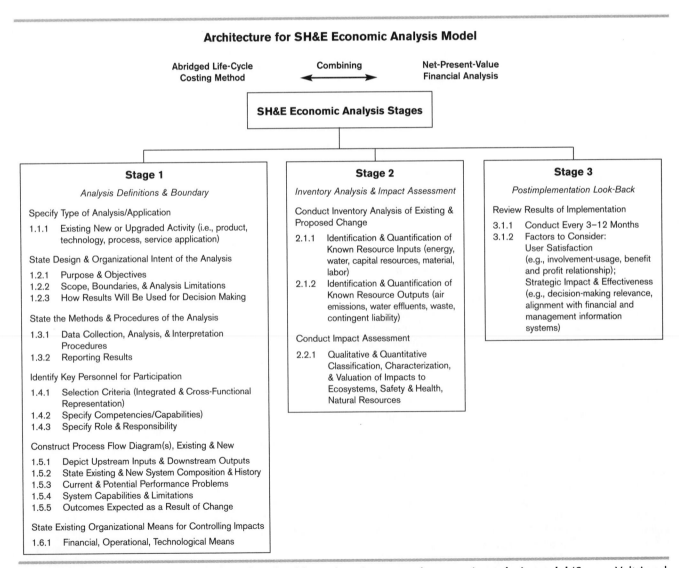

FIGURE 2. Blueprint for constructing a safety, health, and environmental economic analysis model (*Source:* Veltri and Ramsay 2009)

results of implemented solutions are deemed to be in reasonable agreement with the estimated projections.

Stage I: Defining OS&H Economic Analysis Strategy and Boundaries

Defining the OS&H economic analysis strategy and setting its structural boundaries are key aspects of the economic analysis. As outlined in Figure 2, this initial stage should be accomplished through the following five steps. First, the OS&H professional should consider specifying the type of analysis to be conducted, specifically attending to the following components: (a) a description of the existing, upgraded, or new product, technology, process, or service system; (b) the system's expected economic life (i.e., the equivalent of the estimated amount of time that investments in the system can be expected to have economic value or productive uses and the estimated amount of time recurrent savings and reduced contingent liability can be achieved without having to reinvest as the initial investment ages); (c) the firm's hurdle rate (i.e., the required rate of return in a discounted cash-flow analysis that the firm is using for judging investment proposals); and (d) the existing and potential OS&H issues and impacts (e.g., musculoskeletal disorders resulting in workers' compensation claims, CO_2–NOX emissions resulting in global warming potential acidification) that are linked to the firm's activity under analysis.

The second step is to keep the analysis on course and focused. This requires that the design and organizational intent be stated up front. Possible components include: purpose and objectives, key assumptions and analysis limitations, and how information will be used to drive decision-making capabilities.

The third step is to specify the methodology suggested for performing the analysis (i.e., data collection, analysis and interpretation, and reporting procedures). These should be transparent and stated at the outset.

The fourth step is to identify and empower an integrated OS&H economic analysis project team and assist them in carrying out the study. Individuals on this team must be utilized as supportive personnel in order to carry out the project. Note that it is absolutely essential that their assistance be requested and used. Of course, they must be provided with the advisement and encouragement they will need to perform as expected. The team should be cross-functional in makeup and possess skills in finance, design and process engineering, operations, facility management, procurement, legalities, OS&H affairs, and community relations.

The fifth component of this stage is to construct process flow diagrams of the existing organizational activity and the proposed solution change. The process flow diagram should depict upstream inputs and downstream outputs, the existing and new system composition and history, current and potential performance problems, existing and new system capabilities and limitations, and any beneficial outcomes expected as a result of the change.

Stage II: Inventory Analysis and Impact Assessment

Figure 2 shows that the main function of stage two is to conduct an inventory analysis (i.e., the identification and quantification of known resource inputs such as energy, water, capital, resources, materials, and labor, and known outputs such as air emissions, water effluents, waste, and contingent liability) and an impact assessment (i.e., qualitative and quantitative classification, characterization, and valuation of impacts to ecosystems, human safety and health, and natural resources based on the results of the inventory). It is also sensible to provide investment-allocation decision makers with estimates of the firm's ability and means to control or improve the existing OS&H issue. This will add an additional level of robustness to the analysis. Chief factors to assess should include the firm's (1) financial funding capability (i.e., the existing level of funding available to control or improve the OS&H issue: a high level of funding suggests the firm has the financial means to effectively control or improve the issue, whereas a low level of funding suggests the firm has little financial means to affect the issue in the immediate future); (2) human operational capability (i.e., the existing level of human operational wherewithal to control or improve the OS&H issue: a high level of wherewithal suggests the firm has the human means and capability to control or improve the issue, whereas a low level suggests the firm has little human operational means to affect the issue in the immediate future); and (3) available technology (i.e., the existing level of technology that is to control or improve the OS&H issue: a high level of available technology suggests the firm can utilize technology as a way to control or improve the issue, whereas a low level suggests the firm has little technological means to affect the issue in the immediate future).

The use of impact models (e.g., risk and economic) helps guide the decision making and the operating actions that are necessary for keeping the inventory analysis and impact assessment structured and gives a picture of the life-cycle process-flow inputs and outputs linked to the organizational activity under analysis. In addition, it provides investment-allocation decision makers with an understanding of the extent and magnitude of the issue. A large number of risk assessment and analysis models and documents are available for profiling risk impacts and contingent liability linked to the firm's organizational activities.

Stage III: Postimplementation Review

After investing in OS&H practices, it is very important to determine the degree to which the results of the implemented changes are in reasonable agreement with the estimated projections. For example, if a new technology was purchased because of potential reductions in cost and contingent liability, it is important to see if those benefits are actually being realized. If they are, then the economic analysis projections would seem to be accurate. If the benefits are not being obtained, a review to discover what has been overlooked should be performed. A post-implementation assessment helps uncover the reasons why targets were not met. One possible reason could be that economic projections may have been overly optimistic. Knowing this can help analyzers avoid mistakes in economic cost projections in the future. In order to ensure that economic calculations and cost projections are realistic, everyone involved must know that a review of results will take place. Therefore, three to twelve months after a mutually exclusive alternative has become operational, and regularly thereafter, a postimplementation review should be conducted. Factors to be considered in the look-back should include: user satisfaction (i.e., involvement/usage or cost/profit relationship) and strategic impact and effectiveness (i.e., decision-making relevance, alignment with financial and management information technology systems, and organizational objectives).

An economic analysis of a OS&H investment proposal collects cost information associated with the inventory analysis and impact assessment and uses a financial analysis measure for understanding economic impact. The OS&H professional is cautioned that an economic impact analysis of a OS&H investment proposal is only as accurate as the cost information that it collects—quite literally, the euphemism "garbage in, garbage out" applies. In this sense, OS&H professionals are encouraged to work with their finance and accounting colleagues as estimates for necessary costs are obtained. Therefore, a major component of an economic analysis is gathering data to make reasonable estimates of cost. Appendix A provides an outline of usual as well as potentially hidden OS&H life-cycle cost factors and activity drivers that are typically linked to a firm's organizational activities. Estimated costs are referred to in OS&H economic analysis as incremental costs; they are the difference between the after-tax cash flow of the mutually exclusive alternative(s). Net present value (NPV) analysis is the most applicable financial measure for understanding economic impact because it provides the most reliable method for comparing the financial performance of mutually exclusive alternatives on the basis of their projected after-tax cash flows. Net present value analysis can be thought of as the present value of an investment's future cash flows

minus the initial investments required to initiate a particular program (or set of programs). Conventional NPV decision-making rules indicate that projects with profitability indices (PI) of greater than 1.0 should be pursued. When comparing multiple project alternatives, those with higher PIs are understood to be financially more attractive than those with lower, albeit positive, PIs. Alternatively, projects with a PI of 0 will recuperate only the cost of the resources required to make the investment, and, conversely, projects with a negative PI represent a financial loss for the investment. Because investment decisions in OS&H are important, proposals should also be supplemented with qualitative information, such as how the investment is expected to maximize sustainable resource development and use practices, enrich the quality of management information, develop human competency and capability, lower contingent liability, maintain regulatory compliance, reduce nongovernment special interest group concerns, and enhance organizational reputation. This type of qualitative information is sufficiently important that it could influence a decision to fund the investment proposal, in spite of the fact that the proposal may not meet the firm's established hurdle rate (i.e., the required return on a discounted investment).

Many firms discontinue their economic analysis after identifying and quantifying resource inputs and outputs. They simply decide to reduce the amount of resource inputs and outputs, taking on a "less is best" strategy rather than investing in the effort necessary for assessing the estimated economic impact. At times, because of the data requirements of impact assessments, it is difficult to relate inventories to an impact analysis and to provide cost and profitability estimates necessary for advancing investment-allocation decision making beyond what has already been collected in the inventory analysis. On the other hand, making an effort to conduct at least a relative impact assessment should provide investment allocators with information that is more meaningful for decision making. For instance, stating the firm's contingent liability (i.e., an estimate of the firm's probability of an accident/ incident occurring and the range of cost and economic impact) resulting from increased use and disposal of toxic chemicals is just as easy to understand and assess as providing the change in the reduced level of a chemical input use and/or output waste that was identified and quantified in the inventory analysis. Also, when determining the relative impacts using only inventory analysis, the information provided is limiting when investment-allocation decisions must be made. For example, when the exposure to gases emitted is estimated to be higher for the existing process technology, and the exposure to gases of a different pollutant is also estimated to be higher, which mutually exclusive alternative is preferable for reducing contingent liability and what is the economic impact in terms of cost and profitability potential for making a change? An impact assessment provides investment decision makers with additional information to make such choices. This can be best accomplished by identifying the high risk and cost factors that were linked to the existing situation and performing sensitivity analysis so that the effects of certain changes can be studied and forecast. Using this strategy, benefits and costs are reported in monetary terms and can be estimated over the full life cycle of the product, technology, process, or service under analysis. In addition, a risk and cost impact analysis should be conducted on the countermeasure options to ensure that they do not create additional risk and cost impacts that negate their estimated improvement.

One can readily see that constructing an architecture that is reliably gauging costs and profitability potential can be a complicated and time-consuming process with many aspects to consider. The most essential aspect to consider in constructing an OS&H cost model is assuring that the cost-driver information is reliable. Is there sufficient usable, accurate, and timely information from a good data source to make a determination about its usefulness? A peer-reviewed list of cost drivers that should prove useful can be found in the Appendix.

SUMMARY

Questions and uncertainties related to OS&H issues, practices, and investments tend to create business challenges for a firm's internal stakeholders. It is crucial to understand the existing circumstances that drive these issues, their impacts, and their costs. Knowing how to allocate the investment outlays necessary for confronting and managing these issues and how to evaluate the efficacy of those investment outlays is imperative. In fact, an emerging area of research evolving from OS&H economic analysis is that of OS&H performance measurement, which is concerned with discovering ways to assess the financial benefits of improved OS&H performance. For example, there have been numerous calls in the previous five years for incorporating safety, health, and environmental life-cycle costing in operational settings (DOL 2006, ASSE 2008, and RoSPA 2011). Most organizations do not understand which products, technologies, processes, or services provide more or less value comparative to their existing OS&H costs. Traditional OS&H costing systems tend to suffer from imprecise cost collection, poor analysis and interpretation procedures, and distorted cost reporting. They offer little transparency of what comprises their costs, fail to consider the financial returns that can be expected later from the investment, and thus lose their decision relevance. However, it is interesting that, despite these deficiencies, many organizations continue

to invest in OS&H practices, in the authors' experience. It is now time that traditional approaches for justifying OS&H investments yield to a newly fashioned and more economically valued way of thinking.

The last 25 years have shown that changes in a firm's products, technologies, processes, and services are interconnected with its OS&H practices: changes in the firm's products, technologies, processes, and services affect OS&H, and OS&H issues in turn force design changes in the firm's products, technologies, processes, and services. When internal stakeholders are first presented with this connection, many refuse to think about it as an economic opportunity. Viewing it as an additional annoying cost or another regulatory threat, they see it as a move to negotiate a trade-off between operations-related costs and costs related to OS&H practices. This is not the case. In fact, what the safety manager will be able to show internal organizational specialists is that one can set acceptable OS&H performance criteria and then compare the life-cycle cost of ownership for mutually exclusive alternatives that meet or exceed those criteria. The comparative approach will provide them with an improved way of deciding between alternative methods for meeting a specific set of criteria. By looking at investments through the OS&H lens, and looking at OS&H issues and practices through a business lens, internal organizational specialists can derive insights that would otherwise go unnoticed.

The use of economic analysis techniques on OS&H issues is really in its infancy. Economic analysis is not a core accreditation requirement of the Applied Sciences Commission of the Accreditation Board of Engineering and Technology (ABET), which accredits safety programs (ABET 2006). Indeed, the use of economic analysis as applied to OS&H investments currently has reached a point somewhere between the stage of understanding the factors that drive OS&H costs and the stage of using that information to assess economic impact. Any continued developments in this area will require that OS&H professionals put together investment proposals that are based on sound economic analysis and creatively use the results of the analysis for estimating how countermeasure strategies offer opportunities for reducing costs and enhancing revenues. Like any new concept, economic analysis in OS&H areas will go through a predictable life cycle. First, the concept will become increasingly appealing to OS&H professionals as a way to enhance the acceptance of investment proposals and make the business case for OS&H issues and practices. Next, firms will tend to hire outside "experts" with OS&H economic analysis backgrounds to help their internal specialists design an OS&H economic analysis model that is congruent with the way they operate their business and to help pave the way for and steer the use of the model. When the model and its use become functional, OS&H specialists will take over. As the OS&H economic model continues to mature, firms will integrate it into their investment-allocation process. At this point, a firm's ability to respond to OS&H issues associated with its products, technologies, processes, and services with appropriate and economically justified OS&H countermeasures may well become a leading indicator of its competitive advantage in the marketplace.

REFERENCES

Adams, S. "Financial Management Concepts: Making the Bottom Line Case for Safety." *Professional Safety*, August 2002, pp. 23–26.

Adler, P. S., D. W. McDonald, and F. MacDonald. 1992. "Strategic Management of Technical Functions." *Sloan Management Review* 33(2):19–37.

American Society of Safety Engineers (ASSE). 2002. *White Paper Addressing the Return on Investment for Safety, Health, and Environmental (OS&H) Programs* (retrieved September 1, 2010). www.asse.org/professional affairs/govtaffairs/ngposi10.php

Applied Sciences Commission of the Accreditation Board of Engineering and Technology (ABET). 2006 (accessed 4/03/06). www.abet.org

Asche, F., and Terje Aven. "On the Economic Value of Safety." *Risk, Decision and Policy* (July–Sept. 2004) 9(3):283–267.

Behm, M., A. Veltri, and I. Kleinsorge. "The Cost of Safety." *Professional Safety*, April 2004, pp. 22–29.

Bird, F. E. 1996. *Safety and the Bottom Line*. Logansville, GA: Febco.

Brockhoff, K., A. K. Chakrabarti, and M. Kirchgeorg. 1999. "Corporate Strategies in Environmental Management." *Research Technology Management* 42(4):26–30.

Brouwers, W., and A. Stevels. 1995. "Cost Model for the End of Life Stage of Electronic Goods for Consumers." Proceedings of the 3rd International Symposium on Electronics and the Environment, Dallas, Texas, pp. 279–284.

Chatterji, D. 1995. "Achieving Leadership in Environmental R&D." *Research Technology Management* 38(2):37–42.

Cobas, E., C. Hendrickson, L. Lave, and F. McMichael. 1995. "Economic Input/Output Analysis to Aid Life Cycle Assessment of Electronics Products." Proceedings of the 3rd International Symposium on Electronics and the Environment, Dallas, Texas, pp. 273–278.

Coglianese, C., and J. Nash. 2001. "Bolstering Private Sector Environmental Management." *Issues in Science and Technology* 17(3):69–74.

Cohan, D., and D. Gess. 1994. "Integrated Life-Cycle Management." Proceedings of the 2nd International Symposium on Electronics and the Environment, San Francisco, California, pp. 149–154.

Dance, D., and D. Jimenez. "Cost of Ownership: A Tool for Environment, Safety and Health Improvements." *Semiconductor International*, September 1995, pp. 6–8.

Day, R. 1998. "The Business Case for Sustainable Development." *Greener Management International* 23:69–92.

Dorman, P. Three Preliminary Papers on the Economics of Occupational Safety and Health, Chapter 3, "Investments in Occupational Safety and Health." April 2000, International Labour Organization, Geneva.

Environmental Protection Agency (EPA). 1995. *An Introduction to Environmental Accounting As A Business Management Tool: Key Concepts and Terms*. Washington D.C.: Office of Pollution Prevention and Toxics.

Epstein, M. J. 1995. *Measuring Corporate Environmental Performance*. New York: McGraw-Hill.

European Agency for Safety and Health at Work. 2004. *Quality of the Working Environment and Productivity – Research Findings and Case Studies*. Belgium: European Agency for Safety and Health at Work.

Friedman, J. 1987. *Dictionary of Business Terms*. Hauppage, NY: Barron's Educational Series, Inc.

Goetzel, R. Z. Policy and Practice Working Group Background Paper. "Examining the Value of Integrating Occupational Health and Safety and Health Promotion Programs in the Workplace." Steps to a Healthier U.S. Workforce Symposium. NIOSH, October 26, 2004, Washington, D.C.

Graedel, T., B. Allenby, and R. Comrie. "Matrix Approaches to Abridged Life-Cycle Assessments." *Environmental Science and Technology* (March 1995) 29(3):134A–139A.

Harrington, J., and A. Knight. 1999. *ISO Implementation*. New York: McGraw-Hill.

Hart, J., I. Hunt, D. Lidgate, and V. Shankararaman. 1998. "Environmental Accounting and Management: A Knowledge-Based Systems Approach." Proceedings of the 6th International Symposium on Electronics and the Environment, Oak Brook, Illinois, pp. 225–230.

Henn, C. L. 1993. "The New Economics of Life-Cycle Thinking." Proceedings of the 1st International Symposium on Electronics and the Environment, Arlington, Virginia, pp. 184–188.

Jervis, S., and T. R. Collins. 2001. "Measuring Safety's Return on Investment." *Professional Safety* 46(9):18–23.

Kliendorfer et.al. 2005. "Sustainable Operations Management." *Production and Operations Management* vol. 14, no. 4, Winter 2005, pp. 482–492.

Lashbrook, W., P. O'Hara, D. Dance, and A. Veltri. 1997. "Design for Environment Tools for Management Decision Making: A Selected Case Study." Proceedings of the 5th International Symposium on Electronics and the Environment, San Francisco, California, pp. 99–104.

Marelli, A., and M. Vitalli. 2009. "Environmental Accounting in Italy: A Research Note" (retrieved September 1, 2010). www.ssrn.com/sol3/papers.cfm? abstract_id=1480608&CFID=150896418&CFTOKEN= 12252547.

Markku Aaltonen, Kimmo Oinonen, Jari-Pekka Kitinoja, Jorma Saari, Mika Tynkkynen, Henriikka Virta. 2006. "Costs of occupational accidents—effects of occupational safety on company business—a research and development project." Scientific Proceedings of the European Productivity Conference in Finland, 30 August to 1 Sept 2006, pp. 47–51.

Microelectronics and Computer Technology Corporation (MCC). 1996. Report MCC-ECESM001-99, *Environmental Roadmap*. 1st ed. Austin, TX: MCC.

Miles, R., and C. Snow. 1978. *Organizational Strategy Structure and Processes*. New York: McGraw-Hill.

Mizuki, C., P. Sandborn, and G. Pitts. 1996. "Design for Environment—A Survey of Current Practices and Tools." Proceedings of the 4th International Symposium on Electronics and the Environment, Dallas, Texas, pp. 66–72.

Nagle, M. "Environmental Supply-Chain Management versus Green Procurement in the Scope of a Business and Leadership Perspective." Proceedings of the 8th International Symposium on Electronics and the Environment, May 2000, San Francisco, California, pp. 219–224.

Newman, Donald. 1983. *Engineering Economic Analysis*. San Jose, California: Engineering Press, Inc.

Occupational Safety and Health Administration (OSHA). *Making the Business Case for Safety and Health*. www.cdc.gov/niosh/blog/nsb092109_businesscase.html

Oxenburgh, M., P. Merlin, and A. Oxenburgh. 2004. *Increasing Productivity and Profit Through Health and Safety: The Financial Returns from a Safe Working Environment*. 2d ed. Boca Raton, FL: CRC Press.

Porter, M. 1980. *Competitive Strategy*. New York: The Free Press.

Roome, N. 1992. "Developing Environmental Management Strategies." *Business Strategy and the Environment* 1(1):11–24.

The Royal Society for the Prevention of Accidents (RoSPA). 2011. "Making the Business Case for Safety and Health" (accessed December 20, 2011). www.rospa.com/occupationalsafety/advice and information/ business-case.aspx

Santos, A., T. Bourbon, A. Soeiro, J. Taufer, and L. Bazant, 2007. "Economic analysis of safety risks in construction." *WIT Transactions on the Built Environment*, Vol. I, pp. 13–17.

Schot, J., and K. Fischer. 1993. "Introduction: The Greening of the Industrial Firm." *Environmental Strategies for Industry*. Washington, D.C.: Island Press.

Semiconductor Industry Association (SIA). 1997 and 1999. *The National Technology Roadmap for Semiconductors Technology Needs*. San Jose, California: SIA.

Shapiro, S. A. 1998. "The Necessity of OSHA." *Kansas Journal of Law and Public Policy* 3(3):22–31.

Smallman, C., and G. John. 2001. "British Directors Perspectives on the Impact of Health and Safety on Corporate Performance." *Safety Science* 38:727–739.

Society of Environmental Toxicology and Chemistry. 1991. *A Technical Framework for Life Cycle Assessments*. Washington D.C.: Society of Environmental Toxicology and SETAC Foundation for Environmental Education, Inc.

Stead, J., and E. Stead. 2000. "Eco-Enterprise Strategy: Standing for Sustainability." *Journal of Business Ethics* 24(4):313–329.

Suhejla, H., M. McAleer, and Laurent Pawels. 2005. "Modeling Environmental Risk." *Environmental Modeling and Software* 20(10):1289–1298.

Timmons, D. M. 1999. "Building an Eco-Design Toolkit at Kodak." Proceedings of the 7th International Symposium

on Electronics and the Environment, Danvers, Massachusetts, pp. 122–127.

Tipnis, V. 1994. "Towards a Comprehensive Methodology for Competing on Ecology." Proceedings of the 2nd International Symposium on Electronics and the Environment, San Francisco, California, pp. 139–145.

Torres, Katherine. 2008. *Making the Business Case for Safety* (retrieved November 9, 2011). www.ehs.com/mag/making_business_case

Van Mier, G., C. Sterke, and A. Stevels. 1996. "Life Cycle Cost Calculations and Green Design Options." Proceedings of the 4th International Symposium on Electronics and the Environment, Dallas, Texas, pp. 191–196.

Veltri, A. 1997. "Environment, Safety and Health Cost Modeling," Technology Transfer Report #97093350AENG. Austin, Texas: SEMATECH, Inc.

Veltri, A., and E. Maxwell. 2008. "Safety, Health and Environmental Strategies Available to Firms and Being Used by Firms: A Conceptual Framework for Formulating Strategy." *Journal of Safety, Health and Environmental Research*, vol. 5, no.2.

Veltri, A., and J. Ramsay. 2009. "Economic Analysis of Environment, Safety and Health Investments." *Professional Safety* 48(7):30–36.

Veltri, A., D. Dance, and M. Nave. 2003a. "Safety, Health and Environmental Cost Model: An Internal Study from the Semiconductor Manufacturing Industry, Part 1." *Professional Safety* 48(7):30–36.

———. 2003b. "Safety, Health and Environmental Cost Model: An Internal Study from the Semiconductor Manufacturing Industry, Part 2." *Professional Safety* 48(6):23–32.

Venkatesh, S., and T. Phillips. 1992. "The SEMATECH Cost of Ownership Model: An Analysis and Critique." SEMATECH/SRC Contract No. 91-MC-506 Final Report, Texas SCOE, Texas A&M University.

Warburg, N. 2001. "Accompanying the (re) Design of Products with Environmental Assessment (DfE) On the Example of ADSM." Proceedings of the 9th International Symposium on Electronics and the Environment, Denver, Colorado, pp. 202–207.

Ward, P., and D. Bickford. 1996. "Configurations of Manufacturing Strategy, Business Strategy, Environment, and Structure." *Journal of Management* 22(4):597–626.

Warren, J., and K. Weitz. 1994. "Development of an Integrated Life Cycle Cost Assessment Model." Proceedings of the 2nd International Symposium on Electronics and the Environment, San Francisco, California, pp. 155–163.

Welford, R. 1994. "Barriers to the Implementation of Environmental Performance: The Case of the SME Sector." *Cases in Environmental Management and Business Strategy*. London: Pittman.

Wieber, M. 2008. "The Business Case for Corporate Social Responsibility: A Company-Level Measurement Approach for CSR." *European Management Journal*, Volume 26, Issue 4, pp. 247–261.

APPENDIX

LIFE-CYCLE PHASES, COST FACTORS, AND ACTIVITIES

I. UPFRONT. The phase concerned with profiling the OS&H risk and cost burdens associated with an existing, new, or upgraded product, technology, process, or service over its productive/economic life cycle and designing improvement options that maintain a balance between OS&H priorities and other competing business performance factors. The cost of upfront analysis includes all early-stage studies of risk and cost burdens to bring it to a form for decision making.

Note: Activities performed during the upfront phase are considered one-time costs.

Designing for Safety, Health, and Environment. Consideration of OS&H concerns at an early stage in the design engineering of products, technologies, processes, or services to prevent later risk and cost burdens.

> *Stage I. Concept Development - Specification Setting*
> *Stage II. Detail Design – Design of Components, Parts, Subassemblies, Process Steps*
> *Stage III. Prototype Manufacture and Testing*

II. ACQUISITION. The phase concerned with profiling the costs associated with obtaining OS&H permits and procuring capital equipment necessary for controlling hazardous exposures, preventing/controlling pollution, maintaining regulatory compliance, and enhancing business performance. The costs of acquiring a capital asset or permit include both its purchase price and all other costs incurred to bring it to a form and location suitable for its intended use.

Note: Activity performed and capital costs incurred during the acquisition phase are considered one-time costs.

Obtaining Permits. One-time costs associated with obtaining permits (i.e., wastewater discharge; air emissions; handling, storing, and transporting hazardous substances and associated wastes) for the product, technology, process or service. Examples include:

1. **Permit Review/Approval.** Activities performed to study the procedural and performance requirements of the permit, conduct environmental impact studies, make application, lobby for gaining community approval, and sign off on the permit contract.

2. **Permit Fee.** The direct cost associated with the permit.

3. **Process Reengineering.** Activities performed for reengineering and remodeling the process infrastructure to comply with the procedural and performance requirements of the permit, including capital-related equipment and installation and utility hook-up expenses.

Procuring Capital. One-time costs associated with acquiring capital equipment/areas/structures for the product, technology, process, or service (e.g., emission/effluent control equipment for reducing, neutralizing, and minimizing the volume, toxicity, or hazardous properties of process waste; emission/effluent monitoring devices for providing periodic or continuous surveillance, detection, and recording of exposures to process hazards; reclaim equipment for separating process waste for reuse; treatment/storage/disposal facility equipment for the treatment, storage, recycling, or disposal of waste generated by the process, including the consolidation of waste until shipping.

1. **Equipment Review/Signoff.** Activities performed to study capital equipment alternatives; to qualify suppliers; to develop, negotiate, and sign off on equipment contracts; and to make ready the process to receive equipment.

2. **Equipment Cost.** The direct costs associated with capital equipment, including spare parts.

3. **Process Reengineering.** Activities performed for reengineering and remodeling the process infrastructure to accommodate capital, including equipment installation and utility hook-up expenses.

III. USE/DISPOSAL. The phase concerned with profiling the cost burdens associated with protecting and productively using and disposing of process resources in a manner that prevents injury/illness and environmental incidents and that reduces pollution and waste.

Note: Activity costs incurred in the operational phase are considered annual costs.

Operating Capital (CoO). Annual costs associated with operating/owning capital (i.e., equipment, areas, structures). Examples of costs include: utilities, labor, supplies/materials, maintenance, and preventative maintenance.

Resources Consumed. Annual cost of resources consumed by the product, technology, process, or service that has OS&H life-cycle concerns (e.g., effects on natural resource depletion; reduction of raw material; chemical/gas, energy, and water use).

Consumables Used. Annual cost of consumables used by the product, technology, process, or service (e.g., safety, industrial hygiene, ergonomics equipment or supplies for providing employee protection against exposure to process hazards; environmental protection supplies for preventing and controlling environmental incidents; environmental packaging equipment and supplies for consolidating/protecting/improving the handling of waste; hazardous material management equipment and supplies for providing environmental incident response and recovery services; fire-protection equipment and supplies for providing fire prevention and incident-control services; security equipment and supplies for providing process and factory site-monitoring and surveillance; license/certificates for complying with ESH regulations).

Providing Strategic/Technical Support. Annual costs associated with providing strategic and technical support (e.g., strategic management activities such as process strategic planning, reengineering, auditing-process implementation, and managing contracts); technical support activities (e.g., identifying, evaluating, and controlling exposures to hazards; providing training, environmental emission monitoring, and process, safety, and industrial hygiene inspections; advising on regulatory compliance matters; and assisting in manifesting and record-keeping procedures); research/development activities (e.g., testing, conducting studies, and creating innovative ways to protect and use process resources productively).

Training. Annual costs associated with providing training support in areas such as (1) OS&H law required for maintaining compliance with regulatory laws and standards, and (2) OS&H process specific for developing special competencies and capabilities.

Environmental Processing. Annual costs associated with implementing pollution prevention, reuse, and treatment and disposal strategies (e.g., source reduction by process-optimization activities used for limiting pollution before it occurs, including methods for modification of end product to eliminate a waste; revised operating practices; process-modification changes in raw materials, technology, and equipment; reclaim activities used for reusing and recycling a waste based on a closed and open loop system).

Closed Loop: Implies no further processing of a waste material; it is fed directly into the process step.

Open Loop: Implies the material must be processed (e.g., separating a particular component) prior to being reused.

Abatement activities used to control the physical and/or chemical characteristics of a waste; dilution activities used to change the physical and/or chemical characteristics of a waste after its use to reduce the material's volume and toxicity; waste treatment prior to disposal activities used to change the physical and/or chemical characteristics of a waste after its use to reduce the material's volume and toxicity and to improve handling and storage; waste consolidation/packaging activities used to consolidate and store waste before shipping; waste exchange activities used to transfer or sell waste to a brokerage that could use the waste as a raw material; waste shipping and disposal activities for transporting and disposing of a waste.

IV. POSTDISPOSAL. The phase concerned with profiling the cost burdens associated with monitoring the disposal of waste after the waste has left the control of the process and internal factory site and has been transferred to another company for management.

Note: Activity costs incurred during the postdisposal phase are considered to go beyond the productive life of the product, technology, process, or service.

Managing Waste-Site Compliance. Annual costs associated with assuring that waste-site disposal procedures are managed in a manner that maintains compliance with the waste-site disposal contract agreements and federal and state regulations. Examples include:

1. **Waste-Site Review/Selection.** Activities performed to review and select disposal-site alternatives and to develop, negotiate, and sign off on waste disposal contract agreements.

2. **Compliance Monitoring.** Activities performed to assure that the procedural and performance requirements of the contract agreement and federal and state regulations are in compliance.

V. CLOSURE. The phase concerned with profiling the cost burdens associated with retiring the product, technology, process, or service at the end of its useful life and preparing the area for other productive uses.

Note: Activity costs incurred during the closure phase are considered one-time costs.

Decommissioning. One-time costs associated with retiring the product, technology, process, or service following its useful life. Examples include:

1. **Decommissioning Review.** Activities performed for profiling the risk and cost burdens associated with retiring the manufacturing process or factory site.

2. **Dismantling/Cleanup.** Activities required for disassembling components used in the manufacturing process, arranging for disposal, and conducting clean-up procedures.

3. Component Shipping and Disposal. Costs incurred for transporting and disposing of dismantled components.

Remediation. One-time costs associated with remediation and preparing the area for other productive uses.

1. Remediation Plan. Activities required for developing ways to prepare the area for other productive uses.

VI. INCIDENTS. The area concerned with profiling the cost burdens associated with environmental contamination, pollution, alteration, occupational injury/illness, and noncompliance fines that adversely affect the product, technology, process, or service. Examples include:

Internalities. Incidents that only affect the internal manufacturing process and tend to result in (1) an adversity or disablement to a resource, (2) incurred direct and indirect costs, and (3) production interruption to the process. Examples of costs include:

Direct Costs. Those costs that can be easily identified and calculated or directly assigned to the incident with a high degree of accuracy (e.g., employee financial compensation (both current and reserved), damaged manufacturing property resources, capital replacement expenditures, incident fines, and legal expenses).

Indirect Costs. Those costs that can be intangible and difficult to calculate in the short term (e.g., incident investigation, production delays, loss of training investment, loss of future contribution of employee,

replacement of resources, claims management, incident response/recovery/remediation, and business resumption).

Externalities. Internal incidents that affect the outside environment and tend to result in (1) air, water, soil pollution, (2) resource depletion/degradation, (3) chronic/acute health effects, (4) environmental habitat alteration, and (5) social/economic welfare effects.

Direct Costs. Those costs that can be easily identified and calculated or directly assigned to the incident with a high degree of accuracy (e.g., financial compensation for damaged environmental resources, fines, and legal expenses).

Indirect Costs. Those costs that can be intangible and difficult to calculate in the short term (e.g., incident investigation, incident recovery/remediation costs, and claims management).

Noncompliance Fine Facilitation. Citations issued for failing to comply with federal, state, or local environmental, safety, and health agencies.

Direct Costs. Those costs that can be easily identified and calculated or directly assigned to the fine with a high degree of accuracy (e.g., financial payment for the citation; making the facility and the process ready to comply, including any capital expenditures, materials, labor, legal fees, and research).

Indirect Costs. Those costs that can be intangible and difficult to calculate in the short term (e.g., activities needed to study and contest the fine).

Chapter 6

Cost Analysis and Budgeting

Fran Sehn

LEARNING OBJECTIVES

- Understand the problem of traffic crashes and the types of loss analyses needed to identify and minimize the problem.

- Determine a cost-benefit-analysis methodology for fleet safety initiatives.

- Be able to provide useful guidelines regarding what to include in budgeting for fleet safety

- Learn how to analyze the cost of driver training.

- Understand the factors that influence the cost of vehicle maintenance (inspection and repair).

In April 2006, U.S. Transportation Secretary Norman Y. Mineta declared that highway traffic deaths were a "national tragedy" and called on all Americans to respond by wearing safety belts, using motorcycle helmets, and driving sober. According to a report from the Department of Transportation's National Highway Traffic Safety Administration (NHTSA), 33,561 people died on the nation's highways in 2012, up from 32,479 in 2011. Injuries increased from 2.17 million in 2011 to 2,362 million in 2012, an increase of 3.3 percent (NHTSA 2014). Fifty-two percent of passenger-vehicle occupants who died in 2012 were unbelted (NHTSA 2014), despite the fact that overall safety-belt use is at an historic high of 86 percent nationwide in 2012 (NHTSA 2014).

When NHTSA reported safety-belt use at 82 percent in 2006, Mineta stated, "Every year this country experiences a national tragedy that is as preventable as it is devastating . . . We have tools to prevent this tragedy—every car has a safety belt, every motor- cycle rider should have a helmet, and everyone should have enough sense to never drive while impaired" (NHTSA 2006).

This NHTSA report also projected an eighth-straight year of increased motorcycle fatalities. In 2012, 4957 motorcyclists died, a 7.1 percent increase over 2011, when there were 4630 fatalities (NHTSA 2014). Motor vehicle crashes were leading cause of death for age 4 and every age 11 through 27 (NHTSA 2014).

Traffic crashes come at an enormous cost to society, Mineta noted. NHTSA estimates show that highway crashes cost society $230.6 billion a year, about $4820 per person (NHTSA 2006).

While there have been several statistically significant decreases in the estimated number of people injured annually, 2012 shows the first statistically significant increase since 1995. The fatality rate per 100 million vehicle miles traveled (VMT) increased 3.6 percent from 1.10 per million VMT in 2011 to 1.14 in 2012. The overall injury rate increased by 6.7 percent from 75 per 100 million VMT in 2011 to 80 in 2012 (NHTSA 2014).

The data for 2012 reflected higher fatality and injury rates: 1.14 deaths per million miles traveled in 2012 (1.10 deaths were reported for 2011). In addition, the composition of fatalities changed little from 2011 to 2012, with a 0.89 percent in passenger vehicle occupants in 2012 as opposed to 0.88 in 2011 and 0.83 in 2010; the same (0.73) for light trucks in 2011 and 2012 and 0.86 in 2010, 0.26 in large trucks in 2012 versus 0.24 in 2011 and 0.18 in 2010, and 23.97 for motorcycles in 2012, a decrease from 24.94 in 2011 and 24.40 in 2010 (NHTSA 2014). The number of people injured in motor-vehicle crashes in 2012 increased for the first year since 2005, with 145,000 more injuries in 2012 than in 2011 (NHTSA 2014). According to NHTSA alcohol-impaired driving fatalities in 2012 stood at 10,322, up from 9865 in 2011 (an increase of 4.6 percent) (NHTSA 2014). Overall, 18 states and Puerto Rico saw a decline in the number of alcohol-impaired driving fatalities between 2011 and 2012 (NHTSA 2013).

> Today's numbers reflect the tangible benefits of record seat-belt use and strong antidrunk-driving enforcement campaigns. But we are still losing more than 30,000 lives a year on our highways, and about a third of these involve drunk driving. We will continue to work with our state partners to strictly enforce both seat belt use and anti-drunk driving laws across this nation, every day and every night. (NHTSA 2010)

HOW BUSINESS VIEWS TRAFFIC SAFETY

Guidelines for Employers to Reduce Motor Vehicle Crashes, funded by the Occupational Safety and Health Administration (OSHA), NHTSA, and the Network of Employers for Traffic Safety (NETS) state (OSHA, NHTSA, and NETS 2006):

> Motor vehicle crashes cost employers $460 billion annually in medical care, legal expenses, property damage, and lost productivity. They drive up the cost of benefits such as Workers' Compensation, Social Security, and private health and disability insurance. In addition, they increase the company overhead involved in administering these programs.

The Bureau of Labor Statistics (BLS), in 2012 final data, indicated that more work-related fatalities resulted from transportation incidents than from any other type of event. Roadway incidents accounted for 60 percent of the fatal transportation incidents; 565 deaths, or 29 percent, were as a result of collisions with other vehicles (BLS 2014). Drivers/sales workers and truck drivers accounted for 813 fatalities in 2012. This is a rate of 24.3 per 100,000 employed. Transportation incidents accounted for 60 percent of the 353 workers killed in 146 multiple-fatality events (BLS 2014).

NHTSA has determined that "the average crash costs an employer $16,500. When a worker has an on-the-job crash that results in an injury, the cost to their employer is $74,000. Costs can exceed $500,000 when a fatality is involved. Off-the-job crashes are costly to employers as well" (OSHA, NHTSA, and NETS 2006).

These costs are highlighted in a final report for the Federal Motor Carrier Safety Administration. The report noted (Zaloshnja and Miller 2002):

- The cost of crashes with two or more trailers involved was the highest among all crashes—$88,483 per crash.

- Among crashes of all types of trucks (including a single large truck, tractor-trailer or multiple trailers, and buses), bus-involved crashes had the lowest cost—$32,548 per crash. (NOTE: *large trucks* means tractor-trailers, single-unit trucks, and some cargo vans over 10,000 pounds.)

- The cost per crash with injuries averaged $164,730 for large-truck crashes and $477,043 for bus crashes.

- The crash cost per 1000 truck miles was $157 for single-unit trucks, $131 for single combination trucks (tractor and trailer), and $63 for multiple combinations—tractor and multiple trailers.

- The average annual cost of large-truck crashes from 1997–1999 exceeded $19.6 billion, including $6.6 billion in productivity losses, $43.4 billion in resource costs, and $419.6 billion in quality-of-life losses.

These cost estimates exclude mental healthcare costs for crash victims, roadside repair costs, cost of cargo delays, earnings lost by family and friends caring for the injured, and the value of schoolwork lost. These data are prime examples of the hidden costs of crashes and their related outcomes.

Social Media Accident Causation

The use of cell phones has become as common as any other human activity in many countries, including the United States. This wireless communication device is both a benefit and a hindrance to driving activities. The cell phone can be used for emergency contact, but it is often involved in distracting the driver. The National Safety Council (NSC) research shows cell-phone use while driving has been associated with quadrupling the crash risk. The NSC estimated that 28 percent of all crashes per year involve talking on cell phones and texting while driving—accounting for 1.6 million crashes (NSC 2010). According to the the NHTSA, an estimated 11 percent of drivers in 2008 were talking on cell phones at any given time. The NHTSA statistics also show that, in 2008, approximately 5870 people were killed and an estimated 515,000 were injured in crashes in which there was at least one reported form of driver distraction. Drivers younger than 20 years of age accounted for about 16 percent of those deaths (NHTSA 2011).

The same article indicated that, in 1999, only 3 percent of NSC members reported any type of cell-phone ban. Ten years later, nearly 50 percent reported either handheld or full cell-phone bans.

Is banning cell-phone use the answer? In a recent visit to California for business, this author witnessed the impact of no use of handheld cell phones in the Los Angeles area on three major highways used during the business trip. Asking a client what has encouraged nonuse the most, the simple answer was "the fine if caught."

Overview of Distracted Driving

The NHTSA states that driver distraction could pose a serious and potentially deadly danger. In 2009, 5474 people were killed on U.S. roadways and an estimated 448,000 were injured in motor-vehicle crashes that were reported to have involved distracted driving. *Distracted driving* is any nondriving activity that a person engages in, which has the potential to distract him or her from the primary task of driving and increases the risk of crashing.

Distracted driving comes in various forms, such as cell-phone use, texting while driving, eating, drinking, talking with passengers, as well as using in-vehicle technologies and portable electronic devices. Daydreaming and dealing with strong emotions are less obvious forms of distractions.

There are three main types of distraction:

- *Visual:* Taking your eyes off the road
- *Manual:* Taking your hands off the wheel
- *Cognitive:* Taking your mind off what you are doing

Texting while driving is alarming because it involves all three types of distraction (NHTSA n.d.).

The Federal Motor Carrier Safety Administration (FMCSA) states (FMCSA 2010):

New technologies are available that provide objective measures of driver behavior. These in-vehicle technologies are able to provide continuous measures on a wide variety of driving behaviors previously unavailable to the fleet safety manager . . . If behavioral approaches can be integrated with technologies that monitor behavior, fleet safety managers would have an effective tool to improve safety-related behaviors.

This concurs with the information in this chapter that commercial truck and bus drivers typically work alone and in relative isolation, and therefore require alternative strategies.

Using Telemetrics as a Tool to Solve the Problem

In *An Introduction to Telematics*, Tam states (Tam n.d):

The data captured by the devices commonly include the vehicles location, speed, driver behavior, and vehicle diagnostics data determined by the telematics system. The fleet safety manager can in advanced solutions view data in real time. . . . Virtually any fleet operation can benefit from adoption of fleet safety telematics solutions. These solutions enable drivers and companies to proactively reduce costs, improve fleet safety and increase productivity. Some fleet safety solutions also involve installation of an in-vehicle video camera to capture evidence of collisions and other important driving events. The data obtained can be combined with other in-depth analytics to help identify root causes and driving behavior. The fleet safety reports, viewed over an extended period of time are excellent tools for supervisors to use in conducting targeted driver training and counseling programs.

LOSS ANALYSIS METHODS

The employee's cost due to a crash can be significant. The loss of wages and medical costs beyond what Workers' Compensation Insurance pays, as well as pain and suffering, are a burden to the employee, the employee's family, and the employer.

Methods of determining employer costs are varied. Several tools are available to fleet safety professionals to analyze these costs. The goal of analysis should be to determine problem areas, gaps in the safety program, and initiatives needed to minimize future crashes.

When a crash occurs, an initial investigation to determine the cause of the incident should take place. One method employers use for this inquiry includes an incident investigation form (see Figures 1A–E) (NSC 1996).

An effective investigation or analysis of a crash/incident will provide fleet safety professionals with information that can be used to determine

- the root cause of the crash/incident
- its preventability
- appropriate countermeasures to prevent a recurrence

Safety Measurement System (SMS)

In 2010, the FMCSA introduced the safety measurement system (SMS), a new risk-control measurement system

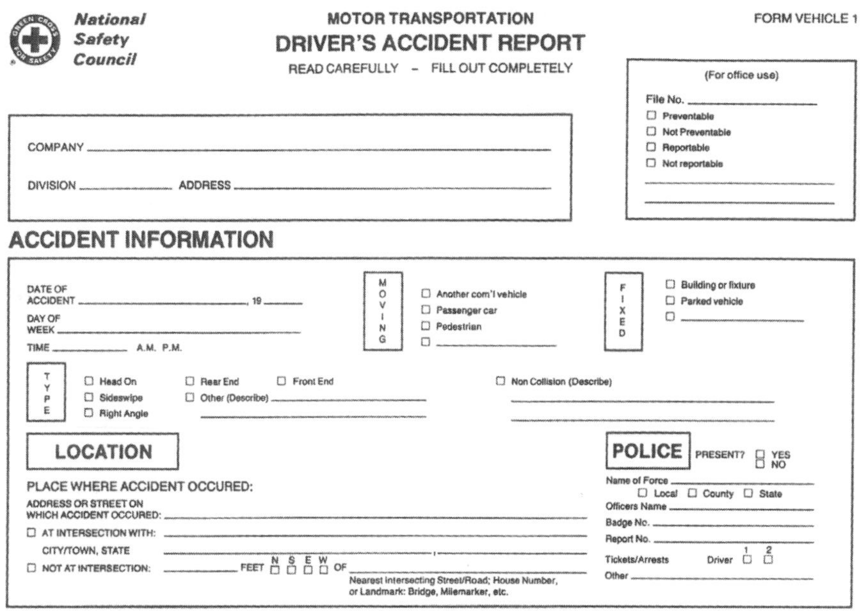

National Safety Council

MOTOR TRANSPORTATION

DRIVER'S ACCIDENT REPORT

READ CAREFULLY - FILL OUT COMPLETELY

FORM VEHICLE 1

(For office use)

File No. ____

☐ Preventable
☐ Not Preventable
☐ Reportable
☐ Not reportable

COMPANY ____

DIVISION ____ ADDRESS ____

ACCIDENT INFORMATION

DATE OF ACCIDENT ____, 19 ____

DAY OF WEEK ____

TIME ____ A.M. P.M.

MOVING: ☐ Another com'l vehicle ☐ Passenger car ☐ Pedestrian ☐ ____

FIXED: ☐ Building or fixture ☐ Parked vehicle ☐ ____

TYPE: ☐ Head On ☐ Sideswipe ☐ Right Angle ☐ Rear End ☐ Other (Describe) ____ ☐ Front End ☐ Non Collision (Describe) ____

LOCATION

PLACE WHERE ACCIDENT OCCURED:

ADDRESS OR STREET ON WHICH ACCIDENT OCCURED: ____

☐ AT INTERSECTION WITH: ____

CITY/TOWN, STATE ____, ____

☐ NOT AT INTERSECTION: ____ FEET N ☐ S ☐ E ☐ W ☐ OF ____

Nearest intersecting Street/Road; House Number, or Landmark: Bridge, Milemarker, etc.

POLICE PRESENT? ☐ YES ☐ NO

Name of Force ____ ☐ Local ☐ County ☐ State

Officers Name ____

Badge No. ____

Report No. ____

Tickets/Arrests Driver 1 ☐ 2 ☐

Other ____

FIGURE 1A. **Accident information** (*Source: Driver's Accident Report*, with permission of the National Safety Council 1996)

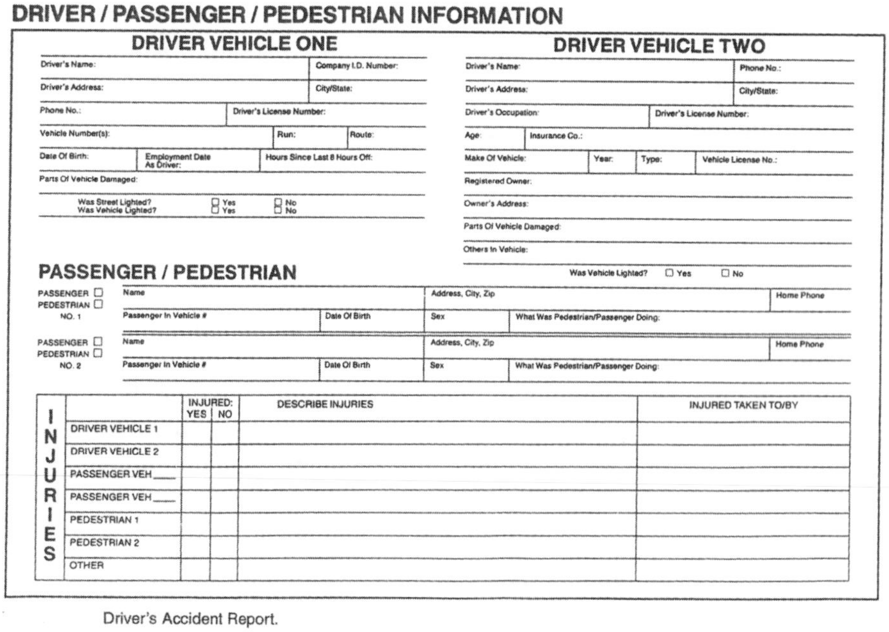

DRIVER / PASSENGER / PEDESTRIAN INFORMATION

DRIVER VEHICLE ONE

Driver's Name: | Company I.D. Number:
Driver's Address: | City/State:
Phone No.: | Driver's License Number:
Vehicle Number(s): | Run: | Route:
Date Of Birth: | Employment Date As Driver: | Hours Since Last 8 Hours Off:
Parts Of Vehicle Damaged:
Was Street Lighted? ☐ Yes ☐ No
Was Vehicle Lighted? ☐ Yes ☐ No

DRIVER VEHICLE TWO

Driver's Name: | Phone No.:
Driver's Address: | City/State:
Driver's Occupation: | Driver's License Number:
Age: | Insurance Co.:
Make Of Vehicle: | Year: | Type: | Vehicle License No.:
Registered Owner:
Owner's Address:
Parts Of Vehicle Damaged:
Others In Vehicle:
Was Vehicle Lighted? ☐ Yes ☐ No

PASSENGER / PEDESTRIAN

PASSENGER ☐ PEDESTRIAN ☐ NO. 1 — Name | Address, City, Zip | Home Phone; Passenger In Vehicle # | Date Of Birth | Sex | What Was Pedestrian/Passenger Doing:

PASSENGER ☐ PEDESTRIAN ☐ NO. 2 — Name | Address, City, Zip | Home Phone; Passenger In Vehicle # | Date Of Birth | Sex | What Was Pedestrian/Passenger Doing:

INJURIES	INJURED: YES	INJURED: NO	DESCRIBE INJURIES	INJURED TAKEN TO/BY
DRIVER VEHICLE 1				
DRIVER VEHICLE 2				
PASSENGER VEH ____				
PASSENGER VEH ____				
PEDESTRIAN 1				
PEDESTRIAN 2				
OTHER				

Driver's Accident Report.

FIGURE 1B. **Driver/passenger/pedestrian information** (*Source: Driver's Accident Report*, with permission of the National Safety Council 1996)

that replaced its older SafeStat system. SMS quantifies the on-road safety performance of carriers and drivers. The primary intent is to identify candidates for interventions, determine the specific safety problems the carrier or driver exhibits, and monitor whether safety problems are improving or worsening. SMS is integral to the compliance, safety, and accountability operational model.

SMS uses the motor carrier's data from roadside inspections, including all safety-based violations, state-reported crashes, and the federal motor carrier census to

VEHICLES/PEDESTRIANS/PASSENGERS

(CHECK ONE OR MORE FOR EACH DRIVER)—YOU ARE No. 1	PREVIOUS TO ACCIDENT		WHEN FIRST IN DANGER		AT IMPACT	
	No. 1	No. 2	No.1	No. 2	No. 1	No. 2
Going straight ahead	☐	☐	☐	☐	☐	☐
Slowing	☐	☐	☐	☐	☐	☐
Stopped in traffic	☐	☐	☐	☐	☐	☐
Park or stopped in zone	☐	☐	☐	☐	☐	☐
Backing	☐	☐	☐	☐	☐	☐
Starting	☐	☐	☐	☐	☐	☐
Passing	☐	☐	☐	☐	☐	☐
Being passed	☐	☐	☐	☐	☐	☐
Changing lanes	☐	☐	☐	☐	☐	☐
Turning left	☐	☐	☐	☐	☐	☐
Turning right	☐	☐	☐	☐	☐	☐
Entering zone/Pulling to curb	☐	☐	☐	☐	☐	☐
Leaving zone/Pulling from curb	☐	☐	☐	☐	☐	☐
Other (explain)	☐	☐	☐	☐	☐	☐

YOUR SPEED ____ MPH ____ MPH ____ MPH
SPEED OF OTHER VEHICLE ____ MPH ____ MPH ____ MPH

DISTANCE YOUR VEHICLE FROM OTHER VEHICLE ____ FEET ____ FEET

DID YOU SOUND HORN? ☐ YES ☐ NO HOW FAR AWAY? ____ FEET
DID YOU APPLY BRAKES? ☐ YES ☐ NO HOW FAR AWAY? ____ FEET

AFTER IMPACT—VEHICLE MOVED ____ FEET   AFTER IMPACT—OTHER VEHICLE MOVED ____ FEET

GIVEN CONDITIONS, WHAT WAS SAFE SPEED FOR:

VEH. 1 _____ MPH   VEH. 2 _____ MPH

VEHICLE

1	2	
☐	☐	Did not have right-of-way
☐	☐	Following too closely
☐	☐	Failure to signal intentions
☐	☐	Speed too fast for conditions
☐	☐	Disregarded traffic signs or signals
☐	☐	Improper passing
☐	☐	Improper turning
☐	☐	Improper backing
☐	☐	Improper traffic lane
☐	☐	Improper parking
☐	☐	No improper driving
☐	☐	Defective brakes
☐	☐	Defective steering
☐	☐	Defective lights
☐	☐	Defective tires
☐	☐	No defects
☐		_____
	☐	_____
		(Specify other)

PEDESTRIAN

☐ Walking with traffic
☐ Walking against traffic
☐ Coming from behind parked vehicle
☐ Crossing at intersection
☐ Crossing not at intersection
☐ Alighting from a vehicle
☐ Working in roadway
☐ Playing in roadway
☐ _____
    (Specify other)

PASSENGER

☐ Boarding vehicle
☐ Alighting from vehicle
☐ Caught in doors
☐ Seated
☐ In motion in vehicle
☐ Other (describe)

_____
_____
_____
_____

FIGURE 1C. Vehicles/pedestrians/passengers information (*Source: Driver's Accident Report*, with permission of the National Safety Council 1996)

ENVIRONMENTAL CONDITIONS (CHECK ALL THAT APPLY)

WEATHER (check one)
☐ CLEAR
☐ CLOUDY
☐ RAINING
☐ SNOWING
☐ FOGGY
☐ OTHER

SURFACE (check one)
☐ DRY
☐ WET
☐ ICY
☐ SNOWY
☐ OTHER

TRAFFIC CONTROL (check one)
☐ STOP SIGN
☐ YIELD SIGN
☐ TRAFFIC SIGNAL
☐ FLAGMAN
☐ NO CONTROL
☐ OTHER

LIGHT (check one)
☐ DAWN
☐ DAY
☐ DUSK
☐ DARK-NO LIGHTS
☐ ARTIFICIAL LIGHT
☐ OTHER

ROADWAY No. of Lanes
☐ DIVIDED ____
☐ UNDIVIDED ____
☐ ASPHALT ____
☐ CONCRETE ____
☐ GRAVEL ____
☐ OTHER ____

ALIGNMENT (check one)
☐ STRAIGHT
☐ CURVE
☐ BRIDGE
☐ INTERSECTION
☐ RAMP
☐ RAILROAD

☐ OVERPASS
☐ UNDERPASS
☐ LEVEL
☐ UPHILL
☐ DOWNHILL

FIGURE 1D. Environmental conditions information (*Source: Driver's Accident Report*, with permission of the National Safety Council 1996)

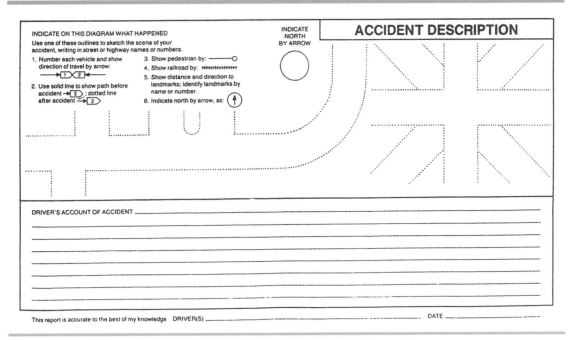

INDICATE ON THIS DIAGRAM WHAT HAPPENED

Use one of these outlines to sketch the scene of your accident, writing in street or highway names or numbers.

1. Number each vehicle and show direction of travel by arrow:
2. Use solid line to show path before accident; dotted line after accident
3. Show pedestrian by:
4. Show railroad by:
5. Show distance and direction to landmarks; identify landmarks by name or number.
6. Indicate north by arrow, as:

INDICATE NORTH BY ARROW

ACCIDENT DESCRIPTION

DRIVER'S ACCOUNT OF ACCIDENT _____

This report is accurate to the best of my knowledge   DRIVER(S) _____ DATE _____

FIGURE 1E. A schematic or diagram of the collision/crash (*Source: Driver's Accident Report*, with permission of the National Safety Council 1996)

quantify performance in the following behavior analysis and safety improvement categories (BASICs):

1. **Unsafe Driving:** Operation of commercial motor vehicles (CMVs) by drivers in a dangerous or careless manner. Example violations include speeding, reckless driving, improper lane change, and inattention (FMCSR Parts 392 and 397).

2. **Fatigued Driving:** (Hours of Service): Operation of CMVs by drivers who are ill, fatigued, or in noncompliance with the hours-of-service (HOS) regulations. This BASIC includes violations of regulations pertaining to logbooks, as they relate to HOS requirements, and the management of CMV driver fatigue. Examples of violations include exceeding HOS, maintaining an incomplete or inaccurate logbook, and operating a CMV while ill or fatigued (FMCSR Parts 392 and 395).

3. **Driver Fitness:** Operation by drivers who are unfit to operate a CMV due to lack of training, experience, or medical qualifications. Examples of violations include failure to have a valid and appropriate commercial driver's license (CDL) and being medically unqualified to operate a CMV (FMCSR Parts 383 and 391).

4. **Controlled Substances or Alcohol:** Operation of CMVs by drivers who are impaired due to alcohol, illegal drugs, and misuse of prescription, or over-the-counter medications. Examples of violations include the use or possession of controlled substances or alcohol (FMCSR Parts 382 and 392).

5. **Vehicle Maintenance:** Failure to properly maintain a CMV. Examples of violations include brakes, lights, and other mechanical defects, and failure to make required repairs (FMCSR Parts 393 and 396).

6. **Cargo-Related Failures:** Failure to properly prevent shifting loads, spilled or dropped cargo, overloading, and unsafe handling of hazardous materials on a CMV. Examples of violations include improper load securement, cargo retention, and hazardous material handling (FMCSR Parts 392, 393, 397, and hazardous material violations).

7. **Crash Indicator:** Histories or patterns of high crash involvement, including frequency and severity. It is based on information from state-reported crashes.

A carrier's measurement for each BASIC depends on the following:

- the number of adverse safety events (violations related to that BASIC or crashes)
- the severity of violations or crashes
- when the adverse safety events occurred (more recent events are weighted more heavily)

After a measurement is determined, the carrier is then placed in a peer group (e.g., other carriers with a similar number of inspections). Percentiles from 0 to 100 are then determined by comparing the BASIC measurement of the carrier to the measurements of other carriers in the peer group. A percentile of 100 indicates the worst performance.

TABLE 1

Fleet Loss Run (Policy Effective Date: 5/15/2010 to 5/14/2011)							
Claim Number	Date of Loss	Claimant Name	Claim Status Description	Accident Narrative	Paid Total	Reserved Total	Net Incurred Total
166123	09/01/2011	S. Jones	Closed	IV was rear ended by CV	$2235.46	$0.00	$98.00
166124	05/01/2011	J. Smith	Closed	Insured was driving north on Rt. 219 when tire blew	$2834.86	$0.00	$2834.86
166125	04/22/2011	F. Washington	Closed	Claimant vehicle hit IV at driver side doors	$1587.95	$0.00	$1587.95
166126	09/05/2011	A. Kennedy	Closed	IV was rear- ended by CV	$0.00	$0.00	$0.00
166127	05/05/2011	R. Jefferson	Closed	Insured was driving on Rt.19 when vehicle struck a deer	$4234.36	$0.00	$4293.36
TOTAL					$10,892.63	$0.00	$8814.17

Note: IV indicates insured vehicle, CV indicates claimant vehicle or the vehicle of others.

NHTSA ISSUES FINAL RULE ON REAR VISIBILITY TECHNOLOGY

Each year in the U.S., an average of 210 fatalities and 15,000 injuries are caused by vehicles striking individuals while the vehicle is in reverse. To help reduce these incidents, the NHTSA has issued a final rule requiring rear visibility technology in all new vehicles weighing less than 10,000 lbs. by May 2018. Affected vehicles will include small buses and trucks.

Under the rule, every vehicle must be equipped with rear visibility technology that expands the drivers' field of view to include 10 × 20-ft zone directly behind the vehicle. Other system requirements of the rule include specifications regarding image size, response time, durability and deactivation (NSC 2014).

Hopefully, this requirement will be expanded to larger vehicles in the future.

Additional Loss-Source Information for the Fleet Safety Professional

Fleet safety professionals have many potential loss sources at their disposal. Insurance carriers and their brokers and agents regularly produce and provide loss runs to assist in the analysis process. A loss run is a historical report of crash/incident information that has been given to an insurance carrier. A typical loss run will include, but not be limited to, the following:

1. date of the incident
2. driver/employee name
3. a brief description of the incident (e.g., "backing" or "struck fixed object")
4. location of the incident
5. anticipated cost or dollars reserved for future costs
6. costs to date

The loss run in Table 1 provides only an overview of needed information—the information it contains is limited by the input data and the ability of the software used to assemble and present the information. A fleet safety professional will need additional information and data in order to determine preventability. One of the goals of a successful fleet safety program is to propose appropriate countermeasures to minimize the possibility of a recurrence.

Exposures and Controls of the "Grey Fleet"

The *grey fleet* is a reflection of business miles traveled by employees using their own vehicles. Sales and service are two categories of employment most frequently associated with this group. These employees are typically paid a fixed mileage allowance for business purposes to cover the cost of operating their own car or truck. The employer has the advantage of minimizing the costs associated with purchasing or leasing a vehicle for this use, but not all costs of risk are eliminated.

While there is very limited data regarding the cost of incidents related to this business risk, the fact that employees are driving on company business presents both liability and worker's compensation exposures that may be significant.

In order to manage this aspect of the business risk, the fleet safety manager should include the following controls at a minimum:

- A copy of the valid insurance certificate should be obtained, including coverage for business use.
- A copy of the employee's driver's license should be obtained.
- A signed declaration should be obtained that the vehicle is fully serviced and maintained to the manufacturer's standards.

The same safety training provided to operators of company-owned vehicles should be mandated for these drivers. There are many appropriate defensive driving courses that are available for this purpose (Businesslink n.d.).

DIRECT AND INDIRECT COSTS OF ACCIDENTS

The image of an iceberg has been used by safety professionals to depict the direct and indirect costs of accidents. The direct costs are easily visible, similar to the section of an iceberg above the water. The indirect costs are buried below the surface of the water. The OSHA $afety Pays eTool discusses the cost of workplace injuries and illnesses in terms of the iceberg model (OSHA 1996).

"Accidents are more expensive than many of us realize. Why? Because there lots of hidden costs. Some are obvious—your workers' compensation claims cover medical and indemnity (lost wages) for an injured or ill worker. These are the direct costs of accidents. But what about the costs to train and compensate a replacement worker, repair damaged property, investigate the accident, and implement corrective action? Even less apparent are the costs related to schedule delays, added administrative time, lower morale, increased absenteeism, and poorer customer relations. These are the indirect costs and the bulk of the iceberg. Studies show that the ratio of indirect costs to direct costs varies widely, from a high of twenty-to-one to a low of one-to-one. We've taken a conservative approach that says that the lower the direct costs of an accident, the higher the ratio of indirect to direct costs" (OSHA 1996).

A worksheet is provided so that fleet safety professionals can determine the direct and indirect costs of accidents (see Figure 2). This worksheet also provides information that can determine the impact of injuries and illnesses on profitability.

These costs, in the context of this chapter, apply to employees of a fleet operator, including drivers, mechanics, sales personnel, administrative personnel, and management. The Federal Motor Carrier Safety Administration's (FMCSA) Accident Cost Table (see Figure 2 and Table 2) shows revenue dollars required to pay for different amounts of costs of accidents from a fleet's standpoint. Table 2 includes the following accident costs that could be considered in relation to a crash (FMCSA 2006).

Direct and Indirect Costs

Direct costs include:

- repair of cargo damage
- repair of vehicle damage
- medical treatment
- loss of revenue
- administrative
- police report
- possible effect on the cost of insurance
- possible effect on the cost of Workers' Compensation Insurance
- towing
- storage of damaged vehicles

Indirect costs include:

- revenue from clients or customers
- revenue from sales
- meetings missed
- salaries (wages) paid to employees in the accident
- lost time at work
- cost to hire and train replacement employees
- supervisor's time
- loss of personal property
- replacement vehicle rental
- damaged equipment downtime

FIGURE 2. How to estimate the impact of accidents on profits and sales (*Source:* OSHA 1996)

TABLE 2

Accident Cost Table

THIS TABLE SHOWS THE DOLLARS OF REVENUE REQUIRED TO PAY FOR DIFFERENT AMOUNTS OF COSTS FOR ACCIDENTS

It is necessary for a motor carrier to generate an additional $1,250,000 revenue to pay the cost of a $25,000 accident, assuming an average profit of 2%. The amount of revenue required to pay for losses will vary with the profit margin.

Yearly Accident Costs	Profit Margin				
	1%	2%	3%	4%	5%
$1,000	100,000	50,000	33,000	25,000	20,000
5,000	500,000	250,000	167,000	125,000	100,000
10,000	1,000,000	500,000	333,000	250,000	200,000
25,000	2,500,000	1,250,000	833,000	625,000	500,000
50,000	5,000,000	2,500,000	1,667,000	1,250,000	1,000,000
100,000	10,000,000	5,000,000			
150,000		7,500,000	3,333,000	2,500,000	2,000,000
200,000	15,000,000	10,000,000			
			5,000,000	3,750,000	3,000,000
	20,000,000				
			6,666,000	5,000,000	4,000,000

REVENUE REQUIRED TO COVER LOSSES

(*Source*: FMSCA 2006)

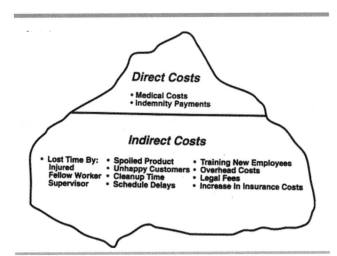

FIGURE 3. Direct/indirect costs iceberg (*Source:* OSHA 1996)

- accelerated depreciation of equipment
- accident reporting
- medical costs paid by the company
- poor public relations/publicity
- increased public relations costs
- government agency costs

If this worksheet is applied to fleet accidents and coupled with the Revenue Required to Pay for an accident chart, it is apparent that even a $5000 accident can impact profitability.

For example, an accident involving $5000 in direct costs would result in $6000 in indirect costs, so the total cost would be $11,000. If a company operates at a 4 percent profit margin, it would need to generate over $250,000 in additional sales to cover the cost of this accident/incident. This example assumes a $5000 deductible by the carrier on a per accident/incident basis. The *iceberg* in Figure 3 "demonstrates the relationship between direct and indirect costs of accidents" (OSHA 1996) and the Accident Cost Table (Table 2) sets out the revenue necessary to pay for accident losses. According to the FMCSA average, indirect costs exceed direct costs by a four-to-one ratio.

ACCIDENT REGISTER

An additional source of information for fleet safety professionals conducting analyses of incidents and crashes is the Accident Register. Part 390.15 of the Federal Motor Carrier Safety Regulations (FMCSR) is reproduced in the sidebar.

A sample accident register is shown in Figures 4A and B.

Fleet safety professionals should use all of the tools detailed in this chapter to conduct regular analyses of their fleets' losses. Detailed analyses will provide opportunities for continuous improvement of safety efforts. An accident register can be used to determine trends, which in turn will provide information for future needs and initiatives for driver selection, equipment, safety training, and related information.

National Safety Council

MOTOR TRANSPORTATION

ACCIDENT REGISTER

PERIOD COVERED _____ TO _____

ACCIDENT NUMBER _____ TO _____

COMPANY _____

LOCATION _____

NATIONAL FLEET SAFETY CONTEST

KEY CODE NO. _____

DIVISION OF CONTEST _____

	ACCIDENT DATE	ACCIDENT NUMBER	DRIVER'S NAME	DRIVER'S HOME TERMINAL	VEHICLE NUMBER	ACCIDENT TYPE	SHOW NEAREST CITY & STATE
1							
2							
3							
4							
5							

FIGURE 4A. Sample accident register (*Source:* NSC 1996)

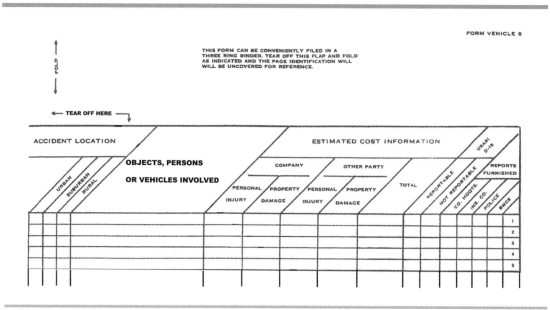

FIGURE 4B. Sample accident register (*Source:* NSC 1996)

COST-BENEFIT ANALYSIS

An effective fleet safety program can produce benefits to the employer, employee/driver, and the customer or client. Well-managed fleets also benefit the community or communities in which they operate.

The National Safety Council (NSC 1996) indicates that some benefits of an effective safety program are:

- reduced costs of operations
- reduced insurance premiums and related costs
- improved customer satisfaction
- lower employee turnover
- improved employee morale

While all of these benefits would be considered logical to anyone operating a fleet, the safety program alone may not achieve them. It is essential that all drivers be aware that the safe operation of vehicles is very important. The standard explains that organizations should periodically evaluate driver performance.

Many types of safety initiatives may have an impact on a company's cost of operations. One is direct observation and feedback from the general public regarding vehicles that are clearly identified with either a company phone number or a commercial safety hotline call-in program. Anyone who drives has probably seen decals on commercial vehicles asking "How is my driving?" along with a vehicle identification number and toll-free phone number. Two companies that provide this early warning service indicate that insurance companies have studied the financial impact of these programs. The Safety Alert Network states that clients have reported a vehicular accident-frequency reduction in excess of 40 percent when using the program (Safety Alert 2006).

Safety Alert charges a one-time fee of $3.95 to place a decal on a trailer plus an annual per-vehicle charge based on the number of vehicles. The company provides this estimated benefits information:

frequency rate of accidents × million miles driven

= number of accidents $\qquad$ (1)

number of fleet accidents × $9000/accident

= cost of accidents $\qquad$ (2)

cost of accidents × 0.10 (a conservative reduction

in accident savings) = minimum net savings $\qquad$ (3)

For example, if a fleet operates 50 vehicles and 100 trailers, the cost of the program is estimated at $5000 for the first year, and $1400 for subsequent years (50 vehicles at approximately $20 per vehicle and 100 trailers at $4 per trailer).

According to the ROI calculator provided on the Safety Alert Network Web site, the ANSI vehicular accident rate for over-the-road vehicles in 1995 was 2.0 per million miles. If the fleet in our example drives 5 million miles per year, the savings would be estimated as follows:

$2.0 \times 5 = 10$ accidents

$10 \times \$9000 = \$90,000$ in accident costs

$\$90,000 \times 0.10 = \$9000$ in avoided accident costs

$\$9000$ in avoided accident costs − $5000 cost

of service = $4000 net savings $\qquad$ (4)

This is a very conservative estimate.

FMCSR, PART 390.15

"Assistance in investigations and special studies.

"(a) A motor carrier must make all records and information pertaining to an accident available to an authorized representative or special agent of the Federal Motor Carrier Safety Administration, an authorized State or local enforcement agency representative, or authorized third party representative, upon request or as part of any investigation within such time as the request or investigation may specify. A motor carrier shall give an authorized representative all reasonable assistance in the investigation of any accident including providing a full, true, and correct response to any question of the inquiry.

"(b) For accidents that occur after April 29, 2003, a motor carrier must maintain an accident register for three years after the date of each accident. For accidents that occurred on or prior to April 29, 2003, motor carriers must maintain an accident register for a period of one year after the date of each accident. Information placed in the accident register must contain at least the following:

"(b)(1) A list of accidents as defined at 390.5 of the chapter containing, for each accident:

"(b)(1)(i) Date of accident.

"(b)(1) (ii) City or town, or most near, where the accident occurred and the State where the accident occurred.

"(b)(1)(iii) Driver name.

"(b)(1)(iv) Number of injuries.

"(b)(1)(v) Number of fatalities.

"(b)(1)(vi) Whether hazardous materials, other than fuel spilled from the fuel tanks of motor vehicle involved in the accident, were released.

"(b)(2) Copies of all accident reports required by State or other governmental entities or insurers."

Paul Farrell of Safety First, which also operates a hotline program, has conducted numerous studies on the benefits of these monitoring programs and has determined that savings can be as high as 20 percent of the cost of accidents.

While Safety Alert and Safety First are only two examples of safety initiatives that produce encouraging results, the use of technology is changing daily and will ultimately be used to improve safe driving habits and reduce risky behaviors. Additional studies are needed to determine the impact of safety training and initiatives similar to those noted above.

BUDGETING FOR FLEET SAFETY

The fleet safety professional or the person responsible for fleet safety in a company should consider the cost of three major components of the safety program in order not only to ensure compliance but also to operate in a safe and efficient manner. These cost components are:

1. record keeping
2. fleet safety training
3. fleet maintenance

In 2008, ORC Worldwide (now Mercer) engaged eighteen occupational health, safety, and environmental professionals and others to provide a comprehensive look at investment decisions and to answer important questions, such as:

- What health and safety or environmental investments should we make?
- When should we make a particular investment?
- Which health and safety of health investments create the greatest value to the organization?
- How do we compare an operational investment decision to an OS&H decision?
- How do we know we are doing the "right things" in the "right way?"
- To which projects should we allocate our human resources?
- How can we demonstrate the business value of our organization?

The return on the health, safety, and environmental investment process and software tools facilitates and encourages a team approach and calculates financial metrics in a common language. This type of tool, along with others referred to in this section, provides the fleet safety manager with the information to make informed decisions for the control and minimization of risk.

Record Keeping

The ANSI/ASSE Standard Z15.1-2012, *Safe Practices for Motor Vehicle Operations*, states, "Organizations shall maintain documentation of the qualifications and driving records of drivers." The data or documents needed for this aspect of fleet safety are noted in the section below.

Either a specific budget for an outside consultant should be established for these compliance efforts or the fleet safety professional should allow ample time in his or her regular work activities to complete these review and administrative activities.

From a driver perspective, the driver file is a critical component for compliance. A small fleet can be audited just as readily as a large one. The driver file and its related documents are a significant aspect of any compliance review. The Federal Motor Carrier Safety Regulations are found in the Code of Federal Regulations (49 CFR) 300–399.

The documents contained in each driver's file must include

- employment application
- current medical certificate
- DOT medical waiver, if applicable
- certificate of road test or equivalent, such as a CDL
- past employment verifications
- motor vehicle record
- annual review of driving record
- annual list of driver violations
- other documents, such as safety training records, pertinent to the driver's ability to operate a commercial motor vehicle

In accordance with 49 CFR 396.3(b), the vehicle maintenance file must contain

- an identification of the vehicle
- a method or document to indicate the nature and due dates of inspections and maintenance
- a record of inspections, repairs, and maintenance, indicating their date and nature or type
- a record of tests conducted on push-out windows, emergency doors, and emergency-door marking lights on buses

In addition to the costs associated with the review and maintenance of these records, fleet safety professionals are responsible for and may incur costs for keeping the written programs, policies, and procedures for the overall safety process current. This could require attendance at seminars or training sessions in order to stay up to date on changes in the regulations. Many organizations offer such seminars throughout the United States.

Fleet Safety Training

The Z15 standard also states, "Organizations shall establish a driver training program. The driver training program shall address requirements for new drivers, continuing education of existing drivers, and instances where remedial training shall be required" (ANSI/ASSE 2012).

The standard further states, "The training should include both classroom and behind-the-wheel training" (ANSI/ASSE 2012). The following topics should be considered for the training sessions:

- defensive driving
- substance abuse
- distracted driving (e.g., cell-phone use)
- aggressive driving (e.g., tailgating)
- vehicle inspection
- commodity-specific training (e.g., hazardous materials, material handling, cargo securement)
- safety regulations
- security procedures
- emergency equipment
- post-incident procedures
- vehicle inspection/maintenance

There are numerous software solutions for the fleet safety manager to consider to manage the data associated with the record-keeping requirements and safety training, as well as other aspects of the operation of a fleet of vehicles. FleetMentor from J. J. Keller, an online toolbox and advisor to assist the fleet safety manager with the myriad of tasks that impact fleet safety, provides tools and resources that include the following (J. J. Keller, Inc. n.d.):

- accident register
- best practices for fleet operations
- cargo securement
- driver and supervisor training
- motor-carrier safety audits
- online safety training
- PM service schedule
- roadside inspection tracking
- repair and maintenance costs
- scoring MVRs

These tools follow the CSA requirements and provide additional resources to adequately manage the fleet's needs. The fleet safety manager is encouraged to review the software products available from J. J. Keller and others.

Evaluating the Risks of Driving

In September 2003, the Health and Safety Executive (HSE) published a pamphlet entitled *Driving at Work: Managing Work Related Road Safety*. A significant portion of this publication is devoted to assessing the risks involved with road safety, including but not limited to the driver, training, vehicles, and the journey itself. The pamphlet suggests that working through a section on evaluating these risks will answer many questions that the fleet safety manager may not have considered. The "Training"

WHITE PAPER SHOWS TRUCK DRIVERS' SAFETY COMPLIANCE KNOWLEDGE LACKING

A white paper from American Transportation Research Institute (ATRI), "Compliance, Safety and Accountability (CSA): Assessing the New Safety Measurement System and Its Implications-2013 Update" shows that truck drivers do not have a clear understanding of CSA, after 3 years of its implementation. According to the Federal Motor Safety Administration, the CSA program was implemented in 2010 "to provide a better view into how well large commercial motor vehicle carriers and drivers are complying with safety rules, and to intervene earlier with those who are not."

The recent report includes 7,800 responses of drivers who were analyzed over the three year period. ATRI reports that the drivers on average, responded to the CSA knowledge test with 42.4% accuracy, which suggests that drivers still do not have a clear understanding of CSA. Despite this lack of knowledge, ATRI also reports carrier provided training has increased since 2011 and drivers job security concerns related to CSA have decreased by about 10% over the three-year period (ATRI 2013). To obtain a copy of the white paper, go to http://atri-online.org.

section asks, "Are you satisfied that your drivers are properly trained?" The following questions help in the risk assessment:

- Do you evaluate whether those who drive at work require additional training to carry out their duties safely?
- Do you provide induction training for drivers?
- Do you arrange for drivers to be trained, giving priority to those at higher risk (i.e., those with high annual mileage, poor crash records, or young drivers)?
- Do drivers know how to correctly adjust safety equipment (i.e., seat belts and head restraints)?
- Do drivers know how to use antilock brakes properly?
- Do drivers know how to check washer-fluid levels before starting a journey?
- Do drivers know how to ensure safe load distribution (i.e., when undertaking multidrop operations)?
- Do drivers know what actions to take to ensure their own safety following the breakdown of a vehicle?

- Do you need to provide a handbook for drivers, giving advice and information on road safety?
- Are drivers aware of the dangers of fatigue?
- Do they know what to do if they feel sleepy?
- Are drivers fully aware of the height of their vehicle, both laden and empty?

The final question of the assessment is appropriate and a great lead-in to the next section of this chapter, "Has money been budgeted for training? To be effective training needs should be periodically assessed, including the requirements for refresher training" (HSE 2003).

The Cost of Driver Training

Several types of safety or driver training sessions are used by fleet safety professionals.

Initial Training

When new employees are hired, a supervisor or a fleet safety professional should communicate the company's safety expectations. The time for this training will depend on the nature of the vehicle to be operated, the experience of the employees, and the organization's level of sophistication with regard to safety. *Many companies find that the more time they spend on initial training, the more likely it is that new hires realize the importance of safety.* The cost of initial training is usually part of the cost of the new-hire orientation process.

Calculating the cost for each hour of orientation should include:

- employee's hourly rate and benefits
- trainer's hourly rate and benefits
- clerical and administration time (hourly rate and benefits)

For example, *The Occupational Outlook Handbook* (BLS 2014) states that in 2012 the median hourly pay for heavy-truck and tractor-trailer drivers was $18.37. If a trainer earns $50,000 per year ($25 per hour) and an administrative employee earns $25,000 per year ($12.50 per hour) and benefits for each category cost approximately 30 percent of earnings, a single hour of orientation would cost

Driver	$18.37 plus $5.51 = $23.20
Trainer	$25.00 plus $15.60 = $40.60
Administrative employee	$12.50 + $3.75 = $16.25
Total cost:	$80.05 for one hour of orientation

Annual Training

Due to the nature of fleet operations, many companies conduct annual safety meetings lasting from as little as one hour to an entire day. In addition to updating drivers on policy or equipment changes, this is an opportunity to review the importance of safe driving techniques and safe behaviors. Often guest speakers are invited to participate in the sessions to provide a new or fresh perspective on safety. This type of meeting/training (if held annually) may also include a *safety awards* recognition program in which drivers are rewarded for years of driving without a preventable accident. The American Trucking Association (ATA) published a study highlighting exceptional approaches to safety management by some of the country's safest carriers, including some that won safety awards. The study notes that the average spent on safety for all surveyed carriers was $1060 per powered unit, but for the award-winning carriers the average was $2500 per powered unit. These expenditures included costs of driver training, compliance, safety awards, and safety meetings (ATA 1999).

- The cost of safety training includes wages and benefits paid to drivers while they are attending training sessions as well as the cost of speakers, video equipment and facilities, refreshments and meals, and rewards (ATA 1999).

Remedial Training

Remedial training may be necessary if employees have safety violations or a certain number of *chargeable* or preventable accidents during a specified time period. During this training, an effort is made to modify employees' behavior or to determine whether they have special needs that should be addressed. The cost of remedial training is an hourly rate for the driver plus the cost of the trainer's time (ATA 1999).

Ongoing Training

Computers have made this type of training readily available and affordable. A search of the Internet using the phrase "fleet safety training" reveals literally thousands of resources, many of which offer online training. The cost of the training depends on several factors, including the number of drivers to be trained and the number of training modules chosen.

Is there a cost benefit for this type of training? Alert-Driving provides an example of the return on investment (ROI) on its Web site with an ROI calculation scenario showing that if eight training modules are presented to 125 drivers, the cost of the program per driver is $43. Several companies that have used the training have reduced their accidents per million miles by an average of 20 percent with a potential savings of $145,000 each. The ROI is over 30 percent per carrier (AlertDriving 2006).

Boorman notes that Occupational Health Services, which operated 48 vehicles in 1994, reduced its average net cost per claim by £1500 over four years and reduced its overall cost by £65,000 in the same time period. The training consisted of a three-pronged approach: (1) raising driver awareness, (2) identifying higher-risk drivers, and (3) providing advanced driver training and providing targeted support to drivers after an incident. The cost per driver was estimated at £125 (Boorman 1999).

Fleet safety professionals are encouraged to find safety training that meets the needs of the fleet and should evaluate the ROI over a three- to four-year period.

The many aspects of ongoing training will also be discussed in the "Best Practices" chapter.

Cost of Vehicle Maintenance

The Federal Motor Carrier Safety Regulations, Part 396.3, require motor carriers to "systematically inspect, repair, and maintain, or cause to be systematically inspected, repaired, and maintained all motor vehicles" under their control (FMCSA 2008). It is considered good business practice to comply with these regulations. In fact, Standard Z15.1 states, "The purpose of the Standard is to provide organizations with a document for the development of policies, procedures, and management processes to control risks associated with the operations of motor vehicles. It is not intended to be a mandate for its use; it has been developed to assist organizations in defining and developing an effective risk management program for their vehicle operations" (ANSI/ASSE 2012).

In Section 6, "Vehicles," Standard Z15.1 states, "Organizations shall institute formal maintenance procedures and record-keeping procedures that meet or exceed the vehicle manufacturer's recommendations, giving consideration to the operating environment" (ANSI/ASSE 2012). The standard also addresses scheduled maintenance, repairs, qualified automotive service personnel, automotive service facilities, and vehicle replacement:

- ***Scheduled Maintenance.*** All vehicles shall be maintained by qualified automotive service technicians at regular intervals based on miles driven, hours of operation, and/or calendar time.
- ***Repairs.*** When defects are reported, the vehicle shall be repaired by a qualified automotive service technician. Safety-related defects shall be repaired before the vehicle is placed back in service, with appropriate records maintained.

• *Qualified Automotive Service Personnel.* All personnel performing maintenance, repair, modifications, or inspections shall possess the requisite skills and be qualified through experience and training.

• *Automotive Service Facilities.* Organizations performing their own vehicle maintenance shall have appropriate facilities and automotive service equipment to perform the required tasks. When maintenance is performed by vendors, the organization shall assess each vendor's ability to adequately perform the required service.

• *Vehicle Replacement.* Organization-operated vehicles shall be replaced according to formal procedures. Factors that affect the need for replacement include total mileage, maintenance cost, condition, operating requirements, operating environment, hours of service, and safety. Additional information below regarding life-cycle costing notes similar considerations and methods of determining these criteria (ANSI/ASSE 2012).

All of the above maintenance considerations are costly to an organization. *Vehicle Maintenance: A Comprehensive Guide to Improved Operations & Compliance* (J. J. Keller and Associates 2001) provides some insight on the expense associated with the maintenance aspect of fleet operations. The section entitled "Organizing Maintenance Programs" emphasizes the importance of tracking costs, stating:

> Operating costs are all the expenses directly related to running a vehicle on the road. Generally, driver expenses amount to about 50 percent or even more of the total costs of operating a vehicle. Vehicle expenses and indirect expenses (clerical staff, office supplies, etc.) make up the rest. Driver expenses include wages and benefits, but for the fleet that employs its drivers, rather than leases them, all employer-paid items must be included.

The guide notes that vehicle expenses are the second major category of costs. They include fixed costs: interest, depreciation, licenses, taxes (federal and state), permits, and insurance (vehicle and cargo) and variable costs: maintenance (labor and parts), fuel, oil, tires, tolls, and other miscellaneous road expenses. While variable costs are difficult to predict, they can be controlled (J. J. Keller and Associates 2001).

The cost per mile is the total dollar amount that it takes to run one truck for one mile. The guide states that cost per mile is the best and most convenient measure of trucking costs and is an easy indicator to use for comparison between vehicles (J. J. Keller and Associates 2001).

TABLE 3

Cost Per Mile	
Labor Costs	**Nonlabor Costs**
Driver—$0.445	Fuel—$0.138
Repair Wages—$0.049	Fuel Taxes—$0.059
Supervision—$0.025	Highway Taxes—$0.028
Other Labor—$0.013	Repair/Parts—$0.059
Fringes—$0.153	Tires/Tubes—$0.026
	Insurance—$0.032
	Depreciation—$0.083
	Other—$0.052
TOTAL—$0.684	TOTAL—$0.476

(*Source*: J. J. Keller and Associates 2001)

In statistics developed by Transportation Services of Fredericksburg, Virginia, (cited in J. J. Keller and Associates 2001, 5) from reports of 46 large general freight carriers, all with revenues above $20 million, the cost of operating a truck over the road was approximately $1.16 per mile. Of that total, 47.6 cents was spent on nonlabor costs and 68.4 cents was spent on labor costs. The study included primarily unionized drivers; this cost could be higher than in nonunion operations. The breakdown is found in Table 3.

Although this study was completed in 1990, it is a good model for determining cost per mile. These formulas can be used to determine the cost per mile and revenue per mile.

$$\text{total cost}/\text{total miles} = \text{cost per mile} \qquad (5)$$

$$\text{total revenue}/\text{total miles} = \text{revenue per mile} \qquad (6)$$

Fleet safety professionals are encouraged to use this data to determine areas where operating costs can be controlled using good risk-management practices.

Life-Cycle Costing

The decision to replace a truck should be based on life-cycle costing (J. J. Keller and Associates 2001). Life-cycle costing can also indicate the need for component replacements. Ideally, fleets replace vehicles the moment it costs more to keep them than to replace them. The guide suggests that the following vehicle records are important in determining when this moment occurs:

• the truck's initial cost and component specifications (which become the vehicle's history)

• the fuel/oil/lube/filter data (from purchase records)

• the vehicle utilization data (from driver reports and mileage logs)

• the maintenance data (from repair orders)

NIOSH OUTLINES STRATEGY FOR REDUCING MOTOR VEHICLE–RELATED WORKER DEATH

In May 2014, the National Institute for Occupational Safety and Health (NIOSH) unveiled a plan aimed at reducing work related deaths caused by motor vehicle crashes, the leading cause of worker fatalities. The Institute's Center for Motor Vehicle Safety (CMVS) defined areas of research and prevention initiatives and set performance measurements in the 2014-2018 plan. Five specific goals of the plan were identified by the CMVS:

1. Advance understanding of the risk factors associated with work-related crashes.

2. Reduce the incidence and severity of work-related crashes through engineering and technology-based safety interventions.

3. Reduce the incidence and severity of work-related crashes through evidence-based road safety management policies.

4. Reduce work-related crashes and injuries through national and international research collaborations.

5. Enhance availability of guidance and products that help prevent work-related crashes.

John Howard, NIOSH Director said the "millions of workers in the United States are exposed to motor vehicle traffic, as vehicle operators, passengers, or pedestrians." In the Foreword of the plan, Howard also said, "the new strategic plan gives the center the flexibility to address emerging issues along with longstanding safety concerns."

The responsibility of reducing the number of motor vehicle-related worker deaths is shared by employers, workers, policymakers, vehicle manufacturers, and research alike, according to Howard (NIOSH 2014).

In the opinion of the author, this important work is long overdue.

A tracking system can aid in determining the cost of operating a fleet and is a key component of vehicle-replacement decision making. A computerized tracking system also simplifies record keeping for fleet management.

A search of the Internet for "Fleet Maintenance" reveals numerous computerized tracking systems that fleet safety managers can use to determine fixed and variable costs. These systems assist in determining the cost of operating an individual vehicle in the fleet as well as the cost of operating the overall fleet. As noted in the Z15 standard, maintenance procedures and record-keeping procedures must meet or exceed the manufacturer's recommendations (ANSI/ASSE 2012).

Tracking systems provide data necessary for deciding when vehicles should be replaced. The Z15 standard states that "organization-operated vehicles shall be replaced upon formal procedures" (ANSI/ ASSE 2012). The standard explains that the factors involved in a decision to replace a vehicle include total mileage, maintenance costs, vehicle condition, operational requirements, operating environment, its hours of service, and vehicle safety (ANSI/ASSE 2012).

For a discussion of software for tracking FMCSA CSA requirements, see the end of the section on record keeping earlier in this chapter.

CONCLUSION

Fleet safety will continue to evolve with the advent of improved training methods, in-cab monitoring, driver professionalism, and maintenance practices. The primary responsibility for these improvements lies in the hands and wallets of the owners and managers of fleets and motor carriers. Without management commitment to safety and adequate resources, little progress will occur. Fleet safety professionals must be creative and innovative in their day-to-day activities in order to lead a safety process that will minimize crashes and prevent injuries.

There is still a need for additional research into this topic. A study of both regulated and nonregulated fleets should be conducted with the conclusions presented as a business case for driver training in all organizations that place drivers at risk on our nation's roads.

REFERENCES

AlertDriving. *ROI Calculations Scenarios* (accessed March 17, 2007). www.alertdriving.com

American National Standards Institute (ANSI) and the American Society of Safety Engineers (ASSE). 2012. Z15.1-2012, *Safe Practices for Motor Vehicle Operations*. Des Plaines, IL: ASSE.

American Transportation Research Institute (ATRI). 2013. "Compliance, Safety and Accountability (CSA): Assessing the New Safety Measurement System and Its Implications-2013 Update." www.arti-online. org/2014/01/28/csa-impacts-on-drivers-and-law-enforcement-explored-in-new-atri-research

American Trucking Association (ATA) Foundation with Parker-Young. 1999. "SafeReturns, A Compendium of Injury Prevention and Safety Management Practices of Award Winning Carriers." Arlington, VA: ATA.

Boorman, S. 1999. "Reviewing Car Fleet Performance After Advanced Driver Training." *Occupational Medicine* 49(8):558–591.

Brodbeck, J., ed. 1996. *Motor Fleet Safety Manual.* 4th ed. Itasca, IL: National Safety Council.

Bureau of Labor Statistics (BLS). 2014. *Occupational Outlook Handbook: Heavy and Tractor-Trailer Truck Drivers.* 2014 ed. www.bls.gov/ooh/transportation-and-materials-moving/heavy-and-tractor-trailer-truck-drivers.html.

_____. 2014. *Census of Fatal Occupational Injury Charts, 2002-2012 (revised).* www.bls.gov/iif/oshwc/cfoi/cfch0011.pdf

BusinessLink. n.d. *The Grey Fleet—Using Private Cars for Business Travel* (accessed November 16, 2011). www.businesslink.gov/uk/bdotg/action/detail

Code of Federal Regulations (CFR). Federal Motor Carrier Safety Administration. Title 49, Subtitle B, Chapter III, Parts 390–399. www.fmcsa.dot/rules-regulations

_____.Hazardous Materials Regulations, 49 CFR Chapter I, Subchapter C. www.fmcsa.dot/rules- regulations

Federal Motor Carrier Safety Administration (FMCSA). n.d.. "Accident Cost Table." www.fmcsa.dot.gov/

_____. 2010. *Evaluating the Safety Benefits of a Low Cost Driving Behavior Management System in Commercial Vehicle Operations* (accessed November 22, 2011). www.fmcsa.dot.gov/facts-research/research-technology/report/FMCSA-RRR-10-333.pdf

_____. n.d. *Compliance, Safety, Accountability* (CSA). "About CSA—What Is It?" (retrieved November 13, 2011). www.csa.fmcsa.for/about/basics.aspx

Health and Safety Executive (HSE). 2003. *Driving at Work: Managing Work-Related Road Safety.* Sudbury, Suffolk, UK: HSE

J. J. Keller, Inc. 2001. *Vehicle Maintenance Manual: A Comprehensive Guide to Improved Operations.* Neenah, WI: J. J. Keller and Associates, Inc.

_____. n.d. *FleetMentor* (accessed November 20, 2011). www.fleetmentor.com

National Highway Traffic Safety Administration (NHTSA). 2006. *Transportation Secretary Mineta Calls Highway Fatalities National Tragedy.* www.nhtsa.dot.gov/portal/site/nhtsa/template

_____. 2010. *U.S. Transportation Secretary LaHood Announces Lowest Traffic Fatalities in Six Decades* (retrieved October 1, 2010). www.nhtsa.gov/PR/ DOT-165-10.

_____. 2011. *Statistics and Facts About Distracted Driving* (retrieved November 13, 2011). www.distraction.gov/stats-and-facts/index.html

_____.2013a. Publication DOT HS 811 856, "2012 Motor Vehicle Crashes: Overview." www.nrd-nhtsa.dot.gov/Pubs/81156.pdf.

_____. 2013b. Publication DOT HS 811 870, "Alcohol-Impaired Driving." www.nrd-nhtsa.dot.gov/Pubs/811870.pdf.

_____. 2014. "Quick Facts 2012." www.nrd-nhtsa.dot.gov/Pubs/812006.pdf.

National Institute of Occupational Safety and Health (NIOSH). 2014. "NIOSH Center for Motor Vehicle Safety Strategic Plan for Research and Prevention, 2014-2018." www.cdc.gov/docs/2014-221pdfs

National Safety Council (NSC). 1996. "Driver's Accident Report." Itasca, IL: NSC.

_____. 2010. "Employers Focus Efforts to Prevent Distracted Driving." *Safety & Health*, June 2010.

_____. 2014. "New passenger cars, other vehicles must have rear visibility systems by 2018." Safety & Health, Vol. 190, No. 1.

Occupational Safety and Health Administration (OSHA). 1996. "Safety Pays: Do You Know How Much Accidents Are Really Costing Your Business?" (Includes the direct and indirect costs of accidents, iceberg and worksheet.) www.osha.gov/SLTC/etools/safetyhealth/ images/safpay1.gif

OSHA, NHTSA, and NETS (Network of Employers for Traffic Safety). 2006. "Guidelines for Employers to Reduce Motor Vehicle Crashes." www.osha.gov/Publications/motor_vehicle_guide.html

Safety Alert Network. 2006. "Cost Benefit Analysis" (accessed November 25, 2007). www.safetyalert.com/costbenefit.asp

Tam, Joyce. n.d. *An Introduction to Telematics* (accessed November 16, 2011). www.zurich.com/insight/insightmagazine/fleet/telematics.htm

Zaloshnja, E., and T. Miller. 2002. *Revised Cost of Large Truck and Bus-Involved Crashes.* Calverton, MD: Pacific Institute for Research and Evaluation (PIRE); prepared for FMCSA (November 18, 2002).

ADDITIONAL READING

CONTROLLING FLEET LIABILITY RISKS THAT COULD DRIVE YOU OUT OF BUSINESS*

Timothy J. Batz, CSP, ARM, CRIS
IMA, Inc.
Denver, CO

Introduction

According to the National Highway Traffic Administration, in 2011 there were 32,367 motor vehicle fatalities in the United States. The Center for Disease Control, in 2011, calculated that the cost of fatal crashes topped $41 Billion. In the 1970's, according to the National Institute of Health, alcohol was a factor in 60% of traffic deaths. In recent years, that percentage has dropped to 32%, according to the Center for Disease Control.

Drivers who use hand-held devices are four times more likely to get into crashes serious enough to injure themselves, according to study by Monash University in Australia. According to the Virginia Tech Transportation Institute (VTTI), text messaging while driving creates a crash risk 23 times worse than driving while not distracted. You may also be surprised to know that a hands-free cell phone use is **not** substantially safer than hand-held use, also according to the VTTI. Many states have enacted laws requiring that drivers must use a hands-free device (Bluetooth) if they choose to talk on the phone while driving. Does that make sense? Finally, a study by Carnegie Mellon University showed that engaging in a secondary task, such as talking on a cell phone, reduces the amount of brain activity associated with driving by 37%. These studies are instructive and we, as safety professionals, need to be aware of the hazards of distracted driving and what we can do to manage them.

What's the Big Deal? We Have Insurance

To answer that question, one needs to understand some basics about our legal system. It's been said of our legal system that it's the worst there is…except for all the rest. One characteristic of our legal system is that it offers access for those who feel that they have been wronged. If a person has no resources to hire a lawyer, there are plaintiffs' lawyers who will take the case on a contingency basis; that is, the attorney's compensation is contingent upon an award or settlement in favor of the plaintiff.

In our system of justice, a person (plaintiff) can bring a legal action against another if they feel the person (defendant) was negligent and that negligence caused them harm.

According to www.legal-dictionary.com, In order to establish negligence as a cause of action under the law of torts, a plaintiff must prove that the defendant had a duty to the plaintiff, the defendant breached that duty by failing to conform to the required standard of conduct, the defendant's negligent conduct was the cause of the harm to the plaintiff, and the plaintiff was, in fact, harmed or damaged.

Is your organization doing what is reasonable? What is "reasonable?" According to www.legal-dictionary.com, the term "reasonable" is a generic and relative one and applies to that which is appropriate for a particular situation. Look again at the definition of negligence.

The standard your company will be held to is what a "reasonable person do in similar circumstances."

Ask yourself if these statements sound reasonable:

- My employee has a driver's license, that's good enough.
- Checking employee driving records is too cumbersome.
- That person makes me a lot of money; I can't put restrictions on him/her.
- I took away the company car and now she drives her own car for business.
- I checked the employee's driving record when he was hired many years ago.
- It's only one DUI, everybody makes mistakes.

These are excuses I commonly hear from businesses. How defensible are your company's acts or omissions? Are your acts/omissions reasonable? Do you have a written fleet safety program? Does your company check employee driving records periodically? If not, why not? You might find that your company is not acting reasonably.

For that matter, who defines "reasonable?" It can be a long and winding road, but juries often are the ones who determine if the defendant acted reasonably. Relying on "common sense" isn't a good idea: Go back to "what a reasonable person who do in similar circumstances."

From a liability standpoint, the good news is that business auto liability insurance is designed to respond to claims of negligence (including gross negligence). For example, if an employee is driving a vehicle for business and negligently injures another, the insurance policy is designed to respond to claims of bodily injury and property damage. That doesn't mean the claimant will be sent a check. It simply means that the policy will respond with your legal defense and pay damages that you're a legally obligated to pay for harm to another person or property.

Of course, with the insurance in place, insurance carriers would like to see some control exercised over which employees drive company vehicles or who drive their own vehicles on company business. An insurance carrier is in a contractual relationship with the policyholder to provide financial responsibility in the event the insured is legally liable. It is understandable that they would want some controls in place to minimize exposure to loss.

The criteria that most insurance carriers like to see include driver selection, such as a periodically checking an employee's driving record against a written criteria, driver safety training and written plan to implement safety procedures. You will also find that carriers are interested in those who drive their personal vehicles for business and expect the same criteria to be applied.

Why do carriers pay attention to employees who drive personal vehicles on company business? Because it's a source of loss.

When employees drive their own vehicles on company business, it is indeed an auto liability exposure for the business. Commonly, if the employee is involved in a crash while driving their own vehicle for a work, their personal automobile insurance will respond if they are legally liable.

But what happens if the employee doesn't have insurance or has very low limits of liability? The business auto liability carrier will likely respond to this legal liability, and that's why business auto liability carriers are interested in the control of this exposure.

Motor Vehicle Records (MVRs)

The value of checking a drivers motor vehicle record (MVR):

- Do you check motor vehicle records (MVRs) for drivers in your organization? If you run MVRs, at what point do you restrict n employee to drive on company business?

- Many organizations have realized the liability exposure of having employees driving vehicles and have chosen to implement a procedure that includes checking MVRs.

- If you do indeed check MVRs, what is a reasonable criterion?

Below are the minimum criteria that businesses should consider:

1. There have been no major violations within the past five years: Major violations are generally defined as convictions for:
   - DUI
   - reckless driving
   - commission of a felony while driving a motor vehicle
   - refusal to take an alcohol test
   - leaving scene of an accident
   - drag race or speed contest
   - eluding a police officer
   - speeding in excess of 25 mph over the posted limit

2. No more than three minor violations within the past three years. Minor violations are defined as convictions for:
   - speeding below 25 mph
   - failure to yield
   - failure to stop
   - any moving violation not considered major

So, what should a business do if drivers don't meet the criteria? The short answer is to not allow the employee to drive on company business, in a company car or in his/her own vehicle. Before you criticize the criteria as unrealistic, realize that legal liability is real and has consequences.

- Here's an actual case: Alicia Bustos was a passenger in the back seat of a Buick when her car was hit by a F150, whose driver was using a cell phone at the time of the crash, which left her severely injured and ventilator-dependent. Following the accident, she sued the driver of the Ford and the driver's employer. A Miami jury awarded Bustos and her husband $20.98 million; the lawsuit was later settled for $16.1 million. *Bustos v. Leive*, No. 01-13370 CA 30 (Miami-Dade Co., Fla., Cir.Ct.) Central to the case was the use of the cell phone while driving.

- The insured *was* a well servicing contractor. I use was in the past tense because the company is not in business any longer as a result of this incident. It had been raining heavily all day so the owner took the crew to a bar for some "team building." After several hours and multiple pitchers of beer, the crew departs in company vehicles. Two employees race side by side on a two-lane road and collide with a vehicle carrying four teenage girls. The crash resulted in three fatalities and one severe brain injury. The auto liability insurance carrier paid policy limits and the court granted a very large punitive damage award.

These types of huge awards are unusual, but it makes the point that these types of losses can drive a company out of business. Insurance can pay for actual damages up to policy limits, but punitive damages are generally not insurable as a matter of public policy.

A Word about Technology

With technology moving at lightning speed, there a new products and services coming onto the market to help employers manage these exposures. Some products can be plugged into the diagnostic port under the vehicle's dashboard and give you very telling data about your drivers' habits, how many hard stops and starts he/she has in a given time period, and even the how much time is spent idling.

Other technologies will allow an employer to see an employees' motor vehicle record in real time, simply with the click of a button. Moreover, vehicles can be equipped with GPS tracking devices that will send a notification to the employer if it leaves a predetermined geographical area.

There is even a product recently available that will disable a phone while located in a moving vehicle.

Technology solutions are readily available and at a relatively low cost.

What Businesses Can Do

How can you as a safety professional help minimize this exposure? Knowing that a one size fits all approach isn't likely to work, you should focus on making incremental progress over time.

The safety professional should also know that what is reasonable will change over time. A generation or two ago, if you were pulled over by the police for driving drunk, law enforcement might tell you to go straight home and sleep it off. Society's view of drunk driving has changed since then. Due to the efforts of organizations such as Mothers Against Drunk Driving (MADD), public health campaigns and state lawmaking, society now takes a much dimmer view of drunk driving. If you are stopped for drunk driving in today's world, you will likely be arrested, spend several hours in the company of law enforcement and lose your driver's license for a period of time.

How can we as safety professionals help?

- Have a written driver safety policy that includes motor vehicle record (MVR) criteria
- Evaluate all employees who will drive company or their own vehicles on company business and review their driving records periodically thereafter
- Formalize driver training
- Enforce disciplinary standards
- Have a distracted driving policy and address cell phone usage
- Require the use of seat belts.
- Know that there is an ANSI standard on the topic, (Z15.1), *Safe Practices for Motor Vehicle Operations*

Chapter 7

Sustainability and the Safety, Health, and Environmental Professional

Kathy A. Seabrook, Robert Stewart,
Jeffrey Camplin, and Mike Taubitz

LEARNING OBJECTIVES

- Understand what sustainability is and what is driving this business strategy.

- Learn about the Global Reporting Initiative (GRI).

- Be able to clarify the relationship between sustainability and social responsibility.

- Recognize the value of the integration model: safety and continuous improvement within sustainability.

- Discuss legislation, standards, and market influences on sustainability.

- Learn about ISO 26000, Guidance on *Social Responsibility*, and its relationship to occupational safety and health.

- Discover from case studies how companies are integrating safety into their sustainability strategies and reporting.

In today's workplace, an OS&H professional can expect to hear or read about sustainability; Global Reporting Initiative (GRI); corporate social responsibility; lean, continuous improvement; and "green." These terms and conditions, while related to each other, can often cause confusion. This chapter puts various strategic issues into context to help readers better understand the big picture of sustainability. Employee safety is currently viewed as one small part of the overall equation, but it should be viewed as a more important ingredient for long-term success in any organization.

The first part of this chapter provides an historical overview of topics related to sustainability. Later sections will describe these topics and present case studies to demonstrate the link between safety and sustainability.

SUSTAINABILITY

Sustainability embodies *stewardship* and *design with nature*—well-established goals of design professionals—and *carrying capacity*, a highly developed modeling technique used by scientists and planners.

The most popular definition of sustainability can be traced to a 1987 UN conference. It defined sustainable developments as those that "meet present needs without compromising the ability of future generations to meet their needs" (WECD 1987). Gilman extends this goal-oriented definition by stating that "sustainability refers to a very old concept (the Golden Rule) . . . do [unto] future generations as you would have them do [unto] you" (Gilman 1990, 1996).

These well-established definitions set an ideal premise but do not clarify specific human and environmental parameters in modeling and measuring sustainable developments. The following definitions are more specific:

- Sustainable means using methods, systems, and materials that will not deplete resources or harm natural cycles (Rosenbaum 1993).

- Sustainability "identifies a concept and attitude in development that looks at a site's natural land, water, and energy resources as integral aspects of the development" (Viera 1993).
- Sustainability integrates natural systems with human patterns and celebrates continuity, uniqueness, and placemaking (Early 1993).

The 1970 National Environmental Policy Act (NEPA) formally established as a national goal the creation and maintenance of conditions under which humans and nature "can exist in productive harmony, and fulfill the social, economic and other requirements of *present and future generations of Americans*" [emphasis added] (EPA1970).

The concept of sustainable development was described in a 1981 White House Council on Environmental Quality (CEQ) report: "The key concept here is sustainable development. If economic development is to be successful over the long term, it must proceed in a way that protects the natural resource base of developing countries" (White House 1981).

A later concept of sustainability that took root in the global arena was an outgrowth of the 1987 Brundt- land Commission (named for the chair) for the United Nations (UN WCED 1987). This concept of sustainability was based upon the concept of the *triple bottom line*—balancing environmental concerns and social needs with economic issues. Sustainability may be envisioned, as depicted in Figure 1, as the confluence of the three pillars (3 Ps): social (people), economic (profit), and environmental (planet). Sustainability is a very complex subject that includes biodiversity, climate change, carbon footprint, and so on. For purposes of discussion in the safety, health, and environmental (SHE) community, it seems best to deal with the practical aspects of the 3 Ps that safety, health, and environmental professionals may impact or influence.

Sustainable growth is not possible without a culture of continuous improvement. This chapter will demonstrate how continuous improvement provides the foundation for an organizational culture capable of attaining the triple bottom line. First of all, there must be an introduction to the current guidelines for organizations that choose to report their progress on sustainable growth. These guidelines are contained in the Global Reporting Initiative (GRI).

GLOBAL REPORTING INITIATIVE (GRI)

The GRI provides the framework for voluntary reporting of initiatives related to sustainable growth. Table 1 presents definitions that pertain to sustainability, including their sources, Web sites, and a discussion of each. It generally addresses the elements of waste from the business process, including time and effort.

GRI Vision

The vision of the GRI is that disclosure on economic, environmental, and social performance becomes as commonplace and comparable as financial reporting, and as important to organizational success.

GRI Mission

GRI's mission is to create conditions for the transparent and reliable exchange of sustainability information through the development and continuous improvement of the GRI sustainability reporting framework.

The GRI is a network-based organization that has pioneered the development of the world's most widely used sustainability reporting framework and is committed to its continuous improvement and application worldwide (GRI 2007).

In an effort to ensure technical quality, credibility, and relevance, the reporting framework was developed through a consensus-seeking process with global participants drawn from business, society, labor, and professional institutions. The cornerstone of the framework is the sustainability reporting guidelines. The third version of the guidelines, known as the *G3 Guidelines,* was published in 2006 and is available free to the public (GRI 2007).

Health and safety is but one small aspect of GRI under the heading of the International Labour Organization's (ILO) decent work agenda for labor practices (GRI 2007). Reporting guidelines from the ILO include the following:

- percentage of total workforce represented in formal joint management: worker health and safety committees that help monitor and advise on occupational health and safety programs
- rates of injury, occupational diseases, lost days and absenteeism, and total number of work-related fatalities by region

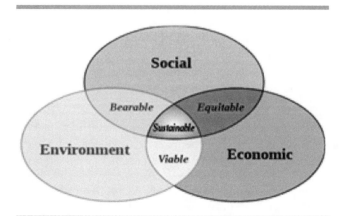

FIGURE 1. Confluence of sustainability
(*Source:* Dréo 2006/2007; adapted by Mike Taubitz)

TABLE 1

Definitions and Discussion

Term	Definition/Source	Discussion
Carbon market	The carbon market grew out of carbon reduction and trading schemes as a result of the Kyoto Protocol and other carbon reduction commitments and regulations. The market tracks and trades carbon (in units of 1 ton CO_2 emissions) like other commodities (UNFCC 2010).	One of the ways organizations are meeting their commitments to their overall carbon emissions targets (locally, nationally and internationally).
Continuous improvement (CI)	Continuous improvement (CI) or continuous improve-ment processes (CIP) ccs.mit.edu/21c/iokey.html	Ongoing efforts to improve products, processes, and services.
Corporate social responsibility	A firm's sense of responsibility toward the community and environment (both ecological and social) in which it operates and draws resources and sustenance from. www.businessdictionary.com/definition/corporate-citizenship.html	Firms express this citizenship (1) through their waste and pollution reduction processes, (2) by contributing educational and social programs, and (3) by earning adequate returns on the employed resources.
Global reporting initiative (GRI)	A network-based organization that has developed the world's most widely used sustainability reporting frame-work and is committed to its continuous improvement and application worldwide. www.globalreporting.org/Home	The global reporting initiative (GRI) is a network-based organization that has pioneered the development of the world's most widely used sustainability reporting framework.
Green/Environment	Green is typically associated with any form of environ-mental initiative that reduces adverse impacts to the planet. www.epa.gov/greenpower	It is sometimes used interchangeably with sustainability. However, green is but one of three legs of sustainable growth.
Greenhouse gases	Gases that trap heat in the atmosphere. www.epa.gov/climatechange/emissions/index.html	Common greenhouse gases derived from human activity are: • Carbon dioxide (CO_2) • Methane (CH_4) • Nitrous oxide (N_2O) • Fluorinated gases
Lean	The suite of tools and thinking employed by companies following the teachings of W. Edwards Deming.	The term lean was first introduced in 1990 with the book, *The Machine That Changed the World*. It generally addresses the elements of waste from the business process, including time and effort.
LEED*	Leadership in Energy and Environmental Design. www.usgbc.org	An internationally recognized green building certification system that provides third-party verification that a building or community was designed and built using strategies intended to improve performance; it is headed by the U.S. Green Building Council.
Kaizen	Incremental efforts driving continuous improvement.	A Japanese term [the translation of kai ("change") and zen ("good") is "improvement"].
PDCA	Plan-Do-Check-Act en.wikipedia.org/wiki/PDCA	Often referred to as the Deming Cycle, PDCA is an iterative four-step problem-solving process typically used in management systems that drive continuous improvement.
Sustainability	Development that meets the needs of the present without compromising the ability of future generations to meet their own needs. www.sustainabilitydictionary.com	An outgrowth of the 1987 UN Commission; referenced as the Brundtland Report and named for the Commission's Chair.
Triple bottom line	Financial, social, and environmental effects of a firm's policies and actions that determine its viability as a sustainable organization. www.businessdictionary.com/definition/triple-bottom-line.html	Sometimes referred to as the "3 Ps" for people, planet, and profit; the triple bottom line strategically balances competing requirements for long-term sustainable growth.

(Adapted by Taubitz from various sources)

- education, training, counseling, prevention, and risk-control programs in place to assist workforce members, their families, or community members regarding serious diseases
- health and safety topics covered in formal agreements with trade unions

To put things into context, the GRI labor practices section is twenty pages and is only a small part of the overall GRI guidelines. The guidelines are comprised of the following major sections (GRI 2007):

- application levels
- G3 guidelines

- the environment
- economics
- human rights
- labor practices
- product responsibility
- society

Considering Dr. Peter Drucker's statement, "What gets measured, gets managed" (Aaron 2008), it would seem that employee safety would not garner much management attention if one relies only on the areas emphasized by the GRI. It is incumbent upon SHE to find ways to integrate with GRI, not the other way around.

Let us turn to how corporate social responsibility fits into the picture.

SOCIAL RESPONSIBILITY (SR) AND CORPORATE SOCIAL RESPONSIBILITY (CSR)

Social responsibility (SR) and *corporate social responsibility* (CSR) are interrelated, and can best be defined through the ISO 2600 standard on social responsibility (ISO 2010). *Social responsibility* refers to any organization's need to preserve resources for future generations and complements the traditional view that only private corporations have a duty to make products and provide services responsibly.

Although these terms are different and are driven by different organizations, they all point in the same general direction. Throughout the industrialized world and in many developing countries, there has been a sharp escalation in the social roles corporations are expected to play. Companies are facing new demands to engage in public/private partnerships and are under growing pressure to be accountable not only to shareholders, but also to stakeholders, such as employees, consumers, suppliers, local communities, policymakers, and the society at large (Noer et al. 2008).

Also known as corporate responsibility, corporate citizenship, responsible business, sustainable responsible business, or corporate social performance, *corporate social responsibility* is a form of corporate selfregulation integrated into a business model. CSR policy is intended to function as a built-in, self-regulating mechanism where the inclusion of public interest into corporate decision making facilitates achievement of a triple bottom line that benefits people, planet, and profit (BNET n.d.). The term corporate social responsibility has been used interchangeably with corporate responsibility, corporate citizenship, social enterprise, sustainability, sustainable development, triple bottom line, corporate ethics, and, in some cases, corporate governance. Social responsibility is used to suggest that all organizations, including government,

nongovernmental organizations (NGOs), and professional organizations, need to be socially responsible.

ISO 26000

The International Organization for Standardization (ISO) finds that sustainability and social responsibility are closely related but different (ISO 2010). Sustainable development from the ISO perspective is about meeting the needs of society while living within the planet's ecological limits, without jeopardizing the ability of future generations to meet their needs. Social responsibility, on the other hand, has the organization as its focus and concerns an organization's responsibilities to society and the environment. Social responsibility is closely linked to sustainable development. Essentially, the main objective of an organization's social responsibility should be to contribute to sustainable development (ISO 2010).

ISO 26000, *Guidance on Social Responsibility,* is an international standard that helps organizations achieve the benefits of implementing policies on social responsibility (SR). Ninety-nine countries and 42 public- and private-sector organizations with liaison status were involved in the ISO working group on social responsibility under the joint leadership of the ISO members for Brazil (ABNT) and Sweden (SIS). The group included a geographical and gender-based balance of participants. Main stakeholder groups represented include: industry; government; labor; consumers; nongovernmental organizations; service, support, and research; and others. The American Society for Quality (ASQ) is the administrator of the U.S. Technical Advisory Group for development of ISO 26000 (ASQ 2010). Published in November 2010, ISO 26000 contains voluntary guidance, not requirements, and therefore is not for use as a certification standard, such as ISO 9001:2008 and ISO 14001:2004. ISO 26000 seeks to help all types of organizations, regardless of their size, activity, or location, to operate in a socially responsible manner by providing guidance on:

- concepts, terms, and definitions relating to social responsibility
- the background, trends, and characteristics of social responsibility
- principles and practices relating to social responsibility
- core subjects and issues relating to social responsibility
- integrating, implementing, and promoting socially responsible behavior throughout the organization
- its sphere of influence on various stakeholders
- identifying and engaging with stakeholders
- communicating commitments and performance related to social responsibility

The OS&H professional can benefit from a general understanding of social responsibility by obtaining a copy of ISO 26000. A review of the new ISO 26000, *Guidance on Social Responsibility,* will help the OS&H professional demonstrate the value safety management contributes to achieving organizational sustainability and social responsibility goals (ASQ 2010).

Whereas sustainability evolved from the United Nations, it is the ISO that has been driving efforts on social responsibility. In October 2010, ISO 26000:2010, *Guidance on Social Responsibility,* was published as a guidance standard for social responsibility (ISO 2010).

It does not matter whether an organization has a foundation based upon sustainability or social responsibility; what is important is to understand that both are similar strategies, often with overlapping goals. By virtue of its seniority and its United Nation's origin, sustainability is probably best thought of as the umbrella for all succeeding initiatives, making CSR one part of an overall approach for attaining sustainable growth.

If sustainability or CSR is not important in your organization, it is safe to assume that the concept of continuous improvement is. Any organization desiring to meet strategic future challenges must have a culture and systems that drive improvement in all facets of the business.

SIDEBAR

> ## ISO 26000 Content List
> (ISO 2010)
>
> The content of ISO 26000 is structured as follows:
>
> Foreword
>
> Introduction
>
> 1 Scope
> 2 Terms and definitions
> 3 Understanding social responsibility
> 4 Principles of social responsibility
> 5 Recognizing social responsibility and engaging stakeholders
> 6 Guidance on social responsibility core subjects
> 7 Guidance on integrating social responsibility throughout an organization
>
> Annex A – Voluntary initiatives and tools for social responsibility
>
> Annex B – Abbreviated terms
>
> Bibliography

GREEN ENVIRONMENT

Green is typically associated with any form of environmental initiative to reduce adverse impacts to the planet. It is sometimes used interchangeably with sustainability. However, green is only one of the three legs of sustainable growth. A significant amount of work and effort is required to link environmental efforts with sustainability. For that reason, this chapter will not repeat what is widely available in publications and on the Internet. However, lean and green are aligning with little mention of safety (Taubitz et al. 2010).

INTEGRATION OF SAFETY AND CONTINUOUS IMPROVEMENT WITH SUSTAINABILITY

Safety

It has already been noted that safety is seen as a small part of sustainability and GRI. Because CSR is also a broad initiative emulating sustainability, safety is therefore viewed as a small part of social responsibility. Social responsibility efforts are often focused *outside* the workplace. Employee safety is rarely, if ever, mentioned in articles and publications that deal with sustainability and corporate social responsibility.

Without safety, the people part of sustainability is missing its core, but this is not well recognized. Baxter International, Inc., is an example of a company that has integrated safety into its sustainability strategies. The case study on Baxter International, Inc., outlines the safety and health performance metrics reported in the Baxter "2009 Sustainability Priorities Report" (Baxter 2010a).

Continuous Improvement: The Bridge

The bridge between dealing with the tactical issue of employee safety and the strategic goal of sustainable growth is depicted in Figure 2.

Safety

Continuous Improvement & Safety

 Sustainability

FIGURE 2. Bridge from safety to sustainability with continuous growth (*Source: Adapted from model by Taubitz*)

Continuous improvement (CI) or *continuous improvement processes* (CIP) are ongoing efforts to improve products, processes, and services. Process management, project management, and quality management are all tools that businesses use to drive continuous improvement. The following section of this chapter provides more detail on comparing strategic and tactical continuous improvement.

Many companies, large and small, are working on the somewhat nebulous issue of sustainability. Even if the term itself is not used, the concept of balancing people, the planet, and profit to achieve long-term success makes sense. Concurrently, leaders everywhere are faced with creating an organizational culture and processes that drive continuous improvement and the opportunity to stay in business for the long term.

Strategic and Tactical Continuous Improvement

Strategic continuous improvement is an ongoing effort to improve products, services, or processes. These efforts can seek *incremental* improvement over time or *breakthrough* improvement all at once. Delivery (customer-valued) processes are constantly evaluated and improved in the light of their effectiveness, efficiency, and flexibility.

CASE STUDY

Baxter International, Inc.

Baxter International, Inc., is working to integrate worker safety performance into its overall sustainability strategies and priorities. With approximately 49,700 employees in 27 countries and gross sales of $12.6 billion in 2009, Baxter International, Inc., and its subsidiary companies manufacture and distribute medical devices, pharmaceuticals, and biotechnology products in 100 countries (Baxter 2010a).

Robert L. Parkinson, Jr., Baxter's Chairman and Chief Executive Officer (June 2010) highlights workplace safety and health, injury, and illness performance, as well as environmental achievements, in Baxter's "2009 Sustainability Priorities Report." The report states that one of Baxter's priorities is to "promote a safe and healthy workplace" (Baxter 2010c). To do this, Baxter has set a 2015 goal to "implement best-in-class programs designed to protect the safety and improve the health of employees that result in performance in the top three industry peers" (Baxter 2010a). This demonstrates Baxter's recognition that occupational safety and health performance is integral to its sustainability strategy and is reflected in its commitment to performance reporting and peer benchmarking. A 2008 ORC benchmarking study ranked Baxter fourth among twelve reporting healthcare companies in days-lost rate performance (Baxter 2010a).

For worker safety and health performance, Baxter primarily reports in the area of injury/illness incident statistics: recordable case rate, cases with days-lost rate, days-lost rate, and restricted days rate as shown in the following table (Baxter International, Inc. 2010a, 2010b).

Lost-cay case rate	0.15 (21% improvement)
Days-lost rate	4.16 (2% Improvement)
Restricted days rate	12.68 (35% improvement)
Recordable case rate	1.07 (17% improvement)
Employee/contractor serious incidents*	12/2
Employee/contractor fatalities	0/0

*A serious workplace incident case "results in an employee or contractor being hospitalized overnight, sustaining an amputation or dying"

According to Baxter, it has realized improvements in its incident rates over the previous year in all areas, with the exception of serious incident cases. According to the ORC report, the company proactively recognized this exception and is assessing the root causes of these serious incidents to prevent potential reoccurrence in the future (Baxter 2010a).

In addition to injury/illness incident statistics, Baxter is also focused on two areas of leading performance metrics: hazard identification and risk assessment (HIRA) and near-miss reporting. Baxter has identified ergonomic risk as a key focus area for its operations globally. To that end, the company has used a risk-based approach (HIRA) to reduce its manual handling-related injuries—11 percent in one year at its Castlebar, Ireland, facility (Baxter 2010a).

The second leading performance indicator used by Baxter is adoption and implementation of a near-miss reporting initiative. By the end of 2009, Baxter reported that 64 percent of its manufacturing, research and development, and distribution sites (more than 100 employees) had implemented this initiative. Baxter's manufacturing site in Cleveland, Mississippi, has seen an 89 percent increase in near-miss reporting since the initiative was implemented there in 2006 (Baxter 2010a). Near-miss reporting allows for incident investigation, root cause analysis, and implementation of control methodologies to prevent reoccurrence of a future near-miss incident or potential injury or illness as a result of the same incident root cause. According to Baxter, this will be an ongoing leading indicator of sustainability performance (Baxter 2010a).

For their 2009 sustainability performance, Baxter International. Inc. was ranked 20th out of America's "100 Best Corporate Citizens" by *Corporate Responsibility (CR) Magazine* (*CR Magazine* 2010). The company has also been recognized as one of the "Global 100 Most Sustainable Corporations" since the list was first published in 2005, has been listed on the Dow Jones Sustainability Index since its launch in 1999, and has been named Medical Products Industry Leader for nine years (Baxter 2010b).

In the experience of author Taubitz, five key criteria for continuous improvement processes include:

1. A core principle of CIP is the (self) reflection of processes (*feedback*).
2. The purpose of CIP is the identification, reduction, and elimination of suboptimal processes (*efficiency*).
3. The emphasis of CIP is on incremental, continuous steps rather than giant leaps (*evolution*).
4. Respect for people is the basis for including everyone in continuous improvement efforts (*empowerment and engagement*).
5. The more strategic elements include deciding how to increase the value of the delivery- process output to the customer (*effectiveness*) and how much flexibility is valuable in the process to meet changing needs.

CASE STUDY

COMAU Inc.: Coping Machine Project Summary—X-Mation Facility (Megan Raines 2009)

This situation involved a metalworking machine which did not have a guard to protect operators from hand/finger injury during machine operation. *(Note:* thankfully, no such injuries had been sustained.) The machine could perform various functions, including coping, and was being used for coping various sizes of angle iron stock. It was actuated using a guarded foot pedal. Upon actuation, the top portion of the machine moved downward to cope the stock. When the point of operation of the machine was opened, it exposed a gap approximately two inches high and several inches wide and deep under the moving area (Figure 3).

In the past, a guard had been added, but it blocked the point of operation, which prevented the machine from being used. Thus, the guard was only in place when the machine was not in use and did not protect the operators. Other protections had been discussed but

were not feasible due to the design of the machine. For example, two-hand controls could not be installed because the operator needed to hold the stock in place during operation for safety and quality reasons. The guard the manufacturer could provide was a sliding guard that had to be moved to expose the point of operation prior to using the machine, which was determined to provide inadequate protection for this task.

On both sides, the machine had a guide to help properly position the stock. The guide was adjustable to allow for different stock sizes. The guide did not have preset locations for the different stock sizes—the operator would have to know exactly where to position the guide during adjustment. Changeover required use of hand tools and four different adjustments. Total changeover time was approximately fifteen minutes.

During operation, the operator had to firmly hold the stock close to the point of operation, to ensure that the stock did not move during machine operation (Figure 4). When the stock

moved, it caused quality problems with burrs on the stock, which required rework to correct and thus added cost. If the stock was not held, it could be ejected from the machine, thereby exposing the machine operator to injury. Repetitive holding of the stock in this manner introduced ergonomic risk factors.

The main goal of the project was to design appropriate guarding for the machine to prevent risk of an injury. A requirement of the design was that it would not negatively impact the productivity or quality of the operation. Operator input for the design was sought to ensure compliance and satisfaction with the result.

With support from management and safety personnel, the machine operator personally developed a design for a guard that met all of the project goals. The guard was manufactured in-house for very little cost. Photos of the new guard were sent to the machine manufacturer, who approved Comau's use of the guard.

The two-piece guard was permanently installed in front of the point-of- operation area. The guard completely prevented the operator's hands/fingers from entering the hazardous gap area, virtually eliminating the risk of a finger/hand injury (Figure 5). The guard allowed the edge of the stock to slide underneath it to enter the machine.

The new guard had two preset settings for stock of different sizes. Changeover required a simple hand adjustment in two locations, which took 30 seconds or less in total. During

FIGURE 3. Before: point of operation configuration creates injury risk *(Source:* COMAU Inc. 2009)

FIGURE 4. Before: operator has to hold stock *(Source:* COMAU Inc. 2009)

operation, the operator would slide the stock into the guard. Because of the design allowing the two sections of guard to work together, the guards would guide the stock into proper position each time without the operator needing to make adjustments. The stock was held in place by the guards and no longer needed to be held by hand during operation, which eliminated an ergonomic risk factor (Figure 6). Because of the ease of use and stock positioning, productivity improved by over 15 percent. Because the stock cannot move around during operation, quality was improved and the need for rework was eliminated.

All of the goals were accomplished and exceeded during this project.

FIGURE 5. After: point of operation no longer exposed (*Source:* COMAU Inc. 2009)

The risk of injury due to the gap was virtually eliminated, while productivity, quality, ergonomics, and changeover time were also significantly improved. The machine operators were fully

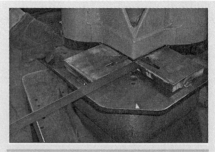

FIGURE 6. After: operator no longer holds stock during operation (*Source:* COMAU Inc. 2009)

involved in the solution and are very happy with the result. Projects such as this demonstrate and uphold Comau's commitment to the health and safety of its workers.

Examples of continuous improvement tools and processes include the following (Taubitz):

- problem solving
- brainstorming
- cause-and-effect diagrams
- check sheets
- flow diagrams

Lean thinking and Kaizen events are developed around the concept of identifying and eliminating waste. The seven forms of lean waste are:

1. Correction
2. Overproduction
3. Motion (people)
4. Material movement
5. Waiting
6. Inventory
7. Process

These make up the acronym COMMWIP, which is a useful way of remembering wastes that negatively impact operational performance. When considered with the wastes of safety (injury and illness) and environmental wastes (air, water, solids, energy, and so on), it is possible to view things in a new light, one that allows the best approach for achieving sustainable growth. A new goal of achieving acceptable risk (safety and environment) with minimized (lean) operational waste fosters daily decisions that contribute to the triple bottom line.

The Kaizen approach from lean manufacturing is another tactical CI tool. Kaizen efforts are small, incremental steps that employ other tools in addition to those cited above. Based upon the experience of author M. Taubitz, Kaizen tools (often associated with lean tools

and thinking) are simple and designed to empower and engage the entire workforce, including:

- 5S
- value-stream mapping
- A3 and one-page reports
- knowledge folders
- standardized work

NOTE: 5S is a simple five-step process to sustain the workplace as clean and organized. A3 reports are a standardized approach used for communication and problem solving.

According to Taubitz, examples of a Kaizen approach include:

- Improvements are based on many small changes rather than on radical changes that might arise from research and development (R&D) and project efforts.
- Since the ideas come from the workers themselves, they are less likely to be radically different, and therefore easier to implement.
- Small improvements are less likely to require major capital investment than major process changes.
- The ideas come from the talents of the existing workforce, as opposed to using R&D, consultants, or equipment, any of which may be very expensive.
- All employees continually seek ways to improve their own performance.
- Workers are encouraged to take ownership for their work and can help reinforce working

in a team, thereby improving overall worker motivation.

Particular attention should be paid to problems associated with process, including:

- too many steps/unnecessarily bureaucratic
- no process, allowing work to be performed that may not be safe or in line with best practice
- process not understood by those who perform the work
- not inclusive of all issues

This latter point is key for safety, health, and environmental professionals. Risk assessment that does not balance safety, environment, and operational performance is likely to suboptimize one leg of the triple bottom line at the expense of the others. Case studies will prove that overall performance is negatively impacted in such instances.

Some see continuous improvement inherently intertwined with management systems. Processes, such as business process management, quality management, and project management, are all part of the strategic toolkit. Deming saw it as part of the system whereby feedback from the process and the customer were evaluated against organizational goals (Deming 1982). W. Edwards Deming's Plan-Do-Check-Act (PDCA) is the foundation for management systems and continuous improvement (Deming 1982):

- *Plan:* Identify and analyze the problem
- *Do:* Pilot/implement the planned change
- *Check:* Analyze results and modify or plan for full implementation
- *Act:* Introduce systemic changes and training

The fact that this can be called a management process does not mean that it needs to be executed by management, merely that it makes decisions about the implementation of the delivery process and the design of the delivery process itself. Plan-Do-Check-Act (PDCA) is the foundation for ANSI/AIHA Z10:2005, *Occupational Health and Safety Management Systems* (ANSI 2005) and is also central to ISO 9000:2008 (ISO 2008), ISO 14000 (ISO 2004), and OSHA's Voluntary Protection Program (VPP) (OSHA 2009) are other examples of management systems that will drive continuous improvement.

A Management System

Though continuous improvement (CI) comes in many forms for different organizations, it is often associated with a management system to drive continuous improvement. CI can provide a foundation for the organizational culture and the goal of zero injuries—identical to the goal of zero defects—and it includes everyone in the desired

FIGURE 7. Management system based on Plan-Do-Check-Act *(Source:* M. Taubitz, adapted from the Lean & Safe Network 2008)

transformation. Achievement of zero defects and zero injuries demands both responsibility and accountability, which is where a management system based on PDCA comes into play (see Figure 7).

A management system is nothing more than a tool for leaders to drive continuous improvement. Goals and objectives are established to accomplish or achieve improvements. Planning and implementation allow for integration into the day-to-day business. Audits, metrics, and evaluation are part of the checking processes that indicate where system adjustments should be made (act) to further reduce injuries (defects). A management system is a series of processes that allows leaders to define responsibility and hold people accountable.

The philosophy of continuous improvement, driven by root-cause analysis of problems, fits perfectly with safety. Use of continuous improvement tools and thinking paves the way for continuously improving safety on and off the job.

Learning to associate integrating safety into continuous improvement will lead the organization to a new way of thinking. Attitudes improve and behaviors change accordingly.

LEGISLATION, STANDARDS, AND MARKET INFLUENCES

International Influences and Regulations

There are several influences that are driving organizations and governments to reduce their greenhouse gas (GHG) emissions and focus on their sustainability strategies. These include international protocols; United Nations Conventions; European Union GHG regulations; carbon trading markets; and instruments used by the investment community that reports on an organization's environmental, social, and governance (ESG) sustainability performance. These instruments include, but are not limited to, the *Carbon Disclosure Market, Dow Jones Sustainability Index* (DJSI), and *MSCI Inc.* These factors have a global reach and impact U.S. organizations. Safety professionals who understand the external financial, voluntary, and regulatory forces that are driving sustainability within their organizations are better able to align safety and health management within the context of the greater dialogue on sustainability. The following provides a brief overview of some of these influences to familiarize the reader with terminology and concepts.

Kyoto Protocol

The Kyoto Protocol is an international agreement that, among other things, sets out binding targets for 37 countries and the European Union to reduce greenhouse gas emissions. Adopted on December 11, 1997, in Kyoto, Japan, it became effective in February 2005, and is linked to the United Nations Framework Convention on Climate Change (UNFCCC). These targets amount to an average of 5 percent reductions from the 1990 emission levels over a 5-year period from 2008-2012 (UNFCCC 2010b).

There is a significant distinction between a *protocol* (e.g., Kyoto) and a *convention* (e.g., UNFCCC or UN labor conventions). In the case of GHG emissions, the UNFCCC convention *encourages* industrialized countries to stabilize their GHG emissions, while the Kyoto Protocol *commits* them to do so.

Under the Kyoto Protocol, countries are expected to meet their targets through GHG emission-reduction strategies; however, the Protocol also offers countries an ability to meet their targets through three market- based mechanisms (UNFCCC 2010b):

- **Emissions trading:** Known as "the carbon market," this allows countries with emission units (permitted to them) they have not used to sell their excess emission units to countries that are over their emission targets (UNFCCC 2010a).
- **Clean development mechanism (CDM):** Allows a country to implement an emission-reduction project in developing countries to earn saleable, certified emission-reduction (CER) credits (equivalent to one ton of CO_2). This can be counted toward meeting their Kyoto targets.
- **Joint implementation (JI):** Allows a country to earn emission-reduction units (ERUs) from a joint emission-reduction or emission-removal project with another country also covered by the Kyoto Protocol. The ERU is equivalent to

one ton of CO_2, which can be counted toward meeting the first country's Kyoto target. The rationale is that the CO_2 emissions overall are being reduced globally, and this mechanism benefits the developing country through foreign investment and technology transfer.

Safety professionals who understand the overall business of carbon trading and what influences their country and organization's decisions in the United States and around the world are better positioned to influence their organization's sustainability strategies for energy and CO_2 reductions. Reducing GHG emissions, whether by implementing processes to reduce energy consumption or reducing CO_2 emissions directly, often impacts safety and health (OSH and product end users) and should to be considered in the design and implementation of these new reduction strategies.

Copenhagen Accord

Representatives from over 190 nations met in Copenhagen to discuss the future of global climate change. The meeting, which produced the *Copenhagen Accord*, was held in conjunction with the United Nations Framework Convention on Climate Change (UNFCCC 2009c). Signing the Copenhagen Accord did not impose any legal requirements or targets on a country, but the country agrees to work to achieve its GHG emissions goals. The signatories of the Accord included countries such as the United States, China, India, Brazil, the European Union (27 countries) and others, accounting for 86 percent of global emissions according to the Climate Action Network's calculations (Broder 2010). The next global climate summit, known as the Conference of Parties (COP) was held in November 2010 in Cancun, Mexico.

European Union Emissions Trading System (EU ETS)

The *EU Greenhouse Gas Emissions Trading System* (EU ETS) is a worldwide system that began in January 2005. The EU ETS is based on the requirements set out in the EU Emissions Trading Directive (Directive 2003/87/EC), which became effective in October 2003 (EU Commission 2010). The system tracks GHG emissions by country and the individual entity owning the emission unit.

The EU ETS is overseen by a central administrator at the EU level, but the accounts in electronic registries are set up by each EU member state. The registry system tracks the ownership of emission allowances in the same way the banking system tracks the ownership of money (EU Commission 2010). This trading system is one of the first carbon markets.

CARBON DISCLOSURE PROJECT (CDP)

The Carbon Disclosure Project (CDP) is a UK-based, global climate-change reporting system. Over 3000 organizations in approximately 60 countries measure their greenhouse gas emissions and disclose their climate-change strategies through the CDP (CDP 2010). This disclosed information is used by institutional investors, corporations, policymakers and their advisors, public-sector organizations, government bodies, academics, and the public. CDP has shaped the harmonization of climate-change data and has significantly influenced the development of international carbon-reporting standards.

According to their Web site, CDP acts on behalf of 534 institutional investors, holding $64 trillion in assets under management, and some 60 purchasing organizations, such as Cadbury, PepsiCo, and Walmart (CDP 2010).

It is important to understand that these socially responsible investors are influencing organizations around the world to develop CO_2 reduction strategies. The designing of processes to implement these strategies can have a direct impact on the work of the safety professional, whose job it is to assure the safety and health of the workforce involved in these processes. Additionally, understanding and anticipating how these various influences are impacting business decisions in an organization, the safety professional is better able to proactively identify new business opportunities, such as new products and services, process improvements, and mitigating OSH and CO_2 implications for product end users, which enhances the marketability of the product.

Dow Jones Sustainability Index (DJSI)

The Dow Jones Sustainability Index (DJSI), derived from the Dow Jones Global Index (DJGI), benchmarks and tracks the financial performance of the leading sustainability-driven companies on a global basis. The DJSI is used by the investment community to identify and select companies for investment purposes based upon their sustainability performance.

The DJSI tracks the financial performance of 57 sectors out of the 2500 in the DJGI, and reports on the top 10 percent in those sectors in the areas of social, economic, and environmental performance (DJSI and SAM 2010); specifically, it defines what a company's business strategy is and how it identifies its risks and opportunities around sustainability.

Sustainability asset management (SAM) is the investment group that manages the DJSI. It provides assessment information on a company's corporate sustainability performance based upon a set of questions. The results of the assessment determine whether the company will be listed on the index. According to the DJSI Web site,

SAM measures a company's strategy, financials, customer relationships, product sustainability, corporate governance, stakeholder engagement, and human resource management (DJSI and SAM 2010).

MSCI Inc.

MSCI USA Broad Environmental, Social, and Governance (ESG) Index provides ESG performance information for the investment community, including asset managers, banks, hedge funds, and pension funds (MSCI Inc. 2010). According to the MSCI Inc., the following criteria are used to rate companies: management of environmental challenges; impacts on communities, employees, contractors, and suppliers (antidiscrimination, labor-management, employee safety, and labor rights) throughout the supply chain; product quality; regulatory compliance; investor relations; board accountability; business ethics; and governance around management, financial, and sustainability reporting practices (MSCI Research 2010).

National Regulations and Initiatives

With sustainability, waste reduction, and energy efficiency becoming more desirable characteristics within communities, national and local initiatives have been developed to address this need and to promote the changes necessary to foster responsible use of natural resources.

The first U.S. government legal initiative toward promoting sustainability was the National Environmental Policy Act (NEPA) of 1970, which laid out the national goal of creating and maintaining sustainable conditions for future generations of Americans (EPA 1970).

The U.S. Environmental Protection Agency (EPA) oversees a number of sustainability regulatory programs, including those involving transportation fuels, fuel economy, and greenhouse gas emissions.

Transportation Fuels

The Energy Policy Act of 2005 (EPA 2010c) and the Energy Independence and Security Act of 2007 (EPA 2010c) authorized the EPA to create standards requiring transportation fuels to contain a minimum amount of renewable fuel content, and to encourage production and use of renewable fuels while reducing dependence on foreign energy sources. The resultant renewable fuels standard (RFS) sets minimum volumes of renewable fuels, such as ethanol, to be incorporated into the nation's transportation fuel supply (EPA 2010c).

Fuel-Economy Standards

The EPA provides annual automotive fuel-economy data for several federal agencies, including the Internal

Revenue Service (IRS), the U.S. Department of Transportation (DOT), and the U.S. Department of Energy (DOE) (EPA 2010a). Among its many uses, the data is displayed on stickers for new vehicles sold in the United States, informing potential consumers about a vehicle's fuel efficiency. Fuel-economy standards for cars and light trucks are continually updated, driving increased efficiency and reduction in fuel use in the U.S. economy.

In January 2007, President Bush signed Executive Order 13423, "Strengthening Federal Environmental, Energy, and Transportation Management" (EPA 2007). The order requires all federal agencies to carry out their missions in a sustainable and energy-efficient manner and to set goals for continuous improvement (EPA 2007).

Greenhouse Gas Emissions Standards

On May 7, 2010, the EPA, in cooperation with the National Highway Traffic Safety Administration (NHTSA), issued the first greenhouse gas emissions standards for manufacturers of light-duty vehicles (EPA 2010g). The standards, which establish limits for carbon emissions in cars and light trucks, start in 2012 and extend through 2016 (EPA 2010g). Similar standards for heavy vehicles are proposed.

Economy, Energy, and Environment (E3) Sustainability Efforts in Manufacturing

Those occupational safety and health (OS&H) professionals looking for ways to capitalize on linking lean manufacturing principles with sustainability initiatives will benefit from the EPA's *Economy, Energy, and Environment (E3) Initiative*. E3 is a coordinated federal and local technical assistance initiative to help manufacturers adapt and thrive in a new business era focused on sustainability. According to the EPA (EPA 2010d), the program provides technical assessments of production processes and training in four key areas:

- lean
- clean
- energy
- greenhouse gas emissions

Depending on the processes of a company, large or small, there are assessments and training target opportunities to:

- maximize energy efficiency
- reduce environmental wastes
- identify opportunities for reducing carbon emissions
- promote sustainable manufacturing practices and growth
- reduce business costs

The EPA offers support to interested companies by providing assistance with:

- a *lean review* that leads to increased productivity and reduced costs
- an *energy audit* that provides tools and insights for reducing energy demand and costs
- a *greenhouse gas evaluation* that teaches manufacturers how to calculate GHG emissions and evaluate reduction strategies
- a clean review that results in water and energy conservation, reduced emissions, and additional cost savings
- *postassessment recommendations* that guide each facility toward improvements in overall efficiency; reduced waste; more efficient use of resources, including energy and water; and cost savings

PILOT PROJECTS

In Columbus, Ohio, six companies participated in an E3 pilot that identified energy savings of $1.7 million and environmental savings of $2.6 million, avoided over 250,000 pounds of water pollutants, and reduced solid waste by 24,000 pounds (EPA 2010d).

E3 is currently completing two pilot projects. In Columbus, Ohio, federal partner agencies are coordinating to conduct technical assessments and provide training by working with six manufacturers, the city government, the Solid Waste Authority of Central Ohio, and American Electric Power. In San Antonio, Texas, the EPA, the Department of Commerce, CPS Energy, and the city government are working with six manufacturers.

The E3 partnership in San Antonio, Texas, resulted in a local manufacturer of detention equipment realizing increased energy efficiency that included $85,000 in energy savings, reduced annual electric consumption of 159,000 kwh, reduced monthly electric demand of 48 kW, and reduced annual natural gas usage of 36,000 CCF.

State and Local Sustainability Initiatives

A number of U.S. states have initiated sustainability programs and requirements without prompting from the federal government. For example, the state of California was granted a waiver of Clean Air Act preemption in 2009 to establish its own light-duty vehicle GHG emission standards. The standards were scheduled to start with model year 2009, but are currently undergoing a regulatory review process (Cal EPA 2007).

The Oregon Sustainability Board works to promote sustainable business practices within Oregon state government. One example is statewide Policy 107-011-140, also known as Sustainable Procurement and Internal

Operations. The policy sets high sustainability standards for purchases and the disposal of electronics and related office waste; it also includes guidance for electronic distribution of meeting minutes, telecommuting, and audio/video conferencing instead of travel (Oregon DAS 2009).

The state of Washington has adopted a number of policies aimed at reducing GHG emissions from transportation, industry, use of buildings, and other sources (ECY 2010). A target of returning to 1990 GHG emission levels by the year 2020 is in place. Facilities emitting over 10,000 metric tons of greenhouse gases must submit an annual emission inventory report to the State Department of Ecology. Certain large employers must have a commute trip-reduction program in place to reduce energy use. A Green Economy Jobs Initiative looks to approximately triple the number of green jobs in Washington by 2020, as compared to a 2004 baseline (ECY 2010).

Sustainable Jersey®, a voluntary New Jersey initiative, was started in 2006 by a group of town mayors. It encourages local municipalities to become certified by implementing a series of sustainable management practices (SJ n.d.). The certification process involves implementing a series of environmental, cultural, and energy-efficiency improvements in accordance with a set of standardized best practices. Certification benefits include cost savings, access to ongoing state and local grant funding for sustainability programs, and a positive public image (SJ n.d.).

Similar to many U.S. states, local municipalities are establishing their own environmental and sustainability programs. For example, within New Jersey, the Princeton Environmental Commission provides counsel and guidance to its host municipalities, Princeton Township, and the Borough of Princeton. Made up of eleven voting community members from various backgrounds and professions, the commission drafts and reviews sustainability-based ordinances for its local governing officials and provides community educational opportunities in accordance with the Princeton Environmental Commission Mission Statement: "To inform local government and residents on environmental issues, laws, and programs" (Wasserman 2010).

Several of the commission's key projects include:

- proposing updates to land-use ordinances to include land preservation provisions
- drafting proposed green building provisions to local construction projects
- encouraging further local recycling efforts

Since its inception in 1977, the commission has provided progressive sustainability guidance to the Princeton community (Wasserman 2010).

U.S. Green Building Council (USGBC)

Prompted by the growing trend toward more efficient and sustainable building design, the U.S. Green Building Council (USGBC) was formed in 1993 as a means to provide measurable criteria for green construction. The organization has grown steadily to its current level of 30,000 members, united across 80 U.S. chapters (USGBC 2010a). The broad spectrum of professional members includes building owners, real estate developers, architects, and engineers (USGBC 2010a).

The USGBC has developed a number of tools to assess and promote green building: educational materials, outreach programs, national and local membership chapters, and the LEED® (Leadership in Energy and Environmental Design) Green Building Certification Program and LEED Green Building Rating System™ (USGBC 2010b). The Council also hosts the Greenbuild International Conference and Expo (Greenbuild 2010).

LEED® GREEN BUILDING CERTIFICATION PROGRAM

In 2000, the LEED® Green Building Certification Program was initiated. Under the program, architects and building owners can apply for and receive LEED® certification for the design and functionality of their green building project. The building project must take into account the entire life cycle of the building, from initial design through construction and end use (USGBC 2010f). The LEED® logo is shown in Figure 8.

Under the program, certification credits are awarded to a building project based on a number of critical areas, including (USBCG 2010f):

- sustainable sites
- water efficiency
- energy and atmosphere
- materials and resources
- indoor environmental quality

Point values for materials and other criteria are contained in a series of tables available from USGBC. From

FIGURE 8. LEED® logo *(Source: USBGC 2010b. "LEED" and related logo is a trademark owned by the U.S. Green Building Council and is used with permission.)*

the maximum of 100 possible points (plus up to 10 bonus points for a combination of innovative design and regional priority, where earned) for certain types of LEED® projects, a building project is rated (USGBC 2010f). Based on the cumulative total points earned, a project will be awarded one of the following LEED® certifications (USBGC 2010e):

- LEED® Certified
- LEED® Silver
- LEED® Gold
- LEED® Platinum

LEED® green building-certification rating systems include: homes, neighborhood development, commercial interiors (including core and shell for applicants responsible for a portion of a building project—their portion can become LEED® Certified), existing buildings, operations and maintenance facilities, schools, and healthcare and retail sales facilities (see Figure 9).

Applying for LEED® Building Certification

Once an individual or project team decides to pursue LEED® certification, a comprehensive registration package is sent to the Green Building Certification Institute (GBCI), the certification body of USGBC (USGBC 2010e). The decision to pursue LEED® certification should be made early in a project, preferably in the design phase, to allow material procurement, site selection and preparation, and waste handling to be managed for the maximum number of LEED® rating points.

Over 35,000 projects are LEED®-registered as of August 2010 (USGBC 2010f). Government agencies, such as the EPA, have set up green building programs for their new acquisitions or for agency remodeling projects based on LEED® registration. The program has resulted in the registration of a number of EPA

buildings, including the EPA's Region I office (Boston, MA), Region IX office (San Francisco, CA), and Region X office (Seattle, WA) (EPA 2010e).

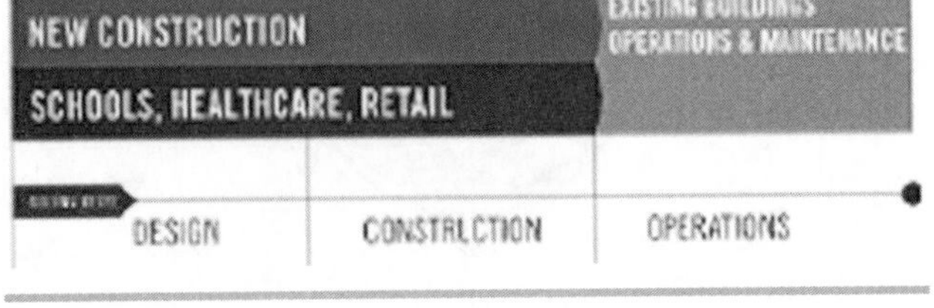

Individual LEED® Certification

Architects, engineers, environmental specialists, and other professionals can obtain certification in the administration of LEED® criteria through the LEED® professional certification program, administered by the GBCI (USGBC 2010f). Certification levels include:

- LEED® Accredited Professional (AP): This is the highest individual LEED® coordinator certification, representing a combination of experience, education, and successful written examination. Successful candidates are awarded the LEED® AP designation for use on individual promotional materials as an indicator of attained professional expertise in green building management. The certification is intended for technical professionals.

  Several specialty LEED® AP certifications are available, including ND (neighborhood development), Homes, O&M (operations and maintenance), ID+C (interior design and construction), and BD+C (building design and construction) (USGBC 2010c).

- LEED® Green Associate: This certification is for nontechnical individuals interested in documenting an attained knowledge of green building concepts, including building design and use (UGBC 2010d).

California Green Building Standards Code®

California is the first U.S. state to adopt sustainability-based building code requirements. The *California Green Building Standards Code®*, known as the CALGreen Code, with its final form appearing first in 2010, became effective in January 2011 (CALGreen Code 2010). The code is made up of the following chapters, each of which contains minimum building requirements for California establishments that meet certain defined criteria (CALGreen Code 2010, vii):

Chapter 1: Administration
Chapter 2: Definitions
Chapter 3: Green Building
Chapter 4: Residential Mandatory Measures
Chapter 5: Nonresidential Mandatory Measures
Chapter 6: Referenced Organizations and Standards
Chapter 7: Installer and Special Inspector Qualifications
Chapter 8: Compliance Forms and Worksheets

Appendices of Residential and Nonresidential Measures are also included

FIGURE 9. LEED® green building-certification rating systems (USGBC 2010f)

The code provides specific construction and renovation requirements for building owners once the applicable occupancy and governing state agency or agencies are determined. It regulates every newly constructed building in California (CALGreen Code 101.3).

Among the code's sustainability requirements are minimum standards for utility use and waste minimization. For example, during residential construction, water use must be reduced by 20 percent through installation of plumbing fixtures or fittings meeting code requirements (CALGreen Code 4.303.1). To minimize waste during residential construction, at least 50 percent of nonhazardous construction or demolition waste must be recycled or salvaged for reuse (CALGreen Code 4.408.1). Similar requirements exist for nonresidential construction.

Linking Safety to Social Responsibility

ISO 26000 outlines key principles for recognizing social responsibility efforts and engaging stakeholders in the process (see the sidebar above on page 21). The OS&H professional can use the structure of ISO 26000 to demonstrate the strategic role OS&H management plays in social responsibility. There are several areas where OS&H issues are directly and indirectly connected to social responsibility principles found in ISO 26000 (Knott 2010). These are discussed in the sections below.

Recognizing Unique Needs of Members of the Organization

Safety management often involves addressing the unique issues related to ergonomics, disabled workers, language barriers, cultural differences, young workers, and an aging workforce. These programs should be highlighted by the safety professional when demonstrating an organization's social responsibility efforts toward recognizing the unique needs of its workforce.

Employee Participation in Safety and Health Efforts

The need for employee participation is highlighted by several safety management systems, including ANSI Z10 (ANSI/AIHA 2005), OHSAS 18000 (20072008), and OSHA. According to OSHA (n.d.), employee participation can take several forms:

- participating on joint labor-management committees and other advisory or specific-purpose committees
- conducting site inspections
- analyzing routine hazards in each step of a job or process, and preparing safe work practices or controls to eliminate or reduce exposure

- developing and revising the site safety and health rules
- training both current and newly hired employees
- providing programs and presentations at safety and health meetings
- conducting accident/incident investigations
- reporting hazards to upper management and/or responsible parties
- fixing hazards within your control
- supporting your fellow workers by providing feedback on risks and assisting them in eliminating hazards
- participating in accident/incident investigations
- performing a pre-use or change analysis for new equipment or processes in order to identify hazards up front before use

EMPLOYEE PARTICIPATION IN HEALTH AND SAFETY MANAGEMENT SYSTEMS

ANSI Z10, *Health and Safety Management Systems* (2005) also specifically itemizes effective employee participation, including a role in activities such as incident investigations, procedure development, health- and safety-related audits, training development, job safety analysis, and all aspects of the planning process. In organizations where social responsibility is already a goal of the organization, the OS&H professional should already be able to identify several activities within the organization that address employee involvement. Areas where employee involvement is lacking or hampered can be more easily implemented by demonstrating that they add value to the organization's social responsibility goals. Examples of obstacles or barriers to employee involvement include: lack of response to employee input or suggestions, reprisals (supervisory and/or peer), or any other forms of discrimination (ANSI/AIHA 2005).

Guidelines for Safety Committee Development

Social responsibility is part of sustainability, involves employees in an organization, and gives them a voice on safety issues. Safety committee development is another way to demonstrate direct employee involvement in the safety program while also satisfying another component of good social responsibility. Safety committees are voluntary in many organizations but may be required by company policy or local regulations. The state of Oregon requires safety committees for most employers. A checklist provided by Oregon OSHA is found in Figure 10 for those OS&H professionals interested in developing, implementing, and/or auditing a safety committee (OR-OSHA 2010).

**Occupational Safety and Health
Safety Committee Evaluation Checklist**

To Do	Done	Item
☐	☐	The safety committee is composed of an equal number of employer and employee representatives.
☐	☐	Employee representatives are volunteers or elected by their peers.
☐	☐	There are at least four representatives on the committee if the workplace has more than 20 employees-at least two representatives if the workplace has 20 or fewer employees.
☐	☐	The representatives elect the committee chairperson.
☐	☐	Representatives are paid their regular wages during safety committee training and meetings.
☐	☐	Employee representatives serve on the committee for at least one year.
☐	☐	Representatives' terms of service are staggered so that at least one experienced representative is always on the committee.
☐	☐	Reasonable efforts are made to ensure that committee representatives represent the company's major work activities.
☐	☐	The committee meets monthly except when representatives schedule quarterly workplace inspections.
☐	☐	Committee meetings follow a written agenda.
☐	☐	The minutes for each meeting are maintained for at least three years.
☐	☐	Minutes are available to all employees.
☐	☐	All reports, evaluations, and recommendations are included in the minutes.
☐	☐	Management has a reasonable time to respond in writing to the committee's recommendations.
☐	☐	The committee has a method for collecting and reviewing employees' safety-related suggestions and reports of hazards.
☐	☐	The committee assists management in evaluating and improving the workplace safety and health program.
☐	☐	The committee's quarterly inspection team follows a standard procedure for identifying safety and health hazards during its inspections.
☐	☐	The inspection team includes employer and employee representatives.
☐	☐	The inspection team documents the location and identity of workplace hazards.
☐	☐	The inspection team-or other persons designated by the committee-inspects satellite locations quarterly.
☐	☐	The committee has a procedure for reviewing the team's quarterly inspection reports.
☐	☐	The committee recommends to management ways to control hazards and unsafe work practices.
☐	☐	The committee makes recommendations to ensure all employees are accountable for following safe work practices.
☐	☐	The committee has a procedure for investigating workplace accidents, illnesses, and deaths.
☐	☐	Representatives understand the purpose of their safety committee and know how it functions.
☐	☐	Representatives have access to applicable occupational safety and health rules.
☐	☐	Representatives have received safety training for identifying workplace hazards and investigating accidents.

FIGURE 10. Oregon OSHA's sample safety and health checklist (OR-OSHA 2010)

Eliminating Workplace Hazards, Including Psychosocial Issues

There is broad recognition that the psychosocial environment at work can affect physical and mental health as well as organizational outcomes, such as work performance and effectiveness (NIOSH 2004). Psychosocial issues can include stress, posttraumatic stress, workplace violence, bullying, substance abuse, absenteeism, racism and racial/ethnic prejudice, sexism and sexual harassment, gender and racial discrimination, work-family integration and balance, and support for diversity in the workplace/workforce. A questionnaire developed to assess psychosocial issues within an organization is available online (Pejtersen 2010). The safety professional may be directly or indirectly involved with one or more psychosocial programs within an organization, yet all safety programs will address workplace hazard identification and abatement methodologies that can be correlated to sound socially responsible actions of the organization.

Two-Way Communication Regarding Safety and Health

Sound OS&H management requires commitment from all levels of an organization but, most importantly, from top management. Management leadership and employee involvement go hand in hand for safety success. In fact, top-management leadership and effective employee participation are crucial for the success of a safety management system (ANSI/AIHA 2005). Management provides the leadership for organizing and controlling activities within an organization. It provides the motivating force, resources, and influence necessary to embed safety as a fundamental value within the organization. In an effective program, management involvement also provides the means through which employees express their own commitment to safety and health for themselves and their fellow workers (OSHA 1989). The ANSI Z10 standard identifies management leadership as the first step toward a successful safety management system (ANSI/AIHA 2005). Since employee involvement is crucial, it is important to establish communication and trust between management and workers.

According to Manuele (2003), an organization's culture consists of its values, beliefs, legends, rituals, mission, goals, and performance measures, and its sense of responsibility to its employees, customers, and its community, all of which are translated into a system of expected behavior. The culture of an organization dictates the effectiveness of a safety management system. Petersen found that the culture of the organization sets the tone for everything in safety. "In a positive safety culture, it says that everything you do about safety is important" (Petersen 1966, 66). Consider this statement

by OSHA: "The best Safety and Health Programs involve every level of the organization, instilling a safety culture that reduces accidents for workers and improves the bottom line for managers. When safety and health are part of the organization and a way of life, everyone wins" (OSHA 2002).

Worker's Rights Regarding the Economics of Safety

In 1986, OSHA issued a program evaluation profile (PEP) for their compliance officers to use when evaluating an employer's safety program (OSHA 1998). Although this compliance directive was rescinded, it serves as guidance in the evaluation of a sound employee training program. The OSHA PEP is available on the OSHA Web site. According to PEP, key indicators include (OSHA 2010):

- Knowledgeable persons conduct safety and health training.
- Training is properly scheduled, assessed, and documented.
- Training covers all necessary topics and situations, and includes all persons working at the site (hourly employees, supervisors, managers, contractors, part-time and temporary employees).
- Employees participate in creating site-specific training methods and materials.
- Employees are trained to recognize inadequate responses to reported program violations.
- A retrievable record-keeping system provides for appropriate retraining, makeup training, and modifications to training as the result of evaluations.

OSHA regulations contain more than 100 standards that include training requirements. OSHA has developed some voluntary training guidelines to assist employers in providing safety and health information, which are available on its Web site (OSHA 1998). These guidelines also provide employers with instructions needed for employees to work at minimal risk to themselves, to fellow employees, and to the public. A summary of the training guidelines (OSHA1998) lists areas designed to help employers:

(1) Determine whether a work-site problem can be solved by training
(2) Determine what training, if any, is needed
(3) Identify goals and objectives for the training
(4) Design learning activities
(5) Conduct training
(6) Determine the effectiveness of the training
(7) Revise the training program, based on feedback from employees, supervisors, and other workers

Social responsibility requires a balance among the three Ps: people, profit, and the planet. Social responsibility should impact the balance between economic decisions and issues related to worker safety and health from the perspective of the workforce. This starts with the OS&H professional linking safety initiatives with profits or demonstrating the business value of safety. ANSI Z10 states that (ANSI/AIHA 2005, 6):

> Organizations and the community may see additional benefits of implementing an OHSMS beyond the reduction of injury and illnesses. Some of these benefits may include: lowered workers' compensation costs, reduced turnover of personnel, reduced lost workdays, compliance with laws and regulations, increased productivity, improved employee health status, improved product quality, higher morale of employees, reduction or elimination of property damage due to incidents, reduced business interruption costs, and reduced impact on the environment due to incidents.

The benefits discussed above are the positive outcomes of an effective safety management system that senior management can see. The job of the OS&H professional is to paint the picture of success and obtain a commitment from management while the vision is fresh. This salesmanship is a means to achieve commitment to safety from management. A little salesmanship can integrate safety into the business model by illustrating incident and accident effects on production and profitability. Integrating the costs of safety into the business and demonstrating a return on investment has been identified and is still a major goal of the OS&H professional (ASSE 2007, ASSE/AIHA 2005). This puts safety into a language to which management, front-line supervisors, and even employees can relate. Unfortunately, many safety initiatives have a negative impact on the bottom line of an organization. In these circumstances, a safety initiative may lose priority within an organization due to its economic impact. Socially responsible organizations will weigh the benefits of an OS&H initiative based on its social and environmental impacts in addition to its effect on the bottom line. The savvy OS&H professional will utilize social responsibility principles involving employee rights in economic decisions as value added to the organization when a profit-based business case for a safety initiative is lacking. The OS&H professional must be able to make a case for safety when there is not a direct positive effect on the bottom line. Various aspects of social responsibility help demonstrate value to an organization interested in sustainability and social responsibility. Active OS&H programs that routinely involve employees in the decision-making process on workplace hazard reduction should be highlighted as examples of meeting this social responsibility initiative.

Health and Safety in an Organization's Value Chain

ISO 26000 (2010) defines a *value chain* as the entire sequence of activities or parties that provide (suppliers, outsourced workers, contractors) or receive (customers, consumers, clients, members, and other users) value in the form of products or services. Organizations have found that sustainability can be reached only through people (Nestle 2009). No other asset in an organization is as important as the people that contribute with their work to the organizational culture and goals. These organizations devote all the necessary energy and attention to protect employees, contractors, and any other people along the value chain, including suppliers, customers, and the public. Organizations can highlight social responsibility by requiring suppliers to meet minimum OS&H program requirements. This can include the procurement of products and services that have a reduced environmental impact, often referred to as a *green supply chain*. Organizations can also mandate OS&H compliance to standards higher than what is mandated by local regulations. Serious organizations will also perform audits of their supply chain's OS&H commitment.

Consumer, Product, and Product Life-Cycle Safety

Organizations often work to address environmental and social issues across a product's life cycle. For instance, Baxter International, Inc., (2010d) incorporates these issues from sustainable design and bioethics during research and development to efficient use of energy and materials during manufacturing and transport, appropriate product advertising and promotion, and, finally, responsible repair, refurbishment, and recycling at product end of life. The OS&H professional should be aware of how his or her organization addresses consumer alerts and product recall information as part of its overall social responsibility goals. This awareness should also extend to products used within one's own organization. Social responsibility should also include a system to make management and employees aware of product defects and recalls on products utilized by the organization.

Personal Protective Equipment

The use of personal protective equipment (PPE) is an important aspect of an organization's social responsibility obligations. However, regulations and best practices require organizations to address workplace hazards using a hierarchy of controls. The use of PPE must be a last resort for protecting workers from workplace hazards. Protective

SIDEBAR

The organization shall implement and maintain a process for achieving feasible risk reduction based upon the following preferred order of controls (ANSI/ASSE 2005):

A. Elimination

B. Substitution of less hazardous materials, processes, operations, or equipment

C. Engineering controls

D. Warnings

E. Administrative control

F. Personal protective equipment (PPE)

Feasible application of this hierarchy of controls shall take into account:

- The nature and extent of risks being controlled
- The degree of risk reduction desired
- The requirements of applicable local, federal, and state statutes, standards, and regulations
- Recognized best practices in industry
- Available technology
- Cost-effectiveness
- Internal organization standards

equipment is acceptable as a hazard control method under the following circumstances (ANSI/ASSE 2005):

- when engineering controls are not feasible or do not totally eliminate the hazard
- while engineering controls are being developed
- when safe work practices do not provide sufficient additional protection
- during emergencies when engineering controls may not be feasible

The ANSI Z10 standard expands upon the traditional hazard-abatement hierarchy of engineering controls, administrative controls, and personal protective equipment. The sidebar outlines the hazard-abatement hierarchy that is provided by the Z10 standard (ANSI/AIHA 2005, 16).

Use of PPE should address workplace hazards. Good social responsibility should include the use of PPE as part of the hierarchy of controls to protect workers.

CASE STUDIES

Following are five case studies, showing how safety and sustainability principles are implemented in the business community.

CASE STUDY 1

Sustainability in Action at BMW Group

The Munich, Germany-based BMW Group encompasses 24 manufacturing facilities in 13 countries. The company traces its roots to the 1917 Bayerische Motoren Werke G.M.B.H., originally producing aircraft engines, and later motorcycles. Several acquisitions and management decisions led to the current focus on individual mobility, primarily through the production and marketing of premier luxury automobiles that include BMW, Rolls Royce, and MINI brands. The group continues to manufacture quality motorcycles and the Husqvarna brand of power equipment.

Sustainability Management

The BMW Group embraces sustainability in all of its operations and publicizes its commitment through the group's Sustainability Strategy Objective: to be the most sustainable company in

the automotive industry. BMW Group's Chairman of the Board of Management, Dr. Norbert Reithofer, succinctly states the group's commitment to sustainability: "...Our aim is to actively shape the future. To achieve this, we are making sustainability an increasingly integral part of our value chain. Sustainability should be a defining principle of how we design our processes and procedures."

To manage its sustainability objective, the group developed three core units (see Figure 11).

The *Sustainability Board* is an internal advisory committee comprised of the Group's entire Board of Management. The Board meets regularly to set future benchmarks and to discuss progress on current sustainability initiatives.

The *Sustainability Circle,* comprised of one representative per division, develops opportunities and enhances crosscommunication throughout the Group. The Circle reports directly to the Sustainability Board.

Each functioning department works with the Sustainability Circle to implement the appropriate waste reduction and conservation initiatives needed to advance the program and to meet the Group's objective.

All BMW Group employees play a key role in implementing the sustainability program. Each has a responsibility to manage resources with the company's sustainability stakeholders and the Group's goals and objectives in mind.

Strategy and Organization

The BMW Group Sustainability Strategy covers all group operations and is a corporate principle of the organization (see Figure 12).

In 2009, the Group set a sustainability target and measures progress through a corporate scorecard. Sustainability in the supply chain is managed through a system of procurement procedures that are managed by specially trained employees. Potential suppliers are carefully screened and audited for environmental and social responsibility. Suppliers and potential suppliers are provided with assistance as necessary to comply with the Group's policy.

The overall sustainability strategy of the BMW Group is demonstrated through reduced environmental impact and increased efficiency in all areas of production, their positive contributions to the surrounding communities, and the uncompromising quality and innovation provided to customers.

Environmental Impact of Its Products

More efficient vehicle emissions and fuel consumption are among the Group's top priorities in its mission to provide value to its stakeholders. The Group is currently conducting the largest field-test of electric vehicles worldwide, with the near-term goal of putting a sustainable, fully electric vehicle into production and distribution. A hydrogen concept car has also been tested in Europe and worldwide; the test scenario in Europe included 100 test vehicles and a series of hydrogen filling stations. Research is ongoing, with focus on liquid hydrogen storage.

With reduction in CO_2 emissions as a long-held corporate objective, BMW has also been successful in engineering vehicles that emit less CO_2.

BMW Group sustainability organisation

Sustainability Board
composed of the entire Board of Management
chaired by: Chairman of the Board of Management
responsible for strategic alignment

Sustainability Circle
composed of one representative per division
chaired by: Group Representative for Sustainability and
Environmental Protection – responsible for drafting proposals

Departments
implement the sustainability targets
by initiating appropriate activities and
processes

FIGURE 11. BMW Group Sustainability Organization (BMW 2008)

Also important are the life cycle of the vehicle itself and production efficiency. Approximately 95% of a new BMW vehicle can be recycled.

Water use in the production process has decreased, as has the volume of waste, and volatile organic compounds per vehicle produced. Additionally,

BMW Group sustainability strategy and key issues

Objective:
To be the most sustainable
company in the automotive industry

Sustainability management

| Environmental radar | Sustainability-based decisions | Evaluation of the value chain | Transparent communication |

Key issues

Ecology	Economy	Society
Product responsibility	Risk management	Responsibility towards employees
Group-wide environmental protection	Corporate governance and compliance	Social commitment

FIGURE 12. BMW Group Sustainability Strategy (BMW 2008)

in 2009 the Group's Spartanburg, SC, plant recycled 85% of plant-generated waste. Details of the Spartanburg plant's waste-handling in 2009 are shown in the table.

All of these innovations are done with the goal of minimizing the Group's use of resources in providing a valuable product to its customers.

2009 Waste (lb)	
Metal	5,030,731
Wood	2,441,280
Cardboard	4,199,280
Plastic	752,787
Glass	107,338
E-waste	34,528
Chemical	1,064,365
Hazardous	226,627
Special	1 7,970
Waste to landfill	2,433,220
Total 2009 Waste	16,308,126
Total recycled	85%
Total disposed	15%

(*Source:* www.bmwusfactory.com - Environmental Responsibility)

Sustainability and Safety

An integral part of the Group's sustainability initiative is the concept of employee health and safety. As with any safety-minded organization, a safe workforce is essential to the Group's success. To further improve performance, the Group has undertaken the goal of establishing occupational health and safety management systems at all locations. At the time of this writing, 50% of locations representing 80% of employees had fully operational systems in place in conformance with internationally accepted guidelines, such as OHSAS.

The remaining sites are scheduled to have systems in place by 2010. The focus on safety has improved the Group's accident frequency to 2.7 accidents per million hours worked, 33 percent less than the industry average of 4.0.

Initiatives for older workers, those with families or elderly relatives, as well as those with financial difficulties, are in place to enhance the overall well-being of BMW Group employees. The investment in these initiatives allows BMW employees to focus their efforts on efficient achievement of the Group's goals through outstanding performance.

Summary

Environmental and social responsibility simply governs the way the BMW Group conducts business. They do not consider sustainable operations as an option, but rather as a guiding principle that is integral to BMW's future success. In partnership with employees, customers, neighbors, and government, the Group is positioned to lead the automotive industry in sustainability and to succeed in its objective: to be the most sustainable company in the automotive industry.

CASE STUDY 2

Integration Failure: When Safety, Lean and Green Are Not Integrated (Bruce Main, September 2010)

Situation

A machine tool was cutting a metal part when the operator working adjacent to the machine heard a whooshing sound, flames shot out the finished parts' exit ports, the guard doors burst open, and he felt a sudden burning sensation on his arm and face. A flash of fire had erupted from ports of the machine. The operator suffered significant burns, resulting in severe pain, lost work time, and residual scarring.

Background

An investigation into the incident revealed a causal chain of factors. The flash fire was caused by a spark from the tooling. During the course of operation, heat and, occasionally, sparks are generated.

The machining oil used to cool and lubricate the cutting operation was relatively benign in liquid form but flammable in a mist above a minimum concentration. During operation, an excessive concentration of airborne cutting fluid, which was in mist form, ignited. The mist concentration exceeded the machine tool supplier's recommendations at the time of the incident because the ventilation system did not provide adequate air flow. The air flow was inadequate because the machine user had installed a third machine on a two-machine system and tapped into the existing ventilation system without making adjustments for increasing the air flow. As a result, the ventilation system, designed for two machines, was inadequate to accommodate the requirements of a three-machine system.

Further investigation revealed that the machine was originally manufactured and sold in the 1980s. The machine supplier offered a fire suppression and mist control system with the machine proposal in the 1980s, but the customer "thrifted out" the fire suppression system at the purchase. The customer also opted to install the machine itself rather than pay for installation by the machine supplier. Historically, such systems and services are often resisted by some customers seeking to minimize the machine purchase price.

The machine was manufactured in Europe, shipped to the United States, and installed at the machine-user facility. The machine was rebuilt in the United States by the machine supplier in the early 2000s with updated control and ventilation systems. Prior to the incident, the customer installed the mist collection system.

Following the refurbishment, the machine supplier performed the startup and qualifying run of the machine at the customer's facility. The qualifying run evaluated the ability of the machine to perform the necessary cutting operations within specifications and general operations of the machine.

More recent evolutions of this type of machine include fire suppression systems, ventilation systems, and interlock door switches on the doors. Following the incident, three new systems were installed on the machines: a retrofit ventilation system, a fire suppression system, and a mist collection system.

Hazards

A task-based, risk assessment of the system identified 145 task-hazard pairs. These hazards include both safety and environmental potential sources of harm, including the following hazards:

- cutting/severing from sharp edges of parts during normal operation
- slip and fall from cutting fluid dripping on the floor
- noise hazards
- environmental/industrial hygiene hazards of oil getting on parts and hands and airborne emissions from the enclosure
- a chemical allergen or irritant from the cutting fluid or, while reaching into the machine, cutting fluid dripping on neck or arms
- ergonomic hazards of posture when reaching into the machine with the doors
- hot surface temperatures from machined parts or motor surface temperatures
- pinch points between tooling in the machine or drive system
- fire from sparks from tool collision if the tooling is misinstalled or incorrectly moved or if the machine

is not reset to accommodate new tooling
- crushing hazards during tool change or parts replacement
- fall hazards during parts replacements or filter changes while accessing the top of the machine
- pressurized lines if not locked out and energy released
- electrical hazards from energized equipment if not locked out during servicing
- fire hazard from heightened oil mist concentration; if fluid gets too low, the impeller can create an ignitable mist
- ergonomic hazards of lifting assemblies out of the machine
- environmental or fire hazards from hazardous waste of grease oils in rags
- environmental hazards of cleaning compounds and chemicals
- unexpected startup or motion if not locked out during servicing
- material movement hazards related to fork-truck delivery and removal of product
- hazards related to installation, hook up, and start up of machinery
- fire hazard of ignitable mist if the concentration exceeds the recommended maximum or the air flow is insufficient, or if the air intake is improperly located

Analysis

This case study highlights safety, environmental, fire, and operational hazards. The connection of a third machine to a ventilation system designed for two machines resulted in an unidentified hazard of inadequate ventilation and mist control. The ensuing fire and injury caused the company significant loss of production because the machines were

unserviceable and required extensive repairs. The machines had to be sent to the U.S.-based service operations for repairs and updates.

Operational wastes that resulted from this incident include added:

- delay/waiting
- motion movement
- process

Additionally, several weeks' delay and significant costs were incurred by both maintenance operations and management personnel in dealing with the incident.

In addition, this case study highlights the challenges the machine supplier can encounter when a legacy machine it built many years ago is involved in injury incident, particularly if the residual risks associated with the older machine differ from those of the current product offerings.

Conclusion

The drive for the triple bottom line of sustainable growth requires that risk assessment concurrently address production, safety, and environmental risks. In this case, failure to address the environmental issue resulted in a significant safety issue, fire damage to equipment, and the consequence of lost production. All of the lean (operational) wastes (correction, motion/movement, and waiting), safety wastes (injury) and environmental waste (air contaminant) could be attributed to the seventh form of lean waste, process. Lack of a process that employed a fully integrated risk assessment overlooked a condition that caused pain, injury, and significant production and attendant costs.

CASE STUDY 3

Safety and Sustainability

A manufacturing company utilizes large vertical and horizontal boring mills to bore complex hole patterns into steel work pieces. Boring mills operate using "ways," which are essentially tracks that allow the body of the mill to move in three dimensions

as needed based on the desired hole pattern. The ways are protected from metal chips by way covers, which adjust to the position of the body of the mill. The way covers require oil as a lubricant to ensure they slide correctly when the machine is moving. This oil drips off the ways over time, and this

oil drip is inherent to the design of the machine.

At this company, the large boring mills are located in pits. In the original process, the excess oil would drip into the pit. Boring mill operators would then soak up the oil using oil absorbent, which was kitty litter.

The absorbent would build up over time until it was several inches deep in the bottom of the pit. Several times per year, the operators would scoop the absorbent out of the pit into collection drums using shovels. Once the absorbent was drained of all free liquids, the absorbent was placed into the general trash which would be sent to a landfill. The drained liquid would be reclaimed.

This process created a number of problems for both safety and sustainability:

- The amount of absorbent used greatly increased the amount of waste generated.
- Nearly all of the waste was being sent to the landfill, which did not support the company's sustainability goals.
- Operators who had to enter the pit to lubricate the machine would be subject to slip and fall hazards because of the unstable absorbent surface, as well as the oil, which would get into the soles of their shoes when inside the pit.
- The soaked kitty litter buildup resulted in an odor near the machine.

Additionally, the process of cleaning the pit was not lean and resulted in significant downtime, the absorbent buildup lowered employee morale, and its appearance did not impress visiting customers.

Therefore, machine maintenance personnel partnered with the safety/environmental department and machine operators to resolve these issues. A temporary fix was put in place as follows. First, the pit was completely emptied and cleaned. Then, absorbent socks were placed along the length of the way covers to contain the oil close to the machine. During this time, the oil in the socks could be squeezed out into drums and reclaimed. This eliminated the landfill waste. It also kept the pit much cleaner and ensured a stable walking surface when operators entered the pit. Additionally, it resulted in much less downtime for cleaning, and was visibly cleaner. However, the downside is that the socks needed to be replaced from time to time, and if they were not emptied soon enough the oil could leak into other areas of the pit.

Ultimately, a long-term solution was developed by the group. A small containment berm was built near the machine in a location that would not pose a trip hazard. When the oil builds up in the containment area, it can easily be pumped out for reclamation. The oil cannot leak into other areas of the pit. The only waste generated is the oil, which is reclaimed. This process significantly improved safety and sustainability for the machine. Productivity improved, while cleaning times decreased. The area looks visibly cleaner, and the employees working in the area are very appreciative. An added benefit is that the pit can now be swept with a broom to pick up metal chips generated by the boring process, and the chips can be recycled, which further improves sustainability. In the original process, the chips would mix with the kitty litter and be sent to the landfill.

The lesson learned is that safety and sustainability can often produce synergistic effects when both are considered together. Also, lean principles can also be applied when implementing safety and sustainability initiatives to improve other business priorities, such as productivity, while simultaneously improving safety and sustainability.

CASE STUDY 4

Safety and Sustainability

The challenge: Reduce safety and ergonomic risks along with cost and environmental impact of using disposable plastic wrapping material to protect parts shipped from a local supplier.

The previous method of wrapping and shipping the covers required annually:

- thousands of square feet of bubble wrap
- over a mile of tape to secure the wrap
- estimated labor and material costs exceeding $10,000

Cuts and complaints of sore wrists and hands were part of the process, along with significant amounts of material waste. Using lean tools and thinking, a team considered modifying the carts used to transport the parts. However, closer analysis suggested that every other part covered with a plastic sleeve would provide necessary protection while using half the material. The bubble wrap was eliminated.

Once removed, the plastic sleeves are returned to the supplier for reuse. Injuries from cuts and repetitive trauma problems were eliminated, and the environmental waste from scrap material was also eliminated. Operational costs were significantly reduced due to reusing the plastic sleeves, and faster performance of the task was achieved.

This real-life case study was driven by a desire to reduce injuries, which led to actions where people, the planet, and profit all won. These tactical steps in today's world are part of the journey to sustainable growth.

CASE STUDY 5

Safety and Sustainability

An automotive company had a significant amount of waste that was being sent to a landfill. The plant assembled a team to investigate methods to reduce the amount of waste being sent to the landfill and increase the amount of waste being recycled. This team included representation from the safety department.

One waste type the team identified for potential recycling was the wooden pallets and "pallet boxes" (pallets with corrugated cardboard containers stapled on the top). Previously, the pallets and pallet boxes had been crushed in a compactor and sent to a landfill. Not only was this very expensive, but it negatively impacted the environment and did not support the company's sustainability goals.

The plant began a process where the pallets were gathered and sent to a third party for reuse/recycling. The cardboard was removed from the pallet boxes by hand to allow the attached pallets to be sent to the third party. The safety department reviewed and approved the pallet box process based on the fact that packaging specifications required the cardboard on the pallet boxes to incorporate a "breakaway" feature to make it fairly easy to remove the cardboard by hand. Overall, the pallet recycling program saved the plant over $25,000 in the first year and significantly increased the overall percentage of recycled waste.

However, the process of removing the cardboard from the pallet boxes by hand was starting to cause ergonomic injuries to employees performing this task because of the amount of upper-extremity force necessary to pull the cardboard from the pallets. Additionally, it was a timeconsuming process and negatively impacted productivity. Although packaging specifications required specific "breakaway" features for the cardboard, some pallet boxes did not have this feature, and others were still too difficult to remove by hand, even with the breakaway feature. Various methods to alleviate the ergonomic risk factors were tested, such as using a powered hand saw and removing the cardboard using the forks of a forklift. However, these options presented other hazards.

Finally, a solution was developed that would alleviate or eliminate the ergonomic risk while still allowing the pallet box pallets to be recycled. First, the suppliers for all nonconforming pallet boxes were contacted to ensure the breakaway features were incorporated. Where possible, employees were allowed to manually pull off the cardboard from breakaway pallet boxes as long as the cardboard came off easily. For nonconforming boxes, and larger boxes where the cardboard was not easy to pull off, a different removal method was developed. A steel "shear plate" was installed directly above the compactor (and with the compactor manufacturer's approval). A forklift would pull the top of a pallet box across the shear plate to easily and quickly shear the cardboard from the pallet. The cardboard would then fall into the compactor and would be recycled. The pallet would be sent to the third party for recycling.

This new process resulted in a 100% reduction of injuries for this process and significantly improved productivity, while still allowing both components of the pallet boxes to be recycled. The lesson learned is that all potential safety hazards must be fully investigated prior to making a change to improve sustainability (or any other business priority).

REFERENCES

Aaron, William. 2008. "What Gets Measured Sometimes Gets Managed." *Entrepreneur* (retrieved October 23, 2010). www.entrepreneur.com/tradejournals/article/ 185487705.html

American National Standards Institute (ANSI) and American Industrial Hygiene Association (AIHA). 2005. Standard Z10-2005, *Occupational Health and Safety Management Systems*. Fairfax, VA: AIHA.

Baxter International, Inc. 2010a. "Baxter 2009 Sustainability Priorities Report" (retrieved September 22, 2010). www.baxter.com/documents/sustainability_report_2009.pdf

_____. 2010b. *Baxter's Sustainability Efforts Support Education, Sustainable Product Design; Earn Dow Jones Sustainability Index Recognition (retrieved September 22, 2010). www.baxter.com/press_room/press_ releases/2010/09_16_10_ sustainability.html

_____. 2010c. *Baxter will promote a safety and health workplace: 2015 Goal* (retrieved September 22, 2010). www.sustainability.baxter.com/sustainability_at_ baxter/priorities_goals/safe_workplace.html

_____. 2010d. *Baxter 2009 Sustainability Report: Health and Safety Approach* (retrieved September 22, 2010). www.sustainability.baxter.com/EHS/health_and_ safety_approach/index.html

Bayerische Motoren Werke, Aktiengesellschaft (BMW). 2008. "BMW Sustainable Value Report 2008." 80788, Munich, Germany: BMW.

BNET. *Business Definition for Corporate Social Responsibility* (retrieved October 23, 2010). dictionary.bnet. definition/Corporate+Social+Responsibility.html

Broder, John M. 2010. *Remember the Copenhagen Accord?* (retrieved October 8, 2010). www.green.blogs.nytimes.com/2010/06/08/remember-the-copenhagen- accord/

California Building Standards Commission. 2010. California Code of Federal Regulations, Title 24, Part 11. 2010. *2010 California Green Building Standards Code* (CALGreen Code). Sacramento, CA: California Building Standards Commission.

California EPA Air Resources Board (Cal OSH ARB). 2007. "Climate Change Emissions Standards for Vehicles." Fact Sheet (retrieved November 22, 2010). www.arb.ca.gov/cc/factsheet.ccfaq.pdf

Carbon Disclosure Project (CDP). 2010. *Overview* (retrieved October 8, 2010). www.cdproject.net/ en-US/WhatWeDo/Pages/overview.aspx

CR Magazine. 2010. "100 Best Corporate Citizens" (retrieved October 5, 2010). www.thecro.com/ content/100-best-corporate-citizens

Deming, W. Edwards. 1982. *Out of the Crisis*. Cambridge, MA: The MIT Press.

Dow Jones Sustainability Indexes (DJSI) and SAM. 2010. *Corporate Sustainability* (retrieved October 5, 2010). www.sustainability-index.com/07_htmle/ sustainability/corpsustainability.html

Dreo, Johann. 2006/2007. *Corporate Social Responsibility* (retrieved October 23, 2010). www.en.wikipedia.org/wiki/File:Sustainable_development.svg

Environmental Protection Agency (EPA). 1970. *National Environmental Policy Act of 1970 (NEPA)* (retrieved November 19, 2010) www.epa.gov/compliance/nepa

_____.2007. *Strengthening Federal Environmental, Energy and Transportation Management* (retrieved November 18, 2010). www.epa.gov/oaintrtn/practices/ eo13424.htm

_____.2010a. *Fuel Economy: Data & Testing/Fuel Economy* (retrieved October 4, 2010). www.epa.gov/fuel economy/data.htm

_____.2010b. *Fuel Economy: EPA's Fuel Economy Programs* (retrieved October 1, 2010). www.epa.gov/fuel economy/420f09067.htm

_____.2010c. *Fuel and Fuel Additives/Renewable Fuel Standard (RFS)* (retrieved October 1, 2010). www.epa.gov/otaq/fuels/renewablefuels/

_____.2010d. *Green Suppliers Network: E3: Economy, Energy and Environment* (retrieved October 29, 2010). www.epa.gov/greensuppliers/e3.html

_____.2010e. *Greening EPA: Green Buildings* (retrieved November 4, 2010). www.epa.gov/oaintrnt/ projects/

_____.2010f. *Sustainability: Basic Information: What Is Sustainability?* (retrieved September 30, 2010). www.epa.gov/sustainability/basicinfo.htm

_____.2010g. *Transportation and Climate: Regulations & Standards* (retrieved November 11, 2010). www.epa.gov/otaq/climate/regulations.htm

European Commission (EU), Directorate for Environment. 2010. *Emission Trading System (EU ETS)* (retrieved November 7, 2011). ec.europa.eu/environment/ clima/emission/index_en.htm

Federal Energy Management Program. 2007. Executive Order 13423, "Strengthening Federal Environmental, Energy and Transportation Management" (retrieved November 15, 2010). www.edocket.access.gpo.gov/ 2007/pdf/07-374.pdf

Global Reporting Initiative (GRI). 2007. *About GRI* (retrieved October 23, 2010). www.globalreporting. org/AboutGRI/

Greenbuild International Conference and Expo. 2010. (retrieved November 22, 2010). www.greenbuild expo.org/expo/internationalexpo.asp

International Organization for Standardization (ISO). 2010. ISO/FDIS 26000:2010(E), *Guidance on Social Responsibility*. Geneva, Switzerland: ISO.

Knott, M. Personal Correspondence "Summary extracted from Lines 1671 through 1705 of ISO/FDIS 26000:2010(E)" by Michael G. Knott, CSP, member of the Industry Group for U.S. TAG TO ISO/TC SR 26000. Email dated September 5, 2010.

Manuele, F. A. 2003. *On the Practice of Safety*. 3d ed. Hoboken, NJ: John Wiley & Sons.

MSCI Research. 2010. *MSCI USA Broad ESG Index* (retrieved October 8, 2010). www.mscibarra.com/ products/indices/thematic_and_strategy/esg_indices/ MSCI_USA_Broad_ESG_Index_Methodology_Jul10.pdf

National Institute for Occupational Health and Safety (NIOSH). 2004. NIOSH Publication #2004-135, *How to Evaluate Safety and Health Changes in the Workplace*. Cincinnati, OH: NIOSH.

Nestle, USA. 2009. *Creating Shared Value in the United States* (accessed November 15, 2011). www.nestleusa.com/ Creating_Shared_Value/ ~/Media/Files/PDFs/NUS ACS/Brochure.asx

Noer, Michael, David M. Ewalt, and Tara Weiss. 2008. "Corporate Social Responsibility: Can Companies Save the World? Should They Try?" *Forbes Magazine* (retrieved October 23, 2010). www.forbes.com/2008/ 10/16/ corporate-social-responsibility-corprespons08- lead-cx_ mn_de_tw_1016csr_land.html

Occupational Safety and Health Administration (OSHA). 1989. *Safety and Health Program Management Guidelines; Issuance of Voluntary Guidelines.* Federal Register Notice 54:3904-3916.

_____.1998 (revised). OSHA 2254, *Training Requirements in OSHA Standards and Training Guidelines. Washington, D.C.: OSHA.*

_____.2002 (revised). OSHA 3071, *Job Hazard Analysis.* Washington, D.C.: OSHA.

_____.2009. *OSHA Fact Sheet: Voluntary Protection Programs* (retrieved November 15, 2010). www.osha. gov/ OshDoc/data_General_Facts/factsheet-vpp.pdf

_____.n.d. *Safety and Health Management System E-tool* (retrieved November 15, 2010). www.osha.gov/SLTC/ etools/safetyhealth/index.html

Oregon Department of Administrative Services (DAS). 2009. *Sustainable Procurement and Internal Operations* (retrieved September 30, 2010). www.oregon.gov/ DAS/OP/docs/ policy/107-011-140.pdf?ga=t

Oregon OSHA (OR-OSHA). 2010. "Occupational Safety and Health Safety Committee Evaluation Checklist." www.cbs.state.or.us/external/osha/pdf/pubs/forms/ eval_checklist.doc)

Pejtersen, J. H. et al. 2010. "The Second Version of the Copenhagen Psychosocial Questionnaire." *Scand J Public Health* 2010 38: 8 (retrieved October 10, 2010). www.sjp. sagepub.com/content/38/3_suppl/8

Petersen, Dan. 2003. *Techniques of Safety Management: A Systems Approach.* Des Plaines, IL: American Society of Safety Engineers.

Sustainable Jersey. n.d. *Certification Benefits* (retrieved October 1, 2010). www.sustainablejersey.com/ about.php

_____.n.d.. *History and Mission* (retrieved October 1, 2010). www.sustainablejersey.com/about.php

United Nations Framework Convention on Climate Change (UNFCCC). 2010a. *Emissions Trading* (retrieved October

8, 2010). www.unfccc.int/kyoto_ protocol/mechanisms/ emissions_trading/items/ 2731.php

_____.2010b. *Kyoto Protocol* (retrieved October 8, 2010). www.unfccc.int/kyoto_protocol/items/2830.php

_____.2010c. *Copenhagen Accord* (retrieved November 23, 2010). www.unfccc.int/home.items/5262.php

United Nations World Commission on Environment and Development (UN WCED) (also known as the Brundtland Commission). 1987. *Our Common Future: Report of the World Commission on Environment and Development* (retrieved November 18, 2010). www.un-documents.net/ wced_ocf.htm

U.S. Green Building Council. 2010a. *About USGBC* (retrieved October 5, 2010). www.usgbc.org/Display Page.aspx?CMSPageID=124

_____.2010b. *What LEED Is: LEED Rating System* (retrieved October 5, 2010). www.usgbc.org/Display Page.aspx?CMSPageID=222

_____.2010c. *LEED AP BD+C* (retrieved October 3, 2010). www.usgbc.org/DisplayPage.aspx?CMSPage ID=2192

_____.2010d. *LEED Green Associate* (retrieved November 22, 2010). www.usgbc.org/DisplayPage.asp? CMSPageID=2191

_____.2010e. "The LEED Green Building Program at a Glance" (fact sheet) (retrieved October 3, 2010). www. usgbc.org/DisplayPage.aspx?CMSPageID=97

_____.2010f. *LEED Project Certifications (retrieved November 22, 2010). www.usgbc.org/DisplayPage. asp?CMSPage=2191

_____.2010g. *LEED Rating Systems* (retrieved November 22, 2010). www.usgbc.org/DisplayPage/aspx?CMS PageID=222

Taubitz, Michael A. 2010. *Lean, Green & Safe: Integrating Safety into the Leans, Green and Sustainability Movement* (Appendix) (retrieved November 22, 2010). www.asse.org/ professionalsafety/docs/Lean- Taubitz_0510.pdf

Washington Department of Ecology (ECY). 2010. *Sustainability Laws and Executive Orders* (retrieved September 30, 2010). www.ecy.wa.gov/sustainability/ exeorders.html

White House. 1981. "Annual Report of the Council on Environmental Quality (CEQ)" (accessed December 21, 2011). www.slideshare.net/whitehouse/august- 1981-the-12th-annual-report-of-the-council-on- environmental-quality

Additional Resources

Manuele, F. A. 2005. "Risk Assessment & Hierarchies of Control" *Professional Safety* 50(5):33-39.

Muller, S, and Braun, C. 1998. *Safety Culture: A Reflection on Risk Awareness.* Zurich: Swiss Reinsurance Company.

Occupational Safety and Health Administration (OSHA). 2009. *Accident Prevention* (retrieved November 15, 2010). www.osha.gov/SLTC/accidentinvestigation/ index.html

Telephone interview with Matthew Wasserman, Chair, Princeton Environmental Commission, October 4, 2010.

Value Based Management. 2010. *The Deming Cycle* (retrieved October 23, 2010). www.valuebased management.net/ methods_demingcycle.html

Womack, J. P., and D. T. Jones. 2003. *Lean Thinking: Banish Waste and Create Wealth in Your Corporations.* 2d ed. Northampton, MA: Free Press.

ADDITIONAL READING

DEVELOP AND SUSTAIN AN EFFECTIVE FLEET SAFETY PROGRAM – Z15 CAN HELP*

Brian S. Hammer, MPA, CDS
Risk Management Consultant, Fleet
Nationwide Agribusiness Insurance
Des Moines, IA

William J. Hinderks, CSP, CPCU, ARM, ALCM
Senior Loss Control Specialist
Artex Risk Solutions (a subsidiary of Arthur J. Gallagher & Company)
Bloomington, IL

Stephanie G. Pratt, PhD, MA
Coordinator, NIOSH Center for Motor Vehicle Safety
National Institute for Occupational Safety and Health
Morgantown, WV

Peggy Ross, RN, MS, CSP, COHN-S/CM, CPE
Corporate Manager, Environment, Health and Safety
Baxter Healthcare Corporation
Deerfield, IL

Introduction

Millions of U.S. workers are at risk for a work-related motor vehicle crash (MVC). Fatality data show that across all industries, MVCs are consistently the leading cause of work-related fatalities. Of 43,025 work-related fatalities reported by the Bureau of Labor Statistics between 2003 and 2010, 10,202 were the result of single- or multiple-vehicle crashes of workers driving or riding in a vehicle on a public roadway, and 2,707 were pedestrian workers struck by a motor vehicle.[1,2] An analysis of the costs of MVCs to U.S. employers using data from 1998-2000 found that on average, each fatality cost a business over $500,000 in direct and liability costs, and each non-fatal injury cost nearly $74,000 (National Highway Traffic Safety Administration 2003). More recently, for MVC-related injuries requiring more than 6 days away from work, workers' compensation costs were estimated to be nearly $2 billion (Liberty Mutual Research Institute for Safety 2).

The risk of work-related MVCs cuts across all industries and occupations. Between 2003 and 2008, workers employed by truck transportation companies had the highest risk of work-related fatality due to an MVC while driving or riding in a motor vehicle on a public roadway (19.6 deaths per 100,000 workers), followed by logging (11.7), wholesale distribution of petroleum products (8.6), waste management services (8.5), and support activities for mining (7.9) (CDC 500). Heavy and tractor-trailer truck drivers account for the highest proportion of fatalities in any single occupation: 39% of the total for 2003-2010.[3]

The history and scope of the ANSI Z15.1 standard

The ANSI Z15 Committee was organized in 2001 to create a consensus standard with requirements for policies, procedures, and management processes for organizations to control risks associated with motor vehicles (ANSI/ASSE 2012 9). The American Society of Safety Engineers (ASSE) has served as the secretariat for the standard throughout its history. The first chairman of the ANSI Committee was Carmen Daecher, who served from 2001 until 2009, when he stepped down and William Hinderks was elected chairman.

The ANSI/ASSE Z15.1 standard, first published in 2006, sets forth practices for the safe operation of

---

[1] Source: Bureau of Labor Statistics online query system at http://data.bls.gov/cgi-bin/dsrv?fi

[2] From 2003-2010, there were an additional 2,487 worker deaths in crashes that occurred off a publicroadway or on industrial premises.

[3] Source: Bureau of Labor Statistics online query system at http://data.bls.gov/cgi-bin/dsrv?fi

organizational vehicles, defined as licensed vehicles designed to be driven primarily on public roads. The standard extends to use of this category of vehicles off public roadways. It provides organizations a template for development of policies, procedures, and processes to better manage the risks associated with vehicle use. ANSI/ASSE Z15.1 is applicable to organizations whose vehicles and drivers are covered by the Federal Motor Carrier Safety Regulations (FMCSRs) ("regulated" fleets), as well as to organizations whose vehicles and drivers do not operate under the FMCSRs ("non-regulated" fleets).

For organizations just beginning to formalize their vehicle operations safety program, the standard provides comprehensive guidance on what a program shall include, but leaves it up to the organization to design the specific detail based on their unique circumstances. For organizations with mature programs, fleet managers can use the standard to audit their existing program or provide a risk-based approach to fleet management.

It is important to point out that the field of vehicle risk management has evolved in recent years. ANSI/ASSE Z15.1-2012 was a moderate revision that includes more guidance in a number of areas (e.g., distracted driving) than its predecessor. Furthermore, the standard provides additional suggestions for measuring performance over time.

Basic Outline of ANSI/ASSE Z15.1-2012

The main body of the ANSI/ASSE Z15.1 standard is divided into seven major sections:

1. Scope, Purpose, Applications, Exceptions and Interpretations
2. Definitions
3. Management, Leadership and Administration
4. Operational Environment
5. Driver
6. Vehicle
7. Incident Reporting and Analysis

Each section of the standard is divided into two columns. The text in the left column contains requirements: what an organization "shall" do in order to be in compliance with the standard. The right column provides non-mandatory guidance and interpretation of the corresponding material in the left column. After the main body of the standard, the Appendices provide valuable supporting information and tools to help organizations apply the standard.

ANSI/ASSE Z15.1-2012 and Non-regulated Fleets: One Company's Experience

The ANSI/ASSE Z15.1 standard was intended to be applicable to both regulated and non-regulated fleets.

The following section discusses one company's experience in implementing the standard in its non-regulated fleet. Baxter Healthcare has approximately 1,000 U.S. employees who drive regularly on business and are considered non-regulated fleet drivers. Most of these employees are part of the sales force. Baxter applies the Occupational Health and Safety Assessment Series (OHSAS) 18001 to assess and manage hazards that pose risk to employees. The Environment, Health and Safety (EHS) management system approach drives continuous performance improvement for Baxter.

In December 2008, the Baxter Corporate EHS audit team engaged an external fleet-safety expert and facilitated the first EHS-focused audit for its U.S. non-regulated fleet. The goal was to understand how Baxter managed its non-regulated fleet and more importantly, *fleet risk*. Managing fleet risk is important because it goes beyond the vehicle and incorporates effective management of drivers and driving behaviors. The audit revealed strong management of fleet operations, vehicle selection, and acquisition, with opportunities to improve upon a risk-based approach to manage fleet risk. Fleet safety audit components included interviews and an assessment of various areas including:

- The current process for managing fleet
- Identification of key stakeholders
- Types and number of vehicles
- Selection and acquisition of vehicles
- Vehicle use (e.g. carrying items, miles per year, type of driving…)
- Inspections, repair and maintenance
- Incident reporting and investigation
- Driver qualification
- Policies and procedures
- Performance evaluation (success metrics)
- Training and communication

Beginning early in 2009, a strong partnership was formed between Corporate EHS and the U.S. Fleet Manager. A strategy was developed and tactical plans defined an action timeline to close gaps identified during the fleet audit and to strengthen management of non-regulated fleet *risk*. Baxter's Fleet Manager led the effort and EHS leveraged a transitional leadership/ partnership style to provide guidance, expertise and support. The U.S. Fleet Manager engaged key stakeholders to support development and deployment of a tailored, Baxter approach.

Baxter referenced the voluntary consensus standard, ANSI/ASSE Z15.1-2006, *Safe Practices for Motor Vehicle Operations*, to support the development of a best-in-class approach to managing fleet risk. Because policies and procedures are the foundation of a non-regulated fleet program, Baxter strengthened the overall driver policy. Further, Baxter developed and deployed a non-regulated fleet safety program and specific guidelines to cover aspects such as authorized driver requirements, safe vehicle use, and expected maintenance. Z15.1 provided the framework for Baxter's policy and guide, tailored to fit Baxter. Measurement systems were also enhanced, leveraging concepts from the standard. In 2009, Baxter was selected to participate on the ANSI/ASSE Z15 committee supporting the review and revision of the ANSI/ASSE Z15.1-2006 standard, *Safe Practices for Motor Vehicle Operations*, and supported revisions for the recently released ANSI/ASSE Z15.1-2012 revised standard.

ANSI/ASSE Z15.1-2012 and Commercial Fleets

When the ANSI/ASSE Z15.1 standard was first issued, it was hailed as a great document to help non-commercial fleets organize a safety effort to reduce costly motor vehicle crashes and reduce risk in motor vehicle operations. The following section of this paper will demonstrate the value of the standard for managing commercial fleets as well. In contrast to non-commercial fleets, commercial motor vehicle fleets are heavily regulated by Federal Motor Carrier Safety Administration (FMCSA) if they are interstate carriers and to a lesser degree by similar state agencies if they are intrastate carriers. It was theorized that commercial motor fleets were heavily regulated, and while parts of Z15 would certainly cover their operations, the FMCSA and its FMCSRs would ensure that commercial fleet operators had the required safety structure in place. Regulatory efforts notwithstanding, injuries and fatalities involving commercial motor vehicles continue to occur, and liability remains. Despite general declines in the number and rate of fatal crashes involving large trucks and buses in past decades, 573 occupants of these vehicles and 3,371 other road users died in large truck and bus crashes in 2010 (Federal Motor Carrier Safety Administration 2012 4). From 2009 to 2010, this represented a 9% increase in the number of large trucks and buses involved in fatal crashes, and a 9% increase in the rate of fatalities per 100 million miles driven (Federal Motor Carrier Safety Administration 2012 3).

Limitations of the FMCSRs

The FMCSRs contain detailed requirements for specific concerns such as hours of service (49 CFR Part 395), but have little to say about the basic policies and procedures that are the foundation of a workplace safety program. Overall, the FMCSRs are limited in scope and nonspecific. For example, the FMCSRs have very few requirements for written policies and procedures or documented annual training. The only required written procedures/policies in the FMCSRs are related to drug and alcohol testing (49 CFR Part 382) and a written security plan for hazardous materials (49 CFR Part 172.800). The FMCSRs have no requirements for a written crash/incident review policy, discipline procedure, driver hiring/orientation, and training in vehicle operation and inspection. There are some training requirements for drivers of longer combination vehicles, entry-level drivers, and HAZMAT drivers, including retraining for HAZMAT drivers every 3 years (49 CFR Parts 380 and 397). However, there are no requirements for annual defensive driving training, hours-of-service training, truck inspection training, or annual drug and alcohol training (although some initial training is required).

In the past, the FMCSA rarely had any interactions with commercial fleets, with the exception of Compliance Reviews (CRs). A CR was a full-blown audit that resulted in a rating of Satisfactory, Conditional, or Unsatisfactory. Fines could result, and an "Unsatisfactory" rating could cause the motor carrier to be shut down. The FMCSA also conducted Safety Reviews, normally after a significant event such as a fatality or too many serious crashes in a short period of time. Generally, however, few carriers interacted with the FMCSA; the number of drivers and carriers was far greater than the number of CRs performed each year (Federal Motor Carrier Safety Administration 2013).

ANSI/ASSE Z15 approach

ANSI/ASSE Z15.1 follows the same approach as Occupational Safety and Health Administration (OSHA) 29 CFR Parts 1910 and 1926 in that it is far more specific and broader in scope in its requirements for written policies/procedures and training than are the FMCSA regulations. It provides an all-inclusive framework for developing, implementing, and monitoring an organizational motor vehicle safety program. OSHA took a proactive and cooperative approach to work with employers to promote worker safety. OSHA also built more flexibility into their approach. They may visit a workplace to address a single issue. Although that issue may lead to a full audit, it is often the sole basis of OSHA's action. OSHA also has the authority and flexibility to forgo or reduce fines based on the individual company's response and actions to abate hazards identified. OSHA audits (those in which the company was fined as well as those in which the company agreed to certain actions to improve safety) seem to be very effective. They work!

The CSA model

The FMCSA introduced the Compliance, Safety, Accountability (CSA) program in late 2010 as a way to make significant reductions in large truck crashes and make this segment of highway transportation safer (Exhibit 1). The program was to be introduced in several phases, with the last part, the Safety Fitness Determination, possibly coming by the end of 2013.

The first phase of the CSA model is Measurement (Exhibit 2). Under CSA, the FMCSA has made a number of changes in the way it reports violations by each motor carrier. Violations are now grouped into seven categories of similar violations, referred to as "BASICs," and assigned weights as to the probability of causing a crash. Since development of the original model (Exhibit 1), the FMCSA has made changes to the original BASICs: "Fatigue" is now "Hours of Service;" the "Cargo" BASIC is now a dedicated "Hazardous Materials" BASIC; and load securement violations are now in the "Maintenance" BASIC.

The final phase of the CSA model, Safety Fitness Determination, is vitally important to a carrier, as this

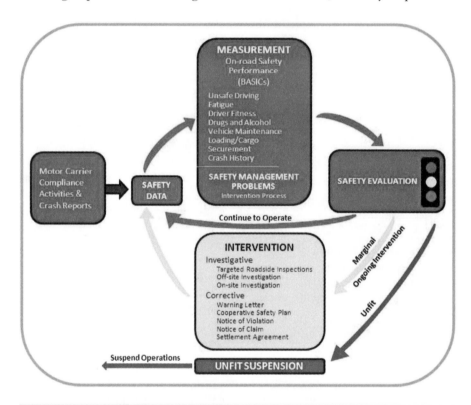

Exhibit 1. This shows the original CSA operational model put out by FMCSA in 2010. Source: http://csa.fmcsa.dot.gov/about/csa_how.aspx.

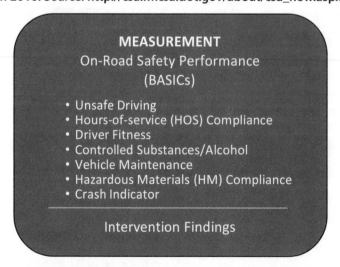

Exhibit 2. For reporting safety performance under CSA, FMCSA now groups violations into seven categories called BASICs.

INTERVENTION

Early Contact
- Warning Letter
- Carrier Access to Safety Data and Measurement
- Targeted Roadside Inspection

Investigation
- Offsite
- Onsite – Focused
- Onsite – Comprehensive

Follow-on
- Cooperative Safety Plan
- Notice of Violation
- Notice of Claim

Exhibit 3. CSA interventions to improve safety performance are progressive in nature.

determination can mean whether they are able to continue to do business or must operate under a "marginal" designation. However, it is the middle phase, Intervention, which makes the ANSI/ASSE Z15.1 standard directly relevant to commercial fleets (Exhibit 3). The FMCSA envisioned a broader array of intervention tools that would be applied directly or in a progressive fashion to "motivate" fleets to be more proactive in their safety efforts.

FMCSA Safety Interventions under CSA

Under the new CSA model, the FMCSA looked for ways to increase interactions with carriers that were having "problems" as indicated by the new safety measurement system (SMS), but using methods that were less intensive than traditional CRs. One "early contact" intervention that has drawn a lot of attention from commercial fleet owners is warning letters, which are generated based on SMS scores. Nationwide's regular customer service outreach includes "DOT Compliance Class," which cover the FMCSRs for motor carriers. Although invitations were sent to a large number of carriers, only a small percentage of carriers attended, unless they had recently received a warning letter.

A second FMCSA intervention targets a company at the roadside, looking for specific violations as indicated by the SMS. This may include off-site and on-site reviews. For instance, if the SMS scores indicate that the company is having hours-of-service problems, FMCSA safety investigators may come to a carrier's main office, reviewing and scanning hours-of-service logs and taking action based on what they find. FMCSA investigators will likely look only at the hours-of-service records, focusing the visit on those violations and not examining other safety items such as maintenance records or driver qualification files. The advantage of this technique is that it allows the FMCSA to have contact with more carriers and to focus only on the areas in which the SMS indicated these carriers have issues. The rationale is that more contacts or higher chance of having a contact will result in carriers paying more attention to their SMS scores and that fearing fines, they will make improvements.

The Cooperative Safety Plan (CSP) is a new "Follow-on" intervention under CSA which to some extent addresses one of the shortcomings of FMCSA's approach: the lack of a model that allows it to work more cooperatively with carriers to reduce violations and improve performance. After intervening at a company, FMCSA may agree to withhold a Notice of Violations (NOV) if the company can devise ways to reduce the violations. While the term is Cooperative Safety Plan, essentially the company is charged with developing effective solutions to the areas in which they have problems. The FMCSA will either agree or disagree as to whether the actions are a good faith effort and will then monitor the company for progress. This is where the gap in the FMCSRs with regard to written policies and procedures is evident, and this is where ANSI/ASSE Z15.1-2012 comes into play.

It is difficult to envision how FMCSA can be assured that the carrier will follow the CSP in the absence of the policies and procedures needed for implementation and the documented training to show commitment and improvement. The answer is simple. Participating in a CSP to ward off a Notice of Violation (NOV) requires a written plan submitted to FMCSA, and such a plan will clearly need to be supported by a policies and procedures manual. Using Z15 as a guide will make this easy.

The Safety Management Cycle

The FMCSA has put forth the Safety Management Cycle (SMC) as a guide to help motor carriers develop the required CSP documents. The SMC starts with the concept that policies and procedures are needed to move forward. The SMC has six elements that are referred to as safety management processes (SMPs) (Exhibit 4). The FMCSA has prepared a document for each of the seven BASICs, which will help companies develop policies and procedures for that BASIC in accordance with the SMC (http://csa.fmcsa.dot.gov/about/smc_overview.aspx).

Safety Management Processes

The six SMPs are the backbone of the SMC. As demonstrated below, the ANSI/ASSE Z15.1-2012 standard matches up well with the SMC and the safety management processes (SMPs) that were recently introduced by the FMCSA:

1. **Policies and Procedures** define the "what" and "how" of a motor carrier's operations. Policies establish the guidelines for how motor carriers and their employees behave in a given situation. Procedures explain how to accomplish policies. The other five SMPs focus on how to implement the policies and procedures. It is important to understand that the FMCSA is basing agreements on improvements on a sound foundational policies and procedures manual, one that covers the areas it sees as having a great impact on safety. Many companies don't have a well-thought-out written policies and procedures manual. ANSI/ASSE Z15.1-2012 provides that foundation.

2. **Roles and Responsibilities** clearly define what each employee should do to successfully implement the policies and procedures. A good policy manual discusses roles and responsibilities at each level of the employee/employer relationship. ANSI/ASSE Z15.1-2012, Section 3.2.1.3, requires that a system of accountability and responsibility be established. It advises implementation of this system through several of an organization's units, including operations, human resources, and safety.

3. **Qualification and Hiring** discusses recruiting and screening applicants to fulfill the roles and responsibilities for positions. ANSI/ASSE Z15.1-2012, Section 3.2.1.3, covers driver recruitment, selection and assessment, and Section 5.1 covers the development of driver qualifications, job descriptions, applications, and background checks. Companies should have a defined policy that lists minimum qualifications or disqualifying events – these should be concrete requirements that don't fluctuate with the job market – and

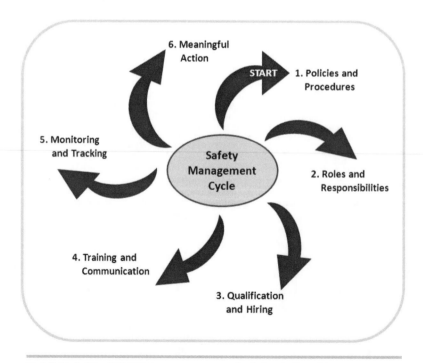

Exhibit 4. The FMCSA has recommended the Safety Management Cycle (SMC) as a guide to implementing CSA and preparing CSPs.
Source: http://csa.fmcsa.dot.gov/about/smc_overview.aspx

systems in place to conduct adequate background checks as required by statute. They should also consider other processes that are not required, such as pre-employment screening, bonding, and criminal checks.

4. **Training and Communication** outlines a motor carrier's communication of its policies, procedures, roles, and responsibilities so that everyone understands the expectations and has the adequate skills and knowledge to perform their assigned function. ANSI/ASSE Z15.1-2012, Section 3.2.1.5 covers orientation and training, and Section 5.3 covers driver training. Ideas from both these sections need to be incorporated into a procedure that tracks how orientation and training goals are achieved. Section 3.2.1.7 highlights the need for communication.

5. **Monitoring and Tracking** concentrates on the need to have a system in place to monitor and track employee performance, enabling a company to be aware of employees' safety performance and compliance with its policies and procedures and how they execute their roles and responsibilities. "Monitoring" represents the motor carrier looking at the performance of the operation, and "Tracking" is assessing the data collected, leading to meaningful action. ANSI/ASSE Z15.1-2012, Section 3.2.1.11 requires a system of management audits to ensure that requirements within a policy/procedure are in fact carried out.

6. **Meaningful Action** gives motor carriers the tools to correct or improve employee behavior, including training and positive reinforcement such as rewards or bonuses, in order to improve the motor carrier's overall safety performance. Sections 7.2.3, 7.2.4, and 7.2.5 all talk about corrective action and incident review, which are meant to spur meaningful action.

Merging ANSI/ASSE Z15.1-2012 with the material provided by the FMCSA results in a very thorough policies and procedures manual. Appendix 2 recommends additional elements to be included in the manual.

A Systems Approach to Z15.1 Implementation

The safe-system approach to road safety

The last two decades have brought a gradual shift in thinking about how road safety improvements can best be achieved. This shift is marked by a new view of the road as a system, and a shift in responsibility for road safety away from the individual road user to designers of the road infrastructure and designers of vehicles (Organization for Economic Cooperation and Development 107-112). The ANSI/ASSE Z15.1 standard is consistent with the safe-system approach in several ways:

- It assumes that the organization is responsible for developing programs, policies, and procedures for managing road risk associated with any motor vehicle operated on behalf of the organization.
- It addresses management of risks related to the driver, vehicle, and operating environment.
- It advocates continuous measurement and review to document successes and identify areas for improvement.

This section provides background information on several safe-system initiatives and explains how ANSI/ASSE Z15.1 is congruent with them.

Vision Zero and the safe system

The safe-system approach to road safety management originated with the "Vision Zero" model developed in the Swedish Road Administration in the mid-1990s. Although road users are still expected to follow the rules of the road, Vision Zero makes designers responsible for continuous modifications to the road system as situations in which human error leads to crash-related injuries are identified (Johansson 827). The goal for traditional road safety approaches was to prevent crashes, while the Vision Zero goal is to eliminate death and serious injury. Vision Zero accepts the idea that road users will inevitably make errors, but its aim is to engineer the road environment and the vehicle to be so forgiving of human error that deaths and serious injuries will be eliminated.

Although Vision Zero was formulated as a framework for managing the entire transport system, it also applies to management of road safety within companies and organizations. In the same way that it sees the road environment as a system that should be forgiving of human error, Vision Zero also calls for a management system at the organizational level that is responsible for modifying the conditions of work to reduce, if not eliminate, the potential for road traffic injury. A primary contribution of Vision Zero to occupational road safety is its support for shifting responsibility away from the individual driver toward the company or organization that employs the driver.

Road safety initiatives similar to Vision Zero have been adopted in other countries, most prominently in the Netherlands through its "Sustainable Safety" strategy and in Australia through its "Safe System" model (Organization for Economic Cooperation and Development 108). In 2009, the United States began to move in a similar direction with the launch of "Toward Zero Deaths," for the first time pursuing a strategy that conceptualized any injury or death on the road as unacceptable (http://safety.fhwa.dot.gov/tzd/).

The ISO 39001 standard

Another outgrowth of the safe-system approach to road safety is a new global standard for road safety management, ISO 39001:2012, *Road Traffic Safety (RTS) Management Systems – Requirements with Guidance for Use*. Because the Swedish Standards Institute serves as the secretariat for ISO 39001, this consensus standard was strongly influenced by Vision Zero. ISO 39001 was designed for use by any public or private organization that wishes to improve its road safety performance, develop and implement a road safety management system, and check its progress toward road safety targets. It is relevant for organizations that transport goods or people, or whose employees or contractors interact with the road system in any way in the course of doing business. Like the ANSI/ASSE Z15.1 standard, ISO 39001's requirements are placed within a framework of roads, vehicles, and users. The main body of ISO 39001 is supplemented by non-mandatory appendices that provide guidance for implementation (International Organization for Standardization).

ANSI/ASSE Z15.1 as a systems approach

All the initiatives described here have common features that are especially relevant to the management of vehicles by companies and organizations – features that they share with the ANSI/ASSE Z15.1 standard:

- They value comprehensive management and communications structures that incorporate all the stakeholders for road safety, including private-and public-sector organizations that are key users of the road system.

- They see road safety as a responsibility shared among all these stakeholders.

- They value continuous data collection and feedback, including cost and economic analysis, as critical to ensuring that investments in road safety are effective and provide a favorable return on investment (Organization for Economic Cooperation and Development 108).

Using ANSI/ASSE Z15.1 to develop and implement a motor vehicle safety program

ANSI/ASSE Z15.1 assumes that management commitment and leadership are the foundation of any organization's road safety management program. It uses a central framework of drivers, vehicles, and operating environment to organize policy areas that should be managed by organizations, and it mandates a process of continuous review and improvement based on in-depth review and response to individual incidents combined with analysis of aggregated data (ANSI/ASSE 2006, 2012). Organizations can use the basic structure of ANSI Z15.1 at several points during development and implementation of a road safety management program: to identify gaps in an existing program, to ensure that policies and procedures are adequately addressing the gaps identified, and to develop key performance indicators (KPIs) that will be used to set program goals and track progress.

Identifying program gaps and implementing interventions

The Haddon Matrix is a tool that can be used in conjunction with the ANSI/ASSE Z15.1 standard to help identify program gaps. It was developed by American epidemiologist William Haddon, Jr., who was a prominent advocate for crash prevention and injury control and the first Administrator of the National Highway Traffic Safety Administration. Haddon conceptualized injury prevention as a problem of reducing or eliminating the exchange of harmful mechanical energy (Haddon, Jr. 1968 1433). The simplest version of the Matrix is a 3 × 3 table (Table 1). The rows denote "phases:" points in time a hazard is present or an intervention can be put in place. The columns denote "factors:" sources of risk or points of intervention to control the risk (Haddon, Jr. 1972 96-97).

The use of the Haddon Matrix is not limited to road safety for the general population. The Matrix can be expanded to fit the needs of any organization that operates motor vehicles, and this expansion can aid in implementing the ANSI/ASSE Z15.1 standard. Haddon himself showed how the "Human" cell could be separated into road user types such as drivers, pedestrians, and motorcyclists, allowing a more refined assessment of risks and interventions (Haddon, Jr. 1968 1436).

For organizational users, research and policy documents have recommended the addition of columns to

TABLE 1

The basic Haddon Matrix combines temporal 'phases' with 'factors' where crash risks and injury prevention opportunities are present

	Human	Vehicle/ Equipment	Environment
Pre-crash			
Crash			
Post-crash			

cover factors related to management and journeys (see, for example, European Transport Safety Council 4-5).[4] Addition of information on management reinforces the ANSI/ASSE Z15.1 standard, where discussion of the importance of leadership, management commitment, and a strong administrative structure precedes any discussion of policies for the driver, vehicle, and operating environment. Published case studies of successful fleet safety programs underscore the importance of having a steering committee charged with implementation and oversight. Not only does this promote broad buy-in across organizational units, but it guards against the danger of entrusting the program to a single key individual whose departure could threaten the program's future (Murray et al. 6-7).

For identifying program gaps, the Haddon Matrix helps an organization to ask the questions: "Which of these risks are we addressing?" and "Where are policies and procedures needed?" For identifying and implementing interventions, the Matrix helps an organization to ask: "What interventions can we put in place to reduce or eliminate these risks?" Table 2 below shows how the Haddon Matrix might be adapted to an initial assessment of program gaps or a check for compliance with ANSI/ASSE Z15.1 elements.

A number of prominent policy documents have cited the Haddon Matrix as a valuable tool for identifying problems and prioritizing interventions. Chief among these is the influential *World Report on Road Traffic Injury Prevention* (Peden et al. 12-13). In addition, the plan of action developed for the UN Decade of Action for Road Safety 2010-2020 is based on five "pillars:" road safety management, safer vehicles, safer roads and mobility, safer road users, and post-crash response (World Health Organization and UN Road Safety Collaboration 11). The pillars for the Decade of Action closely mirror both the Haddon Matrix and sections 3 through 6 of the ANSI/ASSE Z15.1 standard. Finally, and most important, fleet and safety managers, fleet service providers, and researchers have reported successfully using the Haddon Matrix for assessment of program gaps, as discussed above and shown in Table 2 (Darby et al. 437, Murray et al. 4, Wallington et al. 4-5).

Using ANSI/ASSE Z15.1 to develop metrics and track progress

The main portion of the ANSI/ASSE Z15.1 standard requires organizations to follow a process of reporting, reviewing, analyzing, and corrective actions in response to individual motor vehicle incidents and collisions. It also requires organizations to take a broader view by collecting data needed to track road safety performance over time. Early in its deliberations, the ANSI Z15 Committee determined that the standard should not mandate that all organizations use the same outcome measures or the same reporting intervals. Instead, ANSI/ASSE Z15.1 provides appendices with more specific but non-mandatory guidance in these areas, allowing organizations the discretion to select what is most appropriate. The current version of the standard, ANSI/ASSE Z15.1-2012, offers the following:

- Appendix F recommends specific points to be included in instructions for the driver's on-scene response in the event of a collision.

- Appendix G recommends factors to be considered during reviews of incidents and collisions. The list of factors is organized according to those related to the driver, the vehicle, and the environment.

- Appendix H provides several basic measures that may be used to track motor vehicle incidents. (ANSI/ASSE 2012 33-38).

Rate calculation examples from ANSI/ASSE Z15.1

For the rates suggested by ANSI/ASSE Z15.1-2012, the numerator is generally either the number of incidents or the number of incidents resulting in injury. The denominator for a rate is the exposure unit of interest. Key denominator data for tracking fleet safety performance are the number of vehicles and number of vehicle miles traveled (VMT). Depending on its operating environment, an organization may also choose to report rates based on units of service such as the number of deliveries or loads. Selected rates included in Appendix H of the standard are discussed below (ANSI/ASSE 2012 37-38).

An incident rate based on the number of vehicles is essentially the proportion of the vehicle fleet involved in an incident over some pre-determined period of time. It can help an organization assess the proportion of the fleet that may be out of service at any given time, and can also inform decisions about vehicle replacement.

- Incident rate based on number of vehicles operated:

$$\frac{\text{Number of incidents} \times 100}{\text{Number of vehicles}}$$

VMT-based rates are important measures because they are based on exposure to road traffic hazards. They may also be adapted to compare the rate of incidents for

---

[4] The Haddon Matrix has also been suggested as a way to identify gaps and interventions related to an organization's engagement with external partners and its "corporate social responsibility" agenda for road safety (European Transport Safety Council 4-5). This is largely outside the scope of the ANSI/ASSE Z15.1 standard

TABLE 2

The Haddon Matrix is easily expanded and adapted to check for compliance with provisions of the ANSI/ASSE Z15.1 standard. Relevant portions of the standard are referenced in parentheses

Original elements of Haddon Matrix			Additional elements for occupational road safety	
Human	Vehicle	Environment	Management	Journey
Pre-crash				
Formal criteria for: • Driver qualification and selection (3.2.1.3, 5.1.1, 5.1.2) • Motor vehicle record checks (5.1.3) • Driver orientation and training (3.2.1.5, 5.3) Driver management program (5.2)	Formal criteria for: • Vehicle selection and specification (3.2.1.8, 6.1) • Vehicle modifications (6.2) • Regular servicing and maintenance (3.2.1.9, 6.6) • Pre-trip vehicle checks (6.5) • Vehicle replacement (6.7) Policy for business and personal use of organizational vehicles (4.7.1, 4.7.2, Appendix A, B Policy for business use of personal vehicles (4.7.3, Appendix C)	Formal policy on: • Use of occupant restraints (4.1) • Impaired driving (4.2) • Distracted driving (4.3, Appendix E) • Aggressive driving (4.4) System to monitor regulatory compliance (3.2.1.10, 3.2.1.11)	Interest, involvement and commitment to road safety from senior management (3.1) Allocation of adequate staffing and resources to manage and support the program (3.1) Written safety program defining organizational requirements (3.2) Accountability and responsibility throughout the organization (3.2.1.2) Auditing process (3.2.1.11) Procedures to document driver qualification and training (5.4) Procedures to report, record, and investigate incidents, and to track safety performance over time (7.3; Appendix F, G, H) Reporting of major incidents and overall road safety performance to all levels of management (3.2.1.6)	Risk assessment covering: • Need to travel for specific purposes • Modal choice • Journey planning and route selection • Inclement weather • Journey scheduling • Shifts/working time • Means of communicating information about weather emergencies, road construction (4.5, 4.6) Travel policy to cover decision processes for: • Fatigue management • Changes in travel plans due to inclement weather or emergency (4.5, 4.6)
Crash				
Instructions for drivers in the event of a crash (7.1.1, Appendix F, A)	Emergency equipment/ kit for use in the event of a crash (6.3)	Policies for managing crash scene (Appendix F)	Policies for interactions with law enforcement and third parties at the scene (Appendix A)	
Post-crash				
Driver reporting of incident/crash to organization (7.1.2, Appendix A, F) Corrective action directed at driver, if appropriate, to improve skills and behaviors (7.2.4, 7.2.5)	Review of vehicle-related factors and circumstances (7.2, Appendix G) Corrective action related to vehicle policies, if appropriate (7.2.5)	Review of factors and circumstances related to operating environment (7.2, Appendix G) Corrective action related to policies for the operating environment, if appropriate (7.2.5)	Process to report and record incidents (7.1, 7.1.1) Process to review incidents and identify causal and contributing factors (7.2, 7.2.1, Appendix F, G) Incident review report (7.2.3) Corrective action communicated throughout organization, if appropriate (7.2.5)	Review of factors and circumstances related to journey management (7.2, Appendix G) Corrective action related to journey management policies, if appropriate (7.2.5)

different types or models of vehicles in the fleet, or under different operating conditions.

- Incident rate based on vehicle mileage:

$$\frac{\text{Number of incidents} \times 1,000,000}{\text{Vehicle miles traveled}}$$

The calculation of the rate of injury incidence is another good example of the flexibility the ANSI/ ASSE Z15.1 standard affords an organization. Here, the numerator may be adjusted in a number of ways. At the outset, it is important that an organization-wide definition of an injury be established. ANSI/ASSE Z15.1-2012 defines an injury as "Physical harm or damage to a person resulting in the marring of appearance, personal discomfort and/or bodily harm, impairment or death" (ANSI/ ASSE 2012 11). By design, this definition does not dictate specific criteria for an injury; an organization may choose its own threshold. Commonly used thresholds for classifying a case as an injury are the requirement for any kind of medical treatment, restricted work activity, or 4 or more hours of lost work time.

Once a clear definition of an injury is established, if the goal is to supplement data on lost productivity or workers' compensation costs, the numerator might appropriately be the number of injury incidents for workers in the organization only. If the goal is to assess the number of incidents with potential liability for the organization, the number might be the number of incidents involving injury to a third party. If the goal is to assess overall exposure for the organization, the two numbers might be combined.

- Injury incident rate:

$$\frac{\text{Number of incidents with injury} \times 1{,}000{,}000}{\text{Vehicle miles traveled}}$$

Developing and using key performance indicators

Basic rates shown in Appendix H of ANSI/ASSE Z15.1 are useful for summarizing road safety performance within an organization and tracking progress over time. The standard can also help organizations set targets and track progress toward specific program goals and objectives. Again, elements of the standard, organized within the Haddon Matrix, help an organization to select the most appropriate key performance indicators (KPIs) for its needs, and to check to ensure that data are being collected to make it possible to calculate these KPIs.

When considering data collection requirements related to management of a motor vehicle safety program, it is important not to lose sight of which data elements are essential and which are merely "nice to know." Data collection requirements should be linked to specific reporting requirements: those that are needed to calculate basic rates described above, and those that contribute to calculation of KPIs.[5] Data elements are generally a combination of "process" and "outcome" measures. Outcomes are important because they are the end points a program wants to achieve, for example, a certain level in reduction in crashes per million miles. The recommended rates provided in Appendix H of the ANSI/ASSE Z15.1 standard are outcome measures.

Processes are also important, however, because they represent milestones along the way to achieving those outcomes, and they can pinpoint places in the management system where adjustments are needed to continue progress toward the desired outcome (Poister 106-111). A process indicator relevant to the ANSI/ASSE Z15.1

TABLE 3

A KPI should be supported by other data that will help identify opportunities to accelerate progress toward the organization's target for that KPI

Sample KPI: % of 'preventable' incidents in which organization's driver was distracted

Relevant data elements:

- Total number of incidents (based on organization's pre-determined criteria for defining an incident)
- Number of distracted-driving incidents (based on incident review procedures, and including external sources of information such as police reports and cell-phone records, if applicable)
- Number of 'preventable' incidents (based on incident review procedures)

'Process' measures to support this KPI:

- Does organization have a cell-phone policy or a more general distracted-driving policy?
- What percentage of the organization's drivers has signed an acknowledgment of this policy?
- How well do supervisors reinforce importance of the policy?
- Are other organizational practices and policies consistent with workers abiding by this policy? For example, do scheduling practices allow time for organizational business to be completed without incentivizing use of electronic devices or eating meals while driving?
- Are there results from employee surveys on safety climate or safety attitudes that suggest how communications strategies can be adjusted to increase compliance?

---

standard might be the percentage of workers completing behind-the-wheel training within 6 months of hire.

The Haddon Matrix example provided in Table 2 can be a starting point for developing process and outcome KPIs for specific program areas. Table 3 shows how an organization might think through what is needed to support a KPI related to distracted-driving crashes. Some of the more process-related measures are quantitative, while others will be based on more qualitative assessments and knowledge of the organization. Here, it is important to note the distinction between a KPI and a target value for that KPI. The KPI is the measure, but the organization should also determine the value it wants to achieve for that KPI.

Summary and Conclusion

The ANSI/ASSE Z15.1 standard, *Safe Practices for Motor Vehicle Operations*, provides minimum requirements for workplace motor vehicle safety programs. Although the standard was initially conceived as filling a gap by providing guidance for non-DOT-regulated fleets, Z15 is, in fact, applicable to any size fleet and any type of organization that operates motor vehicles. It complements the FMCSRs and FMCSA's new CSA initiative by providing a critical framework for development of a safety management system and policies and procedures — a framework not found in the FMCSRs.

---

[5] There are of course many other reporting requirements related to financial, human resources, and regulatory compliance. These are outside the scope of this discussion.

Because it specifies policies and procedures related to the driver, vehicle, and operating environment, all of these in the context of a safety management system, Z15 is also consistent with other well-established injury prevention models, including those that follow a "systems" approach. Combined with the Haddon Matrix, Z15 can be a starting point for a comprehensive risk assessment for any type of vehicle fleet, leading to development of appropriate interventions.

For more information about ANSI/ASSE Z15.1-2012

For more information, or to purchase a copy, please consult the following resources:

- ASSE Tech Brief on the revised standard, ANSI/ASSE Z15.1-2012: http://www.asse.org/publications/standards/z15/docs/Z15_1_Tech_Brief_4_2012.pdf
- Trifold brochure on the revised standard: https://www.asse.org/ShopOnline/products/docs/ANSI%20Brochure%20Z15%20Std_%20Fi nal.pdf
- Ordering page: https://www.asse.org/shoponline/products/Z15_1_2012.php

The findings and conclusions in this report are those of the authors and do not necessarily represent the views of the National Institute for Occupational Safety and Health.

BIBLIOGRAPHY

ANSI/ASSE. *Safe Practices for Motor Vehicle Operations* (ANSI/ASSE Z15.1-2006). New York, NY: American National Standards Institute, 2006.

ANSI/ASSE. *Safe Practices for Motor Vehicle Operations* (ANSI/ASSE Z15.1-2012). New York: American National Standards Institute, 2012.

CDC. "Occupational Highway Transportation Deaths – United States, 2003-2008." *Morbidity and Mortality Weekly Report.* 2011; 60(16): 497-502.

Darby, P., Murray, W., Raeside, R. "Applying Online Fleet Driver Assessment to Help Identify, Target and Reduce Occupational Road Safety Risks." *Safety Science* 2009; 47(3): 436-442.

European Transport Safety Council. *Fit for Road Safety: From Risk Assessment to Training* (PRAISE Thematic Report 2) (retrieved February 13, 2013 from http://www.etsc.eu/documents/PRAISE%20Report%202.pdf).

Federal Motor Carrier Safety Administration. *Large Truck and Bus Crash Facts 2010* (FMCSA-RRA-12-023). Washington, DC: Federal Motor Carrier Safety Administration, 2012.

Federal Motor Carrier Safety Administration. *Motor Carrier Safety Progress Report, Federal Motor Carrier Safety Administration (as of September 30, 2012)* (retrieved February 21, 2013 from http://www.fmcsa.dot.gov/facts-research/art-safety-progress-report.htm).

Haddon, Jr., W. "The Changing Approach to the Epidemiology, Prevention, and Amelioration of Trauma: The Transition to Approaches Etiologically Rather than Descriptively Based." *American Journal of Public Health* 1968; 58: 1431-1438.

Haddon, Jr., W. "A Logical Framework for Categorizing Highway Safety Phenomena and Activity." *Journal of Trauma.* 1972; 12(3): 193-207.

International Organization for Standardization. *Road Traffic Safety (RTS) Management Systems -Requirements with Guidance for Use* (ISO 39001:2012). Geneva, Switzerland: International Organization for Standardization, 2012.

Johansson, R. "Vision Zero -Implementing a Policy for Traffic Safety." *Safety Science.* 2009; 47(6): 825-831.

Liberty Mutual Research Institute for Safety. *2012 Liberty Mutual Workplace Safety Index* (retrieved February 9, 2013 from http://www.libertymutualgroup.com/omapps/ContentServer?pagename=LMGroup/Views/LMG&ft=2&fid=1138356633468).

Murray, W., Ison, S., Gallemore, P., Nijjar, H. "Effective Occupational Road Safety Programs: A Case Study of Wolseley." *Transportation Research Record: Journal of the Transportation Research Board* 2009; 2096:55-64.

National Highway Traffic Safety Administration. *The Economic Burden of Traffic Crashes on Employers: Costs by State and Industry and by Alcohol and Restraint Use* (retrieved February 8, 2013 from http://www.nhtsa.gov/people/injury/airbags/EconomicBurden/pages/WhatDoTCCost.html) .Washington, DC: National Highway Traffic Safety Administration, 2003.

Organization for Economic Cooperation and Development. *Towards Zero: Ambitious Road Safety Targets and the Safe System Approach.* Paris: Organization for Economic Cooperation and Development and International Transport Forum, 2008.

Peden, M., Scurfield, R., Sleet, D., Mohan, D., Hyder, A., Jarawan, E., Mathers, C. *World Report on Road Traffic Injury Prevention.* Geneva: World Health Organization, 2004.

Poister, T.H. "Performance Monitoring." In: Wholey, J.S., Hatry, H.P., Newcomer, K.E. (ed.), *Handbook of Practical Program Evaluation* (second edition). San Francisco, CA: Jossey-Bass, 2004, 98-125.

Wallington, D., Murray, W., Darby, P., Raeside, R., Ison, S. "Work-related Road Safety: Case Study of British Telecommunications" (Paper No. 12-1196). Unpublished paper presented at the 91st Annual Meeting of the Transportation Research Board, January 22-26, 2012, Washington, DC.

World Health Organization and UN Road Safety Collaboration. *Global Plan for the Decade of Action for Road Safety 2011-2020.* Geneva, Switzerland: World Health Organization, 2010.

APPENDIX 2

<u>Recommended Outline for Policy and Procedure Manuals</u>

Safety Policy/Statement

- Safety mission statement that is conveyed on a constant basis

Responsibility and accountabilities

- Policy setting forth who is responsible for what. **Very Important.**
  - *Assignment of safety functions*
  - *Assignment of auditing requirements*
  - *Chain of command on safety issues*

Driver Recruitment

- Assessment
  - *Job description, with safety expectations*
  - *Road test*
  - *Written test (not required)*
  - *Background check*
    - ○ *Work history documentation*
    - ○ *Drug and alcohol checks*
    - ○ *Criminal history, if required*
- Selection guidelines
  - *Experience required*
  - *Medical examination*
  - *Motor vehicle record (MVR): what is acceptable*
  - *PSP: Pre-employment safety screening program report/ roadside history*
  - *If owner/operator, a review of their DOT number*

Orientation and Training

- New employee training and orientation
  - *New driver checklist*
  - *Driver qualification files*
    - ○ *Biennial review of file*
    - ○ *Annual checks of MVR*
    - ○ *Review of driver qualifications*
      - *Hazmat*
      - *Entry level*
      - *Longer combination vehicles*
      - *Tanker Driver Trainer*
      - *New driver ride-alongs*
      - *Training on your equipment and configurations*
    - ○ *Drugs and alcohol*
      - *Decision on allowing return to work*

- *Retention and storage of records*
- *Procedure for immediate removal*
- Employee retraining
  - *Post-crash*
  - *Post-incident*
- Recurrent training
  - *Hazmat*
  - *OSHA safety training*
- Specialized training
  - *Tanker*
  - *Load securement*
  - *Longer combination vehicles*

Organizational Procedures and Rules

- *General Discipline Procedure* that can be applied to safety and operational violations
- *General Safety Policies*
  - Required by regulations
    - ○ *Drug and alcohol testing procedures/policies (if you employ drivers with a Commercial Driver's License (CDL)*
    - ○ *Security Plan (if you haul hazardous materials)*
  - Company directed
    - ○ *Passengers*
    - ○ *Personal use*
  - Compliance with all traffic and motor carrier regulations and laws – General in nature
- *Crash Countermeasures/ Driving practices*
  - Distracted driving
  - Weather/dispatch policy
    - ○ *General*
    - ○ *Procedures to hold dispatchers accountable for dispatching drivers in runs that cannot be made legally*
  - Speed policy
  - Following distance policy
  - Right lane/ lane change policy
  - Safety belts
  - Hours of Service (HOS)
    - ○ *Adherence to the regulation*
    - ○ *Log retention and submission*
    - ○ *Procedure on how HOS are audited*

Incident and Crash Review

- Evidence retention
- "Black box" retention policies
- Files and photos
- Purpose of incident and crash reviews:
  - *Preventability determination?*
  - *Development of procedures/training to prevent future accidents?*

Rewards and Recognition
- Does the company have a system to reward and recognize achievements of drivers?

Vehicle Specification and Selection
- A policy that details the development of specifications for vehicles and trailers to be used in the operation. This policy should help determine which equipment is proper for the safe operation rather than external factors such as cost, availability or driver wants.

Inspection and Maintenance
- Does the company have a policy describing the system to:
    - Maintain records

- Maintain system of preventative inspections
- Roadside inspections reported
- Driver vehicle inspection report (DVIR)
- If company uses owner/operators (O/O), policy to review O/O equipment prior to allowing use? Policy on repairs of O/O equipment?

Management Program Audits
- Is there a procedure specifying audit functions that management does to insure requirements are being met at all levels? Are they reported back to top management?

Chapter 8

Benchmarking and Performance Criteria

Edward Musal

LEARNING OBJECTIVES

- Be able to develop and administer a fleet accident/incident reporting system.

- Be able to develop and administer a fleet accident/incident record-keeping system.

- Understand the benchmark selection process.

- Be able to perform statistical analysis of fleet accident/incident data, including the ability to calculate incidence rates and to prepare a control chart.

- Understand the importance of accident statistical reporting.

- Understand the uses and limitations of incentive programs.

- Understand the legal implications associated with accident records.

Benchmarking and performance appraisal are as important to fleet safety as they are to any other safety program; indeed, they are important in any management activity. Using benchmarking and performance appraisal will provide a "report card" that can be used to measure the effectiveness of any safety program. The statistical information that supports this activity can also be useful in identifying weaknesses in a safety program so that resources can be allocated for maximum effectiveness. In addition, the incident-reporting and record-keeping framework may be useful in evaluating the effect of proposed activities related to fleet safety.

One must be careful in choosing benchmarks in fleet safety. Choosing them is often quite difficult (see discussion in Benchmarking section). While *Injury Facts*, put out by the National Safety Council (NSC), provides a wealth of statistics for all areas of safety, including fleet safety, safety professionals must consider the unique characteristics of their fleets when choosing a benchmark. Important considerations include the size of the fleet, the type(s) of vehicles that comprise the fleet, and the area in which the fleet operates (road conditions, traffic conditions, weather, and so on).

Much of the information presented in this chapter is based on the author's experience. Where there is no citation in the text to support a specific item, the item is based on the author's experience. At this point it is appropriate for the author to summarize his experience in fleet benchmarking and performance appraisal so the reader may understand the background of the viewpoints presented. He was employed by the New York City Transit Authority, currently Metropolitan Transportation Authority-New York City Transit (NYCT), for 23 years (1973–1996). During most of this time his main function was related to all aspects of accident record keeping, including employee, motor vehicle, and passenger accidents record keeping. His responsibility began with classification. At the end of his career with NYCT, he managed a work unit of five professional employees whose sole responsibility was accident record keeping, analysis, and report preparation. During this period, accident record keeping and analysis at NYCT evolved from a manual system with minimal analysis to a complex computer-based system using sophisticated statistical techniques.

During the author's tenure at NYCT, the Manhattan and Bronx Surface Transit Operating Authority (MaBSTOA), which operates most of the bus service in the Bronx and Manhattan, was integrated into NYCT, which operates most of the bus service in the other three boroughs of New York City. In addition to buses, NYCT operates a fleet of maintenance vehicles for both rapid transit and bus operations as well as supervisory patrol cars. At the time of his employment, NYCT also maintained its own police force. This transit police force was subsequently absorbed into the New York City Police Department. The fleet accident record-keeping system managed by the author included vehicles supporting all of these operations. All the examples presented in this chapter are drawn from his experiences with NYCT.

SOURCES

A list of references is provided at the end of this chapter. As an introduction, however, it is appropriate to identify the four most pertinent sources in the United States. Two American National Standards Institute (ANSI) standards relate to fleet benchmarking and performance appraisal:

- ANSI Z15.1 *Safe Practices for Motor Vehicle Operations* (2006) §6.0 ff presents requirements for incident reporting, record keeping, and analysis.

- ANSI D16.1 *Manual on Classification of Motor Vehicle Traffic Accidents* (1996) provides a classification system that may be used in accident record keeping and analysis.

As indicated earlier, the National Safety Council's *Injury Facts* (previously *Accident Facts*) provides a wealth of accident statistics, including fleet accident statistics, for possible use in benchmarking. The Network of Employers for Traffic Safety (NETS) also provides benchmarking information (www.trafficsafety.org).

In addition to these general sources, there are quite a few industry-specific sources. Some types of motor vehicle fleets are required to report accident statistics to a governmental agency. Statistics on public transit accidents are available from the Federal Transit Administration of the Department of Transportation (DOT). The Bureau of Transportation of the DOT also maintains accident statistics.

Various trade groups catering to specific industry segments also have potentially useful information. These include the American Trucking Association, the American Public Transit Association, the School Bus Information Council, the United Motorcoach Association

(which performed a benchmarking study in 2001), and the American Bus Association (which has a 2000 census of the motorcoach industry). A Web site dedicated to fleet safety benchmarking has been set up in the United Kingdom at www.fleetsafetybenchmarking. net. In addition, an Internet search for a specific type of fleet could be rewarding.

ACCIDENT REPORTING

The foundation on which a fleet's benchmarking and performance appraisal system is built is its accident-reporting system. If this system is not properly designed and implemented, benchmarking and performance appraisal are valueless. People in the computer programming business have an acronym that precisely describes this: GIGO—garbage in, garbage out. It is absolutely necessary to precisely define the criteria for a recordable incident. It is also necessary to implement controls to be sure that all recordable incidents will be captured in the system. These issues will be dealt with in more detail later in this section. The first focus is on the methodology of accident reporting.

There are several means by which fleet management may obtain information about an incident. The usual first report is from the driver of the fleet vehicle involved in the accident. However, the driver may not be aware of an accident or may choose to avoid reporting it (especially if there is minor or no damage to the fleet vehicle), hoping it will be overlooked. Depending on the seriousness of the accident and the fleet's policy, a supervisor may be dispatched to the scene to perform a detailed investigation. It is also possible that a field supervisor may witness the accident. The driver of the other vehicle (if there is one) may be interviewed as part of the supervisor's investigation or may independently contact fleet management. A bystander (or passenger on the fleet vehicle) may be interviewed or may independently contact fleet management. Depending on fleet procedures, the first report of an accident may come after the driver turns in the vehicle from maintenance personnel (or another operator) who inspects the vehicle and notes damage not previously present. Finally, the first notice of an accident might be a lawsuit filed by an aggrieved party. This could occur many months after the alleged incident. The accident-reporting system should provide for all of these potential sources of information. Recent developments in computer technology have allowed several fleets to develop methods of allowing incidents to be reported by computer over the Internet. This provides more timely and accurate accident information as data transcription is eliminated. Several such systems can be found through an Internet search.

If a fleet is large enough to have more than one vehicle dispatch location, such as a nationwide trucking company, its accident-reporting system may be centralized or decentralized. If there is more than one dispatch location, should each location have a person or unit responsible for collecting information about incidents and providing the information to a single fleet location (decentralized), or should the entire fleet have a single unit (centralized) responsible for collecting incident information and providing information to the appropriate dispatch locations? There are certain advantages to each of these methodologies.

The *decentralized* method has the advantage of being closer to the incident. Accordingly, more detailed information can be acquired more quickly, so the initial report of the accident is likely to be more complete and accurate than if a centralized system were used. The major advantage of the *centralized* system is that fewer people collect information and prepare initial accident reports, providing a greater degree of consistency. The centralized system also provides an easier way of incorporating accidents first reported to fleet management (calls to the main office and lawsuits filed) than the decentralized system. Another advantage of the centralized system is that it takes the system out of the control of local management, which may unfairly benefit from not having some accidents reported.

Especially with larger properties, accident reporting may overlap with other reporting systems. If a fleet employee is injured in the accident, the accident may be reported through the employee accident-reporting system, the Workers' Compensation system, and/or the medical reporting system (if the employee sees a physician and the fleet pays for the visit or has its own physician). If a lawsuit is filed with regard to the accident, the accident may be entered into a system used to track lawsuits. It is prudent for people responsible for accident reporting to establish a liaison with people responsible for other reporting systems to see that all systems receive the proper incident reports.

To avoid duplication of effort within an organization, it may be appropriate to expand the accident-reporting system to include nonaccident events of interest to management. As mentioned earlier, the usual sources of accident-reporting information are fleet vehicle drivers, who are also the usual source of information about other incidents related to vehicles and their operation, such as

- criminal activity involving a fleet vehicle (robbery, hijacking, and so on)
- accidents not involving fleet vehicles that are witnessed by fleet drivers
- injuries to a driver or passenger due to nonvehicular accidents
- illnesses of a driver or passenger
- vehicle breakdowns
- other miscellaneous incidents

CASE STUDY 1

Overview of a Sample Accident-Reporting System

This case study presents the NYCT's fleet accident-reporting system for its bus operation and is based on an unpublished master's thesis by the author (1994).

The first verbal report of the incident is directed to the accident desk located within the fleet's centralized communications center, which is manned 24 hours a day, 365 days a year. The report is usually transmitted by radio immediately after the incident by the driver of the fleet vehicle. Occasionally the first report to the accident desk may come from another fleet employee, such as a maintenance employee discovering vehicle damage, a public affairs person taking a complaint from the public, or an attorney receiving notification of a lawsuit. The person at the accident desk enters the information constituting the initial incident report into a structured database (the specific data elements will be discussed later in the Accident Record Keeping section). If appropriate, the accident desk notifies the vehicle dispatch location to send a supervisor to the incident scene to conduct an investigation. More serious incidents (multiple injuries/fatalities) are reported to the fleet safety unit for more thorough investigation.

After completion, the written initial report (referred to as a *brief* because it contains only basic information; see Figure 1 for a sample brief and Figure 2 for an explanation of the information that is included) and a short description of the incident (a few sentences) are immediately transmitted electronically to the dispatch location (both operations and maintenance) responsible for the fleet vehicle involved and to certain fleet management personnel. The briefs are packaged daily and transmitted to the fleet training office, the torts division of the fleet law department, and the safety department. It is important to note that the brief contains only summary information about the incident before any investigation has taken place. It does not contain information regarding fault or preventability. In the NYCT, the safety department has responsibility for fleet benchmarking and performance appraisal as well as internal and external statistical reporting. The brief is the primary data source for this function.

If subsequent investigation determines that any of the information recorded in the brief is incorrect or incomplete, a revised brief is created that replaces the original brief. Revised briefs are necessary relatively infrequently (for fewer than 5 percent of incidents).

BRIEF NO: ENY01177   ACC CODE: 2AAAAAAA   DATE OCC: 05/28/87   TIME: OCC: 1100

DIVISION: Brooklyn   ROUTE: B10 - New Lots Avenue   RUN NO: 5

DEPOT: East New York   DESTIN: HOPKINS ST & SUMNER AVE   SIDE: Near Side

ON: New Lots Avenue   AT: Livonia Avenue

PRIM VEH: 1266   SCHOOL TRIP NO. ____   TOUR OF DUTY: _____

VISIB: Daylight   ROAD COND: Dry   DELAY TO SER: 12   DELAY TO BUS: 35

OP NAME: Smith   OP PASS: 812345   OP BADGE: 44354   OP BIRTH: 03/23/55

TITLE (IF NOT OP):_____ POLICE : (NAS)   OP HIRE: 08/12/79

STUDENT: _____   ST PASS: _____   ST BADGE: _____   ST BIRTH: __/__/__

SUV PASS: 455987   SUV: (AS)   ST HIRE: __/__/__

SUV TITLE: SLD   BUS: GARAGE   NOTIFIED: Control Desk   NO. PSNGR.: 22

DAM PRIM VEH: Slight   DAM SEC. VEH: Moderate   SEC VEH LIC # ABC123   NY

RECD DAT/TIM: 05/28/87   1230   TRAN DAT/TIM: 05/28/87   1300   INITIAL: ABC

Collision-Vehicle

ACTION OF PRIMARY VEHICLE / Forward / Moving in lane

ACTION OF SECONDARY VEHICLE / Forward / Moving in lane

RELATIVE POSITIONS / Other vehicle ahead

CONTACT POINT ON PRIMARY VEHICLE / Front

CONTACT POINT ON SECONDARY VEHICLE / Front

TYPE OF PRIMARY VEHICLE / Bus

TYPE OF SECONDARY VEHICLE / Auto (Jimmy, and so on)

*TOT INJURY: 2

M/23 – Primary Veh. – Treated at scene

F/45 – Sec. Veh. or Ped. – Removed to hosp

*Tot Fat: 1

M/55 – Sec. Veh. or Ped. —

Secondary vehicle failed to observe red signal and entered intersection as bus was entering intersection.

FIGURE 1. Example of a brief (*Source:* Musal 1994)

Even though these events may not be of interest for fleet benchmarking and performance appraisal, they are of interest to other areas of fleet management, and consideration might be given to expanding the fleet accident-reporting system to become a fleet incident-reporting system. Case Study 1 describes a sample fleet accident-reporting system.

The person responsible for fleet benchmarking and performance appraisal must determine which of the reported incidents are to be recorded in the accident record-keeping system.

Before moving on to a discussion of accident record keeping, it is appropriate to discuss the establishment of criteria for including reported incidents in an accident record-keeping system.

One of the pioneers of the industrial safety movement in the United States, H. W. Heinrich, introduced the concept of the accident pyramid in 1931. According to Heinrich, for every major accident (serious injury or death) there were 29 minor-injury accidents and 300 no-injury accidents (property damage or disruption) (Heinrich 1969).

As the subject of his doctoral dissertation in 1963, William E. Tarrants added a new, broader-base layer to Heinrich's pyramid. Tarrants realized that analysis of the number of accidents was not an effective preventive technique for small work units. Due to statistical constraints, several years' worth of accident records would have to accumulate before any meaningful statistics could be generated. Tarrants interviewed workers in a small work unit to identify critical incidents—events that could have resulted in an accident but by luck did not. He gathered sufficient information about critical incidents to perform meaningful statistical analysis so that he could direct efforts to prevent accidents (Tarrants 1963).

The main purpose of fleet benchmarking and appraisal should be to direct accident prevention efforts so they will have maximum effectiveness. Comparison of fleet accident experience with appropriate benchmarks shows how safe a specific fleet is compared to similar fleets. This will show the need for additional accident-prevention efforts. Only through accident record keeping and analysis can comparisons be made of accidents experienced before and after a safety initiative so that the effectiveness of that initiative can be determined. The more incidents in the accident record-keeping system, the more precise statistical analyses can be, so there is a rationale for including as many accident or near-miss events in the accident record-keeping system as possible.

There are other factors to consider. A conscientious operator or supervisor who meticulously reports every critical incident may be considered to have a poor safety record compared to that of a colleague who successfully hides many accidents. There is a strong incentive for both operators and local supervisors to avoid reporting accidents if they think they can get away with it. Above all, the accident-reporting and record-keeping system must be fair.

Reporting of critical incidents may be especially useful in a small fleet where the emphasis is on safety and not discipline. The practice of examining each fleet vehicle for damage every time it returns to the dispatch location or changes drivers is a good way to ensure that every accident is reported.

Whatever threshold is set for recording incidents, it is always possible to maintain nonrecordable incidents in the record-keeping system for use in statistical analyses even if they are not counted for internal and external reporting purposes. Knowing that critical incidents will not count against their safety record is an incentive for operators and supervisors to report them.

Some fleet safety officers (in the author's experience) believe that preventability by the fleet operator should be a criterion in determining whether an accident is recorded. There is certainly a strong incentive for both the safety officer and fleet management to not record incidents unless the fleet operator is found to be at fault, because if fewer accidents are recorded, the fleet's safety record appears to be better. The author disagrees with this position, because even accidents the fleet operator could not prevent might result in injury, damage, and disruption of fleet activity, and the elimination of preventability by the fleet operator as a criterion removes a subjective variable from statistical analysis and makes the accident record-keeping system more complete. Also, recording the accident but noting that the operator was not at fault puts the fleet in a stronger legal position should a lawsuit follow an incident.

ACCIDENT RECORD KEEPING— DESIGNING A SYSTEM

The author's first involvement with accident record keeping occurred before personal computers were introduced into the office environment. He vividly remembers being part of a team of five employees searching through piles of paper accident reports to determine how many of a certain type of vehicle accident happened in the previous year to answer a top management question.

Development of a computer-based accident record-keeping system is necessary with a large fleet, because manual searches through accident records are very time-consuming. While it would be possible to use a spreadsheet program such as Microsoft Excel to record incidents, a database program such as Microsoft Access is more suited for use when organization policies require report generation, statistical analysis, and searching for incidents or trends. Both of these programs are frequently provided as part of the software package on office computers. The person responsible for accident record keeping must become familiar with the capabilities and basic operations of the database program selected to support the accident record-keeping system.

The first step in creating an accident record-keeping system is choosing the data elements to be recorded. Figure 2 provides a suggested list of data elements to consider. This list should not be considered comprehensive; additional elements may be added or removed depending on the scope of the system (see discussion below).

No matter how much thought is put into developing an accident record-keeping system, some odd incident will occur that will provide a record-keeping challenge. The data elements in Figure 2 are intended to capture information about a typical two-vehicle collision, but what if more than two vehicles are involved? A suggestion is to collect information on the first vehicle to collide with the fleet vehicle (no matter where that vehicle falls in the chain of events in the overall accident). Include the total other vehicle injuries and fatalities in the secondary vehicle numbers. If the fleet vehicle collides with two or more other vehicles simultaneously, pick the one with the most serious injuries or damage to record. Other potential events to consider are pedestrian accidents, collisions with objects, noncollision accidents involving passengers on the fleet vehicle, and employee accidents on the fleet vehicle.

As was previously mentioned, there is a possibility that information gathered within the fleet accident record-keeping system may overlap information in other record-keeping systems. It is also possible that information reported, such as crimes, witnessing of events, and other miscellaneous occurrences, while not useful to the fleet safety benchmarking and performance appraisal system,

Data Element	Explanation
Date	Date of incident
Time	Time of incident (suggest using 24-hour time)
Work unit	Dispatch location of fleet vehicle
Driver	Identity of operator of fleet vehicle (employee number or name)
Driver demographics	Date of birth, date of hire, gender, and so on, for possible use in statistical analyses. This information might be acquired by linking with a personnel database.
Primary vehicle number	Identity of the fleet vehicle
Primary vehicle type	E.g., bus, truck, car
Primary vehicle point of impact	E.g., left front, front, right front. Consider using a numbered diagram instead of wording to identify.
Primary vehicle action	What the fleet vehicle was doing at the time of the incident (e.g., stopped in traffic, stopped at curb, starting forward, moving forward, turning left)
Driver of secondary vehicle/pedestrian	Identity of other vehicle operator
Registered owner of secondary vehicle	Identity of other vehicle owner
Secondary vehicle/object type	E.g., bus, truck, car, emergency vehicle, other fleet vehicle, bicycle, pedestrian
Secondary vehicle point of impact	E.g., left front, front, right front. Consider using a numbered diagram instead of wording to identify.
Secondary vehicle/pedestrian action	What the other vehicle/pedestrian was doing at the time of the incident
Relative position of vehicles/object/pedestrian	E.g., other vehicle ahead, other vehicle behind, other vehicle overtaking and passing, other vehicle approaching from left
Fleet employees injured, primary vehicle	Number of employees injured
Fleet employees killed, primary vehicle	Number of employees killed
Other injuries, primary vehicle	Number of passengers injured
Other fatalities, primary vehicle	Number of passengers killed
Injuries secondary, vehicle/pedestrian	Number in other vehicle injured
Fatalities secondary, vehicle/pedestrian	Number in other vehicle killed
Damage, primary vehicle	Estimated dollar value or subjective estimate (e.g., none, minor, moderate, severe)
Damage, secondary vehicle/object	Estimated dollar value or subjective estimate (e.g., none, minor, moderate, severe)
Geographical location	E.g., nearest intersection, milepost. Consider using a mapping program to provide precise longitude/latitude.
Number of passengers on primary vehicle	To assist law department; occasionally more lawsuits are filed claiming injury than there were passengers on the bus
Demographics on injured persons	Age, gender (to assist law department)
Identity of responders	E.g., police, ambulance
Detailed narrative of accident	Include potentially useful information that doesn't fit elsewhere.

FIGURE 2. Vehicle accident record-keeping system data elements (*Source:* Musal 1994)

might be useful to other areas of fleet management. The administrator of the fleet accident record-keeping system should communicate with the administrators of other record-keeping systems within the fleet and coordinate management of information sources and record keeping for mutual benefit. Case Study 2 presents a sample fleet accident record-keeping system. The details of the coding system are provided in the Appendix.

BENCHMARKING

Perhaps the most difficult task of fleet benchmarking and performance appraisal is to determine what benchmark, or benchmarks, to use. ANSI Z15.1 *Safe Practices for Motor Vehicle Operations* (ANSI 2006) establishes incidents per million miles as a standard rate for comparing motor fleet accidents, but what does the person responsible for fleet safety performance appraisal compare against? There are many possible answers to this question.

The National Safety Council's *Injury Facts*, published annually, provides a wealth of accident statistics for possible use in benchmarking. Incidence rates per million miles are presented in it for many types of fleets. In addition, industry-specific organizations may provide statistics for benchmarking comparisons. Membership in the Network of Employers for Traffic Safety (NETS) allows fleet participation in their benchmarking efforts. Even within the same industry, the selection of benchmarks may be difficult. Is it fair to compare a fleet of eighteen-wheelers with a fleet of smaller trucks? Is it fair to compare a fleet of articulated buses with a fleet without such vehicles? What about a fleet with mixed vehicle types?

Can the fleet accident rate of a post office delivering primarily to RFD routes with dirt roads be compared with a suburban post office delivering to town houses on well-paved roads? Traffic density is another issue. NYCT accident rates for Queens and Staten Island depots, which have relatively low traffic density as well as express routes on superhighways that provide many miles to the denominator of the equation, always have significantly lower accident rates than Manhattan depots providing crosstown service, where it may take as much as an hour to traverse the two-mile-wide island in very dense stop-and-go traffic. Is it fair to use a Queens or Staten Island accident rate as a benchmark for a Manhattan bus depot? Of course not.

Another confounding variable in using accident rates from other fleets as a benchmark is the use of different accident record-keeping methodologies. (In the Accident Reporting section of this chapter, this issue was raised during the discussion of preventability being used as a factor in determining whether an incident should be recorded.) While the NYCT did not use preventability as a factor in determining whether to record bus traffic accidents, the author discovered that several other transit properties in the United States did not report accidents that they determined were not their fault. NYCT accident rates are compared directly with the accident rates of other fleets in American Public Transit Association (APTA) safety contests and are published alongside the rates of other fleets by the Federal Transit Administration (FTA).

CASE STUDY 2

Overview of a Sample Accident Record-Keeping System

This case study presents the fleet incident record-keeping system of the bus operation of NYCT and is based on an unpublished master's thesis by the author (1994).

A database was set up to accept most of the information suggested in Figure 2. Rather than establish multiple fields or have a narrative to describe the incident, an eight-character coding system occupying one field in the database was established for accident classification. The details of this coding system are provided in the Appendix. The structure of the coding system is summarized in the table.

The structure of this coding system makes it easy to select accidents when either responding to inquiries or performing detailed statistical analyses. For example, pedestrian accidents may be found by selecting all records with a first character of "1." Collisions with taxis

		Coding System							
		Character							
Type	1	2	3	4	5	6	7	8
Collision pedestrian	1	Primary vehicle action	Pedestrian action	--	Primary vehicle contact point	--	Primary vehicle type	--
Collision vehicle	2	Primary vehicle action	Secondary vehicle action	Relative positions	Primary vehicle contact point	Secondary vehicle contact point	Primary vehicle type	Secondary vehicle type
Collision object	3	Primary vehicle action	--	--	Primary vehicle contact point	--	Primary vehicle type	Object type
Passenger	4	Primary vehicle action	Passenger action	Passenger location	Event	--	--	--
Crime	5	Crime category	Crime details	--	--	--	--	--
Misc.	6	Misc. category	Misc. details	--	--	--	--	--

would be found by selecting all records with the eighth character "J." Collisions involving the right front of the fleet vehicle would be found by selecting all records with the first character "1," "2," or "3" and the fifth character "F."

The most accurate benchmark is often a fleet's own prior history unless the fleet changes its accident record-keeping methodology. Many of the variables mentioned above are eliminated if a work unit's own history is selected as a benchmark. There are, however, still variables that must be looked at in considering a fleet's own history as a benchmark. Seasonality is one important factor. Aside from weather conditions, there may be other seasonal issues. For example, as birds migrate, so do some people, and traffic conditions in the southern parts of the United States may be heavier in the winter than in the summer. When school is in session, the presence of school buses may appreciably increase traffic density. Special factors, such as a heavy snowstorm, temporary construction traffic patterns, or the occurrence of a special activity, such as a political convention, may drastically alter accident statistics. Such issues should be addressed in the notes presented with statistical reports.

While the most accurate benchmark may be the fleet's own prior experience, totally neglecting the experience of other fleet operators would be a serious mistake. Continued comparison of a fleet that has an abysmal safety record with its own record alone would provide little incentive to improve. Such benchmarking would perpetuate poor safety performance. Selection of benchmarks outside the fleet must be made with care, understanding the limitations of using such benchmarks.

The United States has adequate fleet accident-reporting systems, public and nonprofit, as described earlier. There is, however, little fleet safety benchmarking information available for many other countries (P.A.U. Education 2005). Case Study 3 shows how one company developed fleet safety benchmarking information where little was available.

Even where international data is available, it may be difficult to make proper comparisons due to differences in data-collection methodologies, population distribution, and traffic conditions. This is illustrated in "Benchmarking Australian Bus Safety" (Hildebrand and Geoff 2002), a study that compared bus accident rates in Australia with those in the United States and Canada. This study found that the bus fatality rate per kilometer in Australia is about 50 percent of that in Canada or the United States. However, the population-based fatality rate among bus passengers is more than ten times that in the United States or Canada. Lumley General Insurance of Australia provides statistical information on fleet accidents to clients. Included is information on how each client compares to other clients. Lumley also provides training materials and safety giveaways to clients, but believes the benchmarking initiative is their most effective tool (Haworth et al. 2000).

Prompted by unusually high fleet accident costs in 2006–2007, the British Royal Mail conducted a benchmarking audit, comparing their fleet safety practices to British Telecom, British Gas, and other organizations. They found that while they had good vehicle safety practices and reporting of accident information, they were deficient in driver assessment. Subsequently, they improved driver risk assessment, including license checks and installing telemetry in vehicles to identify driver performance (Murray and Keeler 2008).

The preceding discussion of benchmarking has been confined to vehicle accidents. It should be noted that ANSI Z15.1 provides a means for calculating incidence rates for other fleet operations. For example, delivery vehicles or dump trucks might use the *number of incidents per 10,000 deliveries made* or *number of incidents per 10,000 loads carried*, and fleets carrying passengers might use the *number of incidents resulting in passenger injury per million passengers carried*.

Benchmarking must be done with caution. While a fleet's own previous accident experience may be the most accurate benchmark, other benchmarks should also be considered, comparing judiciously and taking confounding factors into account.

CASE STUDY 3

Fleet Safety Benchmark Survey: Europe, Middle East, and Africa

The Europe, Middle East, and Africa (EMEA) division of the Johnson & Johnson Company realized there was little data available for fleet safety benchmarking in their geographic area, so it conducted a survey to develop such data. Initially pharmaceutical companies in the area were included, but the scope was expanded to include medical and consumer products companies. In all, 23 multinational companies participated in the survey.

For the calendar year 2004, vehicle mileage and accident data, safe driving programs, and environmental and risk management issues were included in the survey for all of the respondents' operations in Europe, the Middle East, and Africa.

The survey was initiated with three conference calls during which the questionnaire was explained and questions responded to. A second similar survey, which is global in scope, was begun in May 2006 (P.A.U. Education 2005).

STATISTICAL ANALYSIS

An intensive study of statistical analytical methods is beyond the scope of this book. Many statistical tests have been developed to perform all sorts of different analyses. It is important for the statistician to understand exactly what is to be measured and the limitations of the statistical test proposed. It is quite possible for different statistical tests to result in what appear to be contradictory findings. Having said this, it is necessary to use some statistical analysis techniques when carrying out performance appraisals.

Whether it is intended to compare one work unit with another within the fleet or to compare the fleet's accident experience with that of another fleet, it is necessary to consider the activity of the fleet as well as the number of accidents.

The most frequently used standard rate for comparing fleet accidents is *accidents per million miles traveled*. This is calculated by multiplying the number of accidents recorded (see discussion on recordable accidents in the Accident Reporting section of this chapter) by one million and dividing the result by the number of miles traveled by all vehicles in the work unit (see Case Study 4 for a sample calculation). Other rates noted in the Benchmarking section are similarly calculated using the appropriate incidents and the constant specified in the rate instead of 1,000,000.

Now that an accident rate has been calculated, the accident experience of one fleet work unit (or a whole fleet) may be directly compared with that of another. Such comparisons should be considered carefully, as there are many possible confounding variables, such as traffic conditions, weather, and different vehicle types, that would make the comparison invalid.

One note of caution: it is not statistically proper to add or average rates. Once rates have been calculated for subsidiary work units, do *not* add or average the rates. Each accident rate must be calculated separately using the incidents and miles traveled (or deliveries made or passengers carried) for the work unit being examined.

As has been noted in the Benchmarking section, the author recommends a work unit's own accident record as an appropriate benchmark because it is likely that using it will introduce the fewest confounding variables. The use of the unit's own record as a benchmark facilitates an ongoing analysis of the effectiveness of accident prevention efforts within that unit. One very useful tool to perform this analysis is the *control chart*.

Accident occurrences vary daily. This variation may be due to chance or some extraneous factor, such as a snowstorm or the implementation of a safety initiative that may have caused the accident rate to go up or down.

CASE STUDY 4

To calculate the standard rate for comparing fleet collision accidents, first, determine the work unit for which the rate is to be calculated. Almost any work unit may be selected; it could be one vehicle, one driver, one route, one dispatch point, or the whole fleet. Next determine the time period for which the rate will be collected: a day, a month, a year, and so on. Then identify the number of recordable collision accidents and the cumulative number of miles all vehicles in that work unit traveled.

For example, for a given work unit and time period, assume that there were three recordable collision accidents and the total number of miles traveled was 50,000. These numbers are put in the following equation:

$$\text{accidents per million miles} = \frac{\text{accidents} \times 1,000,000}{\text{miles traveled}} =$$

$$\frac{3 \times 1,000,000}{50,000} = 60 \text{ accidents per million miles}$$

A control chart uses statistical techniques to measure each individual time unit (day, month, and so on) against all other similar time units included within the calculation. A statistical technique is used to set control limits at levels of statistical significance [e.g., 95 percent confidence interval—approximately two standard deviations (actually 1.96) above and below the mean, or 99 percent confidence interval—approximately three standard deviations (actually 2.576) above and below the mean]. After application of this statistical technique, the user may state that any data point above the upper control limit or below the lower control limit was influenced by a factor other than chance with 95 percent (or 99 percent) certainty. Regular use of the control-chart technique is especially useful in measuring the continued effect of a particular safety initiative. Does the initiative result in a permanent accident reduction, or is its effect temporary?

A word of caution: before attempting to use a control chart, one should understand some fundamental statistical concepts, such as a normal distribution, probability distribution, and standard deviation.

Before introducing the preparation of a control chart, a brief discussion of time intervals and statistical significance is helpful. Statistical calculations by their nature are estimates. For example, in the previous paragraph the reader was given choices of 95 percent or 99 percent certainty; statistical analysis used as an estimating tool does not provide 100 percent accuracy. The more data points within a statistical analysis, the more accurate it will be, because the number of values is one of the factors used in determining the accuracy of the statistical calculation. Thus, a weekly analysis (with seven days of accidents) will be more accurate than a daily analysis (with only one day of accidents), and a monthly analysis (with 28 to 31 days of accidents) will be more accurate than a weekly analysis. Using longer time periods reduces variability, thereby allowing control limits to be tighter so that developing trends may be identified earlier.

Besides selecting the time period measured (day, week, month), it is also necessary to select the time interval used to establish the control limits. This selection should be made based on what the chart is intended to show. If the intention is to show the long-term effectiveness of the implementation of a safety initiative started several years in the past, it may be appropriate to create a control chart showing yearly accident rates over a period of twenty or more years. If the effectiveness of a current safety program is being evaluated, it may be more appropriate to start the control chart after the previous safety initiative was fully implemented and use monthly intervals. If the intention is just to watch accident statistics to see if any trends develop, 24 months is suggested, with monthly data points.

The formulas for calculating the upper control limit (UCL) and the lower control limit (LCL) at the 95 percent confidence level are

$$\text{UCL} = \bar{p} + 1.96 \sqrt{\frac{\bar{p}(1-\bar{p})}{n}} \tag{1}$$

$$\text{LCL} = \bar{p} - 1.96 \sqrt{\frac{\bar{p}(1-\bar{p})}{n}} \tag{2}$$

where

$$\bar{p} = \text{sum of } \frac{\text{accidents}}{n}$$

$$n = \text{sum of miles traveled}$$

Depending on the accident rate used, the value for n might also be the sum of passengers carried, deliveries made, and so on. Should the 99 percent confidence level be desired, substitute 2.576 for 1.96 in the above equations (Tarrants n.d.). The numbers 1.96 and 2.576 are used because those are the numbers of standard deviations required for the 95 percent and 99 percent confidence intervals, respectively. These numbers are derived from the standard normal (z) distribution table, which shows the areas under a normal curve for different numbers of standard deviations from the mean. Any number of standard deviations may be selected based on the degree of accuracy desired.

Case Study 5 is presented to show the calculations necessary to prepare a control chart with a 95 percent confidence level for vehicle accidents based on miles traveled in a work unit. The data are fictitious. An interpretation of the control chart is also presented with fictitious events used to explain any anomalies.

The primary purpose of accident record keeping and analysis is for performance appraisal and benchmarking. Occasionally, however, it is necessary to use these tools to evaluate the effectiveness of accident-prevention efforts. The accident record-keeping database becomes a useful tool in performing these analyses. Depending on the situation, it may be necessary to perform a prospective or retrospective study, and the appropriate statistical tests must be selected. A prospective study is one in which the ground rules of the study are set and participants are selected before the study is begun. A retrospective study is one in which preexisting data is used for the study. Care must be taken in establishing the ground rules of the study to eliminate or reduce confounding variables and to ensure the validity and reliability of the findings.

Case Study 6 presents an analysis of the effectiveness of an accident-prevention effort. No documentation of this study remains; its description is based on the author's memory only. The presentation focuses on the methods followed in setting up the study rather than the exact statistical techniques used in the study.

It would not be appropriate to conclude this discussion of statistical analysis without touching on nonstatistical analysis—specifically, the human element. People processing accident reports sometimes notice odd things or come up with ideas that can be very productive in reducing accidents. Hence, Case Study 7 is presented.

Statistical Reporting

Maintaining accident statistics is valueless unless something is done with them. Their use in initiating and measuring accident-reduction efforts has already been discussed. Accident statistics are also reported as a measure of work-unit safety. Such reports may be made to entities outside the organization as well as those inside the organization.

Certain motor fleets may be required to report accident statistics to regulatory agencies. For example, public transit properties are required to submit annual statistical reports to the Federal Transit Administration (FTA). Most business organizations are also required to make annual reports of employee accident statistics to the Occupational Safety and Health Administration (OSHA). Local public agencies often must report employee accident statistics to regulatory bodies similar to OSHA.

CASE STUDY 5

Preparing a Control Chart

This case provides a chart showing fictitious data for a fleet unit and the calculations necessary to prepare the control chart.

The individual monthly data points as well as the upper and lower control limits may then be plotted on a line graph.

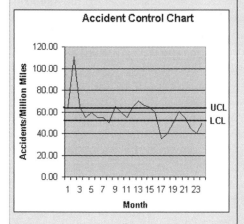

Accident Control Chart

It is now necessary to interpret the control chart in light of (fictitious) events that happened related to the work unit under examination. Months 1 through 24 represent January of the first year through December of the second year. The spike in month 2 represents a very snowy February of year 1 with icy road conditions through much of the month resulting in more accidents than usual. The ticks below the lower control limit in month 8 and above the upper control limit in month 9 are unexplained. A 95 percent confidence level was chosen, so it is possible that some points outside the control limits are due to chance. Had a 99 percent confidence level been used in the calculations, both of these points would have been within the control limits. Note that due to the relatively small size of the work unit, only about three accidents separate the lower control limit from the upper control limit. Had the monthly number of accidents varied more widely than those presented here, the control limits would have been farther apart because

Time Interval	No. of Accidents	Miles Traveled	Accidents Per Million Miles
1	13	200,923	64.70
2	21	190,013	110.52
3	13	201,198	64.61
4	11	200,201	54.94
5	12	201,989	59.41
6	11	200,805	54.78
7	11	199,879	55.03
8	10	199,987	50.00
9	13	200,113	64.96
10	12	201,198	59.64
11	11	200,098	54.97
12	13	201,175	64.62
13	14	200,123	69.96
14	13	197,013	65.99
15	13	201,213	64.61
16	12	200,197	59.94
17	7	201,112	34.81
18	8	200,891	39.82
19	10	199,979	50.01
20	12	199,998	60.00
21	11	200,250	54.93
22	9	201,213	44.73
23	8	200,118	39.98
24	10	201,200	49.70
Sum	278	4,800,886	57.91
$\bar{p}$	5.7906E-05		
$\dfrac{\bar{p}(1-\bar{p})}{n}$	1.20608E-11		
$\sqrt{\dfrac{\bar{p}(1-\bar{p})}{n}}$	3.47287E-06		
$1.96\sqrt{\dfrac{\bar{p}(1-\bar{p})}{n}}$	6.80682E-06		
UCL	6.47128E-05		64.71
LCL	5.10992E-05		51.10

the standard deviation would have been greater. Months 13 and 14 represent January and February of year 2 with snow and ice again, but not as severe as in year 1. In month 17, the safety director implemented an incentive program focusing on accident reduction. There was a significant reduction in accidents for three months, but the novelty of the program wore off (see discussion of incentive programs) and things were back to normal in month 20. In month 22 the traffic department installed a traffic light at an especially dangerous intersection that most fleet vehicles had to pass through. This resulted in a permanent drop in traffic accidents to a new lower plateau. Month 22 would be a logical starting point for a future control chart because it represents a permanent change in traffic conditions that makes prior data a poor benchmark.

Members of the National Safety Council (NSC) are requested to voluntarily report their accident statistics to the NSC. These statistics are amalgamated and presented in the NSC's annual publication *Injury Facts*, previously mentioned in this chapter. Members with especially noteworthy accident records receive recognition from the NSC. Industry groups, such as the American Public Transit Association (APTA), also collect accident statistics from members for publication within the industry. Again, fleets with excellent safety records receive recognition.

Publications from and inquiries for statistical information from all of these organizations become sources of information fleets can use to develop benchmarking criteria to measure their overall safety. Care must be taken in selecting benchmarking criteria (see the discussion on benchmarking earlier in the chapter).

Finally, and perhaps most importantly, accident statistics are reported internally to management. They become a tool local management can use to measure their success in safety. Statistical reports may also be among the measures used to rate managers for promotions and possible bonuses. For these reasons it is especially important that accident-reporting, record-keeping, and analysis systems be above reproach (see the discussion on criteria for recording accidents in the Accident Reporting section of this chapter).

An internal fleet accident statistical reporting system may include charts and graphs showing accidents geographically by fleet unit and showing accident trends by time. Accidents may be presented as raw numbers and/or as rates (see Case Studies 4 and 5).

CASE STUDY 6

Analysis of the Effectiveness of an Accident-Prevention Effort

This case study presents a real accident-prevention effort at the NYCT. It is drawn from memory, as no documentation of the study remains.

Statistics showed that collisions involving the bus rear represented a significant number of accidents. A suggestion was made that if the bus rear were to be more visible, fewer vehicles might collide with it. Further investigation revealed two possible ways to make the bus rear more visible. One was to paint the rear with chevron-shaped alternating yellow and black stripes ("zebra stripes"), as is done with some construction vehicles. A second was to install a third brake light (a "cyclops light") below the rear window of the bus and centered above a horizontal line drawn between the two existing brake lights.

Discussions were initiated with the bus operations and maintenance departments. They agreed on a preliminary test protocol for a prospective matched control study calling for participation by four bus depots: one each in Queens and Staten Island, which serve areas with relatively light traffic conditions, and one each in Brooklyn and the Bronx, which serve areas with heavy traffic volume. Thirty regular buses were to be chosen at random from each depot. (This test excluded high-mileage express routes

that used a different type of bus and included significant amounts of highway travel.) All 120 buses were to have rear advertising signs removed because the signs were a potentially confounding variable. Ten buses at each depot were to be repainted with zebra stripes, ten were to have the cyclops light installed, and ten were to remain as is (with the advertising signs removed). The study was to last one year.

The concept of removing the advertising signs from the buses brought vehement objections from the real estate department, which produced revenue from renting space for the signs. Negotiations resulted in an agreement that only the 20 zebra-striped buses would have their advertising signs removed, and the signs would remain in place on the other 40 buses. Should the zebra stripes prove effective in reducing rear-end accidents, further discussion would take place with the real estate department.

After the buses were prepared, the study began. The test buses were randomly assigned to routes and drivers using regular procedures at the depots. Test buses withdrawn from service for more than a few days due to accident damage or mechanical breakdown were replaced by other regular buses selected at random from the same depot and prepared appropriately. On a monthly basis all accidents involving the test

buses where the point of impact was either left rear, rear, or right rear (see the Appendix for coding structure) were abstracted from the accident record-keeping system, and copies of the accident brief were maintained in a separate file for the duration of the study. Special procedures were established to obtain monthly mileage counts from each depot for the buses in the study.

At the end of the first month of the study it was noted that the zebra-striped test buses had more rear accidents than the other test groups. Approximately four months into the study, sufficient data had been collected to indicate that the zebra-striped test buses had significantly more rear accidents than the other test groups. At that point a decision was made to withdraw the zebra-striped buses from the study, have them repainted, and have the advertising signs remounted. This resolved issues with the real estate department.

The study continued with only two test groups. Analysis of the results at the conclusion of the twelve-month test period showed the cyclops-light-equipped buses had significantly fewer rear collisions than the control group. The study results were presented to management. Management determined that all future new bus orders would include the requirement that a cyclops light be factory installed. Moreover, management directed that all existing buses be retrofitted with a cyclops light.

CASE STUDY 7

Bus Operators Falling from Doors

This case study presents a real event at the NYCT. It is related from memory, as no documentation remains.

The person responsible for classifying employee accidents noted that several incidents had been classified as "bus operator falling from door." This was identified from the NYCT employee accident record-keeping system, which has not been described here but was fully described in *The Development of an Accident Record-Keeping System at the New York City Transit Authority* (Musal 1994). Why do bus operators fall from the door of a bus? Interest was piqued and further investigation of accident records and a visit to a bus depot resolved the mystery.

For safe driving, it is necessary that both right and left outside rearview mirrors be properly adjusted for the height and seat position of the driver. Accordingly, when drivers enter a bus, the first thing they adjust is the seat and the second is the mirrors. It is easy to adjust the left outside mirror by opening the window and manually moving it. The right outside mirror is more difficult. The driver sits in the seat, looks at the mirror, estimates how it must be adjusted, and then opens the front door of the bus and places his or her left foot on the door hinge while grasping a railing with his or her left hand. The right hand adjusts the mirror while the right foot moves in the air, trying to maintain balance. The driver then returns to the seat to check the mirror position and repeats the adjustment process as necessary.

As is known from ladder safety rules, three points of secure contact are required for safety. Drivers have two secure points: left foot and left hand, making mirror adjusting less than safe. Two additional factors make the mirror-adjusting operation even more unsafe. A properly maintained door hinge is well oiled or greased, and therefore slippery. Also, quite often bus drivers relieve other drivers on the road, not in the depot, and in winter ice and snow tend to accumulate on the door hinge.

The findings of this study were presented to management along with a recommendation that small servomotors be attached to the right outside mirrors to permit them to be adjusted by the driver from the seat. Management directed that all future bus orders have servomotors factory installed.

INCENTIVE PROGRAMS

The use of incentive programs as accident-prevention tools is somewhat controversial in the safety profession. Because such programs raise safety awareness, they do prevent some accidents. Their continued effectiveness requires constant effort to keep employees interested. Where funding is limited, incentive programs must take second place to efforts to ameliorate unsafe conditions.

The effectiveness of incentive programs has come to be linked to an industrial research phenomenon known as the "Hawthorne effect." From 1927 to 1932, Elton Mayo and Fritz Roethlisberger conducted research on methods of enhancing employee productivity at the Hawthorne Works of the Western Electric Company (now Alcatel-Lucent) near Chicago. The key experiment in the series occurred in the relay assembly test room, where six female employees were isolated and working conditions could be controlled. The researchers measured productivity under various working conditions: rest breaks were provided or withheld; the length of the workday was changed; temperature and lighting levels were increased and decreased. After a year of experimentation, no correlation could be discovered between the varying working conditions and the women's productivity, but productivity increased throughout the experiment. Finally, interviews with the women uncovered the secret to their enhanced productivity. They felt special because they had been chosen from all other workers in the plant. They appreciated the communications and openness to questions by the researchers. A degree of team cohesiveness developed among these six women, who became fast friends. Productivity increases had nothing to do with the test conditions. They related directly to the attention given to the employees as part of the research study and the cohesiveness and dedication that developed as a result of it (Rieger 1995).

Similarly, an incentive program as an accident-prevention tool succeeds only to the extent that employees are genuinely interested in the program and modify their behaviors to align with those promoted by the program. When that interest wanes, money spent on incentive programs is as good as thrown away.

Case Study 8 describes an incentive program in use in 1988 and 1989 at NYCT to promote employee safety.

Several studies have found that a significant number of fleets use driver incentive programs as part of their accident-reduction efforts. One study found that 70 percent of trucking firms surveyed use them (Barton and Tardiff 1998). Another found that 41 percent of surveyed fleets and 66 percent of award-winning fleets use them (American Trucking Associations Foundation 1999). Still another found that 73 percent use them (Knipling et al. 2003).

CASE STUDY 8

A Safety Incentive Program

This case study presents a safety incentive program used in 1988 and 1989 at the NYCT and is reconstructed from the author's memory.

It began as an annual program recognizing the bus maintenance shop with the best lost-time accident record. Suitable publicity announced the program before it began. After the annual accident records were compiled, a ceremony was held at the winning work location. A trophy was presented by the chief executive officer followed by coffee and cake. Coffee mugs imprinted with the winning maintenance shop's name, year, and achievement were presented to all employees.

During the second year of the program a second award was added to recognize the maintenance shop with the most improved lost-time accident record. A similar presentation ceremony was held at each winning maintenance shop. After the 1989 awards were presented, in 1990 that particular program was brought to a close and another safety initiative was implemented.

LEGAL IMPLICATIONS

Vehicle accidents often result in legal action by injured parties. To protect the interests of the employer, the custodian of vehicle accident records must be very careful in responding to requests for accident information from outside the organization.

Public agencies are especially at risk. Many public bodies are required by various freedom-of-information laws to provide their internal information to members of the public upon request, and accident information is included. Accident information may also be useful to researchers doing academic investigations. As such information is accessible to anyone, it is quite possible, and not illegal, for a person to submit a request as a private citizen without indicating in the request that he or she is an attorney representing a client. Accordingly, it is prudent for all freedom-of-information requests to be funneled through an agency's legal department.

Both public and private fleet operators may receive subpoenas requiring the presentation of accident records as part of the discovery process of a lawsuit. Upon receiving a subpoena, it is likewise important to consult with the fleet's attorney to determine how it will be handled.

The custodian of the accident records and the fleet's attorney can determine how best to handle the issue to protect both the employer and the custodian. For example, the author remembers one freedom-of-information request submitted by an attorney suing the NYCT. The request sought information to show that the specific type of accident suffered by the attorney's client had previously occurred and that the NYCT was negligent in not correcting the hazard that caused the accident. The request was worded quite broadly, requesting information for all accidents occurring during a particular period of time. After consultation with the legal department's freedom-of-information officer, the attorney was provided with precisely what he asked for, not what he wanted. The accidents he was searching for were scattered throughout the hundreds of printed pages he was given precisely in the order in which they had been entered into the computer. The NYCT successfully defended this particular lawsuit.

CONCLUSION

Benchmarking and performance appraisal are critical parts of an effective fleet safety program. There are several components of a benchmarking and performance appraisal system. An accident/incident-reporting system must be established to ensure that incidents are reported with adequate details. A record-keeping system must maintain easy availability of all of the accident data to facilitate analysis and reporting. Appropriate benchmarks must be selected so that fleet performance can be adequately judged. Proper statistical tools must be used to meaningfully analyze accident data. Appropriate methodologies must be used to create understandable reports of statistical results. All of the above should be accomplished with an understanding of how the total benchmarking and appraisal system might be used to prosecute or defend fleet management should legal action be commenced.

Without an effective accident-reporting and record-keeping system, there can be no safety management. Benchmarking and performance appraisal are the tools used to identify problem areas for accident-reduction efforts and to evaluate the effectiveness of those efforts.

Acknowledgements

The author acknowledges Robert J. Crain, P.E., who worked for many years with the author in developing the computer-based accident record-keeping systems at the NYCT that were used in most of the case studies presented in this chapter. The author also thanks Bram D. Weiser, M.S., who was intimately involved in the evolution and operation of the fleet accident record-keeping and analysis system and kindly consented to review a draft of this chapter.

REFERENCES

American National Standards Institute (ANSI). 1996. Standard ANSI D16.1. In *Manual on Classification of Motor Vehicle Traffic Accidents*. Washington, D.C.: ANSI.

_____. 2006. Standard ANSI Z15.1. In *Safe Practices for Motor Vehicle Operations*. Washington, D.C.: ANSI.

American Trucking Associations Foundation. 1999. *Safe Returns: A Compendium of Injury Reduction and Safety Management Practices of Award Winning Carriers*. Alexandria, VA: American Trucking Associations.

Barton, R., and L. P. Tardiff. 1998. *Incentive Programs for Enhancing Truck Safety and Productivity*. Montreal, CAN: Transportation Development Centre.

Haworth, Narelle, Claes Tingvall, and Naomi Kwadlo. 2000. *Review of Best Practice Road Safety Initiatives in the Corporate and/or Business Environment*. Melbourne: Monash University.

Heinrich, H. W. 1969. *Industrial Accident Prevention*. New York: McGraw-Hill.

Hildebrand, Eric, and Rose Geoff. 2002. "Benchmarking Australian Bus Safety." *Road & Transport Research*. Vermont South, Victoria, Australia: ARRB Group Ltd.

Knipling, Ronald R., Jeffrey S. Hickman, and Gene Bergoffen. 2003. *Commercial Truck and Bus Safety Synthesis Program, Synthesis 1: Effective Commercial Truck and Bus Safety Management Techniques*. Washington, D.C.: Transportation Research Board.

Murray, Will, and Cathy Keeler. 2008. *Summary Report from the Fleet Safety Benchmarking Seminar*. London, 16 January 2008. (accessed April 28, 2011) www.virtualriskmanager.net/main/news/Benchmarking-Workshop-Report-Jan-08.pdf

Musal, Edward A. 1994. "The Development of an Accident Record-Keeping System at the New York City Transit Authority." Unpublished master's thesis. New York: Hunter College.

National Safety Council (NSC). 2010. *Injury Facts* (previously titled *Accident Facts*) Itasca, IL: NSC.

P.A.U. Education. (Barcelona, Spain.) 2005. *European Road Safety Charter—Sharing of Best Practices*. (Retrieved January 14, 2007.) www.paueducation.com/comm/transport/roadsafety/charger/media/media1252.doc

Rieger, Bradley J. 1995. "Lessons in productivity and people." *Training & Development* 49:56–58.

Tarrants, William E. Undated, approximately 1960. *Measurement of Safety Performance*. Unpublished manuscript used as text for course. New York: New York University.

_____. 1963. "An Evaluation of the Critical Incident Technique as a Method for Identifying Industrial Accident Causal Factors." Unpublished doctoral dissertation. New York: New York University.

APPENDIX

BUS FLEET INCIDENT CODES

Character 1: Incident Type

1	Collision-Pedestrian
2	Collision-Vehicle
3	Collision-Object
4	Passenger
5	Crime
6	Miscellaneous
7	Industrial (employee) accident

Collision

Character 2: All Collisions (Pedestrian/Vehicle/Object) – Action of Primary Vehicle

Forward/Reverse

A/B	Moving in lane
C/D	Changing lanes
E/F	Turning right
G/H	Turning left
I/J	U-turn
K/L	Pulling into curb
M/N	Pulling out from curb
O/P	Starting (not from curb)
Q/R	Stopping (not from curb)
S	Standing in traffic
T	Standing/parked at curb
X	Unknown

Character 3: Pedestrian Collision – Pedestrian Action

A	In street
B	On sidewalk
C	In crosswalk—crossing from left
D	In crosswalk—crossing from right
E	Not in crosswalk—crossing from left
F	Not in crosswalk—crossing from right
X	Unknown

Character 3: Vehicle Collision – Secondary Vehicle Action

Forward/Reverse

A/B	Moving in lane
C/D	Changing lanes

E/F   Turning right
G/H   Turning left
I/J   U-turn
K/L   Pulling into curb
M/N   Pulling out from curb
O/P   Starting (not from curb)
Q/R   Stopping (not from curb)
S   Standing in traffic
T   Standing/parked at curb
X   Unknown

Character 4: Vehicle Collision – Relative Positions

A   Other vehicle ahead
B   Other vehicle behind
C   Other vehicle overtaking and passing left
D   Other vehicle overtaking and passing right
E   Primary vehicle overtaking and passing left
F   Primary vehicle overtaking and passing right
G   Other vehicle approaching from left
H   Other vehicle approaching from right
I   Other vehicle approaching from opposite direction
J   Both vehicles standing (e.g., slide on ice, open door)
X   Unknown

Character 5: All Collisions (Pedestrian/Vehicle/Object) – Contact Point on Primary Vehicle

A   Front
B   Left front
C   Left side
D   Left rear
E   Rear
F   Right front
G   Right side
H   Right rear
I   Left open door (including engine door)
J   Right open door (including engine door)
X   Unknown

Character 6: Vehicle Collision – Contact Point on Secondary Vehicle

A   Front
B   Left front
C   Left side
D   Left rear

E   Rear
F   Right front
G   Right side
H   Right rear
I   Left open door (including engine door)
J   Right open door (including engine door)
X   Unknown

Character 7: All Collisions (Pedestrian/Vehicle/Object) – Primary Vehicle Type

A   Bus
B   Van
C   Truck
D   Auto (e.g., Jimmy)
E   Industrial truck (e.g., forklift)

Character 8: Vehicle Collision – Secondary Vehicle Type

A   Auto (e.g., Jimmy)
B   Van
C   Truck
D   Fleet bus
E   Fleet auto
F   Fleet truck
G   Fleet industrial truck (e.g., forklift)
H   School bus
I   Nonfleet bus
J   Taxi
K   Emergency vehicle (e.g., police, fire, ambulance)
L   Motorcycle
M   Moped
N   Bicycle or tricycle
O   Other person-powered vehicle (e.g., pushcart)
P   Animal-drawn vehicle
Q   Nonfleet industrial truck (e.g., forklift)
X   Unknown

Character 8: Object Collision – Object Type

A   Fixed object (e.g., abutment, pole, building, tree, curb)
B   Movable object on roadway
C   Movable object on sidewalk
D   Movable object elsewhere (e.g., depot)
E   Animal
X   Other

Passenger Accident

Character 2: Passenger Accident – Bus Action

Forward/Reverse

A/B	Moving in lane
C/D	Changing lanes
E/F	Turning right
G/H	Turning left
I/J	U-turn
K/L	Pulling into curb
M/N	Pulling out from curb
O/P	Starting (not from curb)
Q/R	Stopping (not from curb)
S	Standing in traffic
T	Standing/parked at curb
X	Unknown

Character 3: Passenger Accident – Passenger Action

A	Boarding
B	On board standing
C	On board walking
D	On board seated
E	On board sitting down
F	On board arising
G	On board action unknown
H	Alighting
X	Unknown

Character 4: Passenger Accident – Passenger Location

A	Front door/steps
B	Near fare box
C	Front seat area
D	Rear door/steps
E	Rear seat area
X	Unknown

Character 5: Passenger Accident – Event

A	Slipped/tripped/fell
B	Bumped into object/person
C	Struck by doors
D	Caught by doors and dragged
E	Struck by vehicle/object (part of body extended through window)
F	Object through window (not thrown)
G	Defective equipment

H	Bus fire
I	Actions of other passengers (not assault)
X	Unknown

Crime

Character 2: Crime Category

A	Robbery/larceny (theft)
B	Assault (injury or intent to injure person)
C	Criminal mischief (damage or intent to damage property)
D	Violation (no damage or injury intended)

Character 3: Crime Details – A. Robbery/Larceny

A	Robbery operator (theft with force or threat of force)
B	Robbery passenger (theft with force or threat of force)
C	Larceny operator (theft without force, e.g., pickpocket)
D	Larceny passenger (theft without force, e.g., pickpocket)
E	Larceny fleet property (theft without force)
F	Larceny fleet revenue (theft without force)
G	Larceny non-fleet property (theft without force)

Character 3: Crime Details – B. Assault

A	Other operator assault
B	Other passenger assault
C	Assault by operator
D	Operator struck by thrown object
E	Passenger struck by thrown object

Character 3: Crime Details – C. Criminal Mischief

A	Missiles
B	Graffiti
C	Other

Character 3: Crime Details – D. Violations

A	Harassment
B	Hitching (no injury)
C	Hitching (injury)
D	Hitching (fatal)
E	Other violation

Miscellaneous

Character 2: Miscellaneous Category

A   Person leaving after alighting

B   Person approaching to board

C   Equipment damage or failure

D   Involvement—passenger/other person

E   Miscellaneous other

F   Incident observed

Character 3: Miscellaneous Details – A. Person Leaving after Alighting

A   Other fall in roadway or on adjacent ground

B   Fall in bus stop zone

C   Struck by vehicle in roadway—other

D   Struck by vehicle in roadway—alongside bus

E   Miscellaneous other and indeterminate

Character 3: Miscellaneous Details – B. Person Approaching to Board

A   Other fall in roadway or on adjacent ground

B   Fall in bus stop zone

C   Struck by vehicle in roadway—other

D   Struck by vehicle in roadway—alongside bus

E   Miscellaneous other and indeterminate

Character 3: Miscellaneous Details – C. Equipment Damage or Failure

A   Window/bus damage—no injury, not a crime

B   Bus fire

Character 3: Miscellaneous Details – D. Involvement – Passenger/Other Person

A   Illness/death on bus including sick employee

B   With passenger—fare or transfer

C   With passenger—other reason

D   Between passengers

E   With person other than passenger

F   Miscellaneous other and indeterminate

Character 3: Miscellaneous Details – E. Miscellaneous Other

A   Clothing soiled or damaged on bus

B   Other property damaged on bus

C   Miscellaneous other and indeterminate— also denial by operator

Character 3: Miscellaneous Details – F. Incident Observed

A   Vehicles colliding

B   Vehicle striking person

C   Person falling

D   Injury off bus

E   Other

Industrial (Employee) Accident

Character 2: Cause

A   Animal or insect

B   Contact—e.g., electricity, surface, molten metal, liquid

C   Fall—elevation

D   Fall—surface

E   Falling object

F   Flying object

G   Flying particle—source unknown (wind, dust)

H   Gas, fume, compressed air, heat

I   Handling object

J   Striking object (including pothole)

K   Stepping on object

L   Struck by object

M   Struck by train or vehicle

N   Dropped operator seat (seat collapses)

O   Miscellaneous

R   Trip, slip, or stumble boarding or alighting from bus

Chapter 9

Best Practices

Phil Moser, Carmen W. Daecher, and Amy Stewart

LEARNING OBJECTIVES

- Understand what *best practices* means for fleet operations.

- Be able to define the risk elements associated with fleet operations.

- Know the ten steps used to develop a fleet operations' driver-safety initiative.

- Be able to define *reportable* crashes.

- Understand the classes of Commercial Driver's Licenses (CDLs) and the use of endorsements and restrictions.

- Summarize the hours-of-service rules that were revised in 2005.

- List three types of provisions of laws pertaining to CDL drivers that regulate the use of drugs and alcohol.

The term *best practices* is often heard in organizations today. In this chapter, *best practices* describes consistently applied principles and activities that have produced consistently positive results in fleet management.

Over time, many misconceptions or myths have crept into our collective thinking regarding vehicle fleets. This chapter will discuss two such myths as a prelude to the discussion of best practices. The first is that fleet managers manage vehicles. If that is all they did, fleet management would be less challenging than it is. After all, vehicles cannot talk back or offer criticism to make the fleet manager's job more challenging.

The second myth is that the lowest-cost vehicle is best for an organization. While cost is always an important consideration, the quality of the ride and the vehicle's safety features are fundamentally important to its effective and efficient use and to the employee/driver being able to operate it safely and remaining safe while in it.

Most of the myths associated with fleet management overlook a critical element in fleet operations—the driver. Most fleet-operations management systems do not fully encompass all of the risk elements associated with the operation of vehicle fleets. Because of this, the term *fleet management* is inaccurate if an organization has employees who operate fleet vehicles. *Fleet operations management* is a far better general description of the process and its challenges.

BEST PRACTICES FOR RISK MANAGEMENT OF FLEET OPERATIONS

Managing fleet operations is managing risk. Best practices for managing these risks start with the identification of risk elements associated with fleet operations. They are drivers, vehicles, and operations associated with the use of vehicles.

These three elements comprise the core around which any effective management program for fleet operations is built. Not addressing any one of these elements allows risk to be uncontrolled.

187

Based upon this author's twenty years of experience in studying and assisting fleet operations of all sizes and types, three key management principles are important in effectively managing fleet operations:

- *Hiring the best person for the job.* The job description, if it includes driving a vehicle, should include consideration of driving abilities or the ability to learn the driving task effectively.

- *Training people to succeed.* Providing employees with the knowledge to effectively drive vehicles and understand critical behaviors associated with vehicle operations is essential to managing fleet operations. Fleet managers must ensure proficiency through repetition and/or testing during training.

- *Managing consistently.* With the knowledge that new employees receive, they should be expected to behave consistently according to the standards provided to them during training. Celebrating consistently good behavior and addressing unacceptable behavior are critical to keeping employees focused on behaviors that are critical in mitigating risk associated with fleet operations.

Too often, some or all of these principles are compromised. People are hired because of need rather than ability. Training is minimized or overlooked, and management is personal rather than objective. By objectively implementing and using these three key management principles, an effective and successful process of fleet operations management can be established.

A subtle but fundamentally important difference in managing fleet operations compared to other types of operations is the environment in which critical behaviors occur. In most situations, a supervisor is with employees on the floor or in the field and can identify critical behaviors and address them on the spot. Or, because of the interconnectivity between many job tasks, one employee's unsafe behavior is viewed as dangerous to the health and well-being of other employees. Thus, employees also assist in identifying and changing unacceptable behaviors.

This type of environment hardly ever exists while an employee is driving a vehicle. Usually, the driver is the captain of the ship. He or she is also the chief cook and bottle-washer. Drivers control their own destinies as well as those of others on the roadway with no direct supervision or oversight while operating the vehicle. The old paradigm *management by walking around* (MBWA) is not applicable in fleet operations. Rather, a new paradigm must be established for successful fleet operations: *management by driving around* (MBDA).

Expected Outcomes of Best Practices

With all of this in mind, best practices for management of fleet operations occur after the following components are in place:

- Enhancement of existing policies or establishment of new policies directed at fleet operations and critical behaviors associated with vehicle operations.

- Provision of adequate training to ensure that people have the proper skills to operate and maintain vehicles and understand critical behaviors and the importance of attitude and alertness while driving.

- Establishment of a progressive system of discipline for those who fail to behave acceptably. This system should attempt to refocus and retain employees rather than be purely negative in consequence. However, if employees cannot maintain consistently acceptable behavior, the company must limit the risk and liability associated with the unacceptable behavior.

- Implementation of a positive behavior-reinforcement strategy that is intended to celebrate good behavior on a regular basis and as soon as possible after such behavior is observed or acknowledged. Safety bonus programs by themselves are not always the best answer. A more fluid and interactive approach to positive reinforcement and a system in which all employees are focused on critical behaviors is more effective. The intended result of these programs is to keep people conscious of their own actions and behaviors as they drive. Positive communication may also take on the form of reminding employees of what is important as well as rewarding good behaviors after they are performed.

- Implementation of an improved fleet-efficiency program. By properly selecting and maintaining vehicles and establishing standards for their use (maximum speed, fuel usage, and so on) a more efficient and effective use of the vehicle fleet—in conjunction with vehicle performance standards that incorporate safe operation—can be established and measured.

- Revisions to organizational operations as they relate to critical behaviors and fleet efficiency. Through reassessment and adjustment to company operations that affect safe vehicle-fleet operations (such as scheduling, routing, and provisions for replacing vehicles), company employees other than drivers and service technicians become involved in safe fleet operations. Through this process, others who influence safe fleet operations are aware of the company's commitment to safe fleet operations in combination with customer service and satisfaction and profitability.

• Establishment of a measurement and accountability process to monitor results and to help safety records to continue to improve. Regular reporting and analyzing will identify processes, policies, personnel, and other key performance items that may need change or improvement.

After an effective fleet-operations management system is in place, what should be expected? A consistently applied, effective fleet management program should produce the following sequence of results:

• elimination of poor performers

• reduced turnover

• improved communication regarding performance

• higher-quality training

• a more efficient vehicle fleet

• improved customer services and profitability

• more consistent and effective management of fleet operations

References that Can Help the Fleet Manager

The following standards, in addition to referenced publications, offer guidelines that organizations can use to shape and implement a fleet improvement program:

• ANSI Z15.1-2006, *Safe Practices for Motor Vehicle Operations* (ANSI/ASSE 2006) (for all fleet operations)

• Code of Federal Regulations (CFR) Title 49 (Parts 40, 171–180, 325, 380–399) (for commercial fleet operations)

These standards define the framework for achieving best management practices for fleet operations and detail regulatory requirements for commercial fleets. By implementing a well-defined and measurable risk-management process that also complies with all applicable regulations, an organization can achieve best practices for fleet operations.

A Ten-Step Outline for Creating a Fleet Safety Initiative

Year in and year out, traffic crashes are the leading cause of death for American workers. Annually, approximately 21 percent of worker fatalities occur as a result of motor-vehicle collisions (BLS 2011). Nevertheless, driver safety has rarely received the same level of attention as other areas of employee safety, but this is changing. Since the ANSI Z15.1-2006 standards on driver safety were published, the awareness level for driver safety has been elevated. This is great news, because in order for a problem to be corrected, there must be an awareness that the problem exists. The ANSI Z15.1-2006 standard is just one source that can be used by organizations to achieve their driver-safety goals. While many of the suggested strategies for achieving success with a driver-safety initiative are discussed in ANSI Z15.1-2006. (ANSI/ASSE 2006), the information covered in this chapter originated from the author's experiences, training, and knowledge regarding driver safety.

Many safety professionals are not familiar with the steps necessary to create a comprehensive fleet safety initiative within their organization. The following ten-step best-practices approach will help them to create a driver-safety initiative for their organization.

Step 1: Understand the Problem

In order to justify taking on a major driver-safety initiative, it is first necessary to understand the problem. This justification can begin at the national level. In 2008, according to the *Fatality Analysis Reporting System Encyclopedia* on the NHTSA Web site (NHTSA 2008), there were 34,017 fatal motor-vehicle traffic crashes. That is an average of 93 people dying every day. Early estimates for 2009 are that 33,963 people died in motor-vehicle traffic crashes, a decline of 8.9 percent from 2008, in which 37,261 people died.

Looked at in terms of risk factors, this means that one average American driver in fifteen will be involved in a motor-vehicle collision during the next year. One average American driver in forty-five will be involved in an injury collision during the next year. And one average American driver in sixty-five will be involved in a fatal collision during his or her driving lifetime. The term used for these statistics is *average American driver*. People who drive as part of their job may not be considered average. Chances are they drive quite a bit more than the *average* driver.

A National Household Travel Survey (NHTS) conducted from 2001 to 2002 by the Bureau of Transportation Statistics found that contrary to the stereotypical image of the business traveler heading off to catch a cross-country flight, the majority of long-distance business trips in the United States are taken to destinations within 250 miles of home and are by automobile. The personal vehicle is the dominant travel mode for business travel, comprising 81 percent of all trips. Air travel accounts for about 16 percent of all business trips (BTS 2003). The average driver logs approximately 10,000 to 12,000 miles a year. The typical business driver logs approximately 25,000 miles a year. The exposure of business drivers to collisions and all of their associated risks is greater than that of the average driver—they are not *average*.

In fact, data analysis by the U.S. Department of Labor, Bureau of Labor Statistics (BLS), has shown that transportation incidents cause more work-related deaths in the United States (at 40 percent) than any other single incident type (BLS 2014). As illustrated in Figure 1, (page 16) motor-vehicle crashes were responsible for 22 percent of all worker fatalities in 2013, causing over one in five work-related deaths. The next most frequent cause of worker fatalities—contact with objects and equipment—accounted for less than half as many fatalities.

To fully understand the problem, it is necessary to look at more than just national statistics. Each organization should determine its own crash rate as well as the number of crash-related injuries, lost workdays, and workers' compensation claims that resulted from motor-vehicle collisions.

Step 2: Set Achievable Goals

The ultimate goal is to create a safe driving culture throughout an organization. Organizations that have created such a culture have had great success. As an example, in the manufacturing environment, there are some areas employees would never think of entering without the proper safety equipment, such as hard hats or eye protection, because, in this work environment, wearing protection is part of the culture. Nobody questions it. Employees adhere to these safety practices as a matter of course. This is the type of culture that must be achieved when it comes to driver safety. To reach this important overall goal, it is necessary to set achievable goals along the way. Each step listed in this chapter should be viewed as an incremental goal that is necessary to achieve a successful driver-safety initiative.

Another important goal is setting timelines for reducing the number of crashes. Quarterly, semiannual, and annual goals can be set. They should be realistic but not too easy to achieve. If an organization does not ask for quality, it will not achieve quality.

Step 3: Enlist Help

Safety professionals should seek help from people in various divisions of their organization, such as human resources, fleet management, risk management, and legal department personnel.

Human resources personnel can provide information that can justify a safe-driving initiative. They have an obvious understanding of the human element of such an initiative and can be very beneficial in trying to move it forward.

Fleet personnel see the damages and lost assets that result from motor-vehicle collisions and can also be of great assistance.

Risk-management personnel should work hand in hand with safety professionals on this initiative because managing risk is what it is all about. If an organization is insured, a reduced number of vehicle crashes has benefits in the form of reduced insurance rates. If an organization is self-insured, the savings from a reduced crash rate will improve its bottom line.

Involving the legal department provides a couple of benefits. The first is they will make sure that the initiative is within legal guidelines. The second is legal advisers can emphasize the benefits of a comprehensive driver-safety initiative from the viewpoint of exposure to litigation.

Step 4: Obtain Management Buy-In

No initiative will work if upper management is not behind it. They control the purse strings, but they also set the tone of the organization. If it is important to the boss, it will be important to the employee.

Most managers understand that creating a safe work environment is a fundamental requirement of running a successful business. Many organizations have mission statements that express the need for a safe work environment for all employees, and the driving environment should be no exception. With upper-management support, much can be done to create the safest work environment possible for employees who drive as part of their job.

In order to obtain upper-management support, it is important to look at the human element. This is where a relationship with human resources personnel is helpful. They can provide information about workers' compensation, lost workdays, and quality-of-life issues as they relate to employee motor-vehicle collisions.

The human element aside, all organizations look for ways to save money. The return on investment from a successful driver-safety initiative can be tremendous. Safety professionals should create mathematical models that take into consideration all losses caused by motor-vehicle collisions, including workers' compensation, lost productivity, litigation, and vehicle repairs and replacement, and contrast them with the savings that can be achieved with a reduced crash rate. The fiscal benefits of a driver-safety initiative will soon become apparent.

A number of companies in the United States have achieved tremendous savings as a result of their reduced crash rates (OSHA 2006).

Table 1 depicts an actual case study and Table 2 shows the savings the organization achieved.

During this six-year period, Company A's fleet grew by 534 vehicles—32 percent. At a time when the fleet's total number of claims might have been expected to increase, it actually decreased by 16 percent. In fact, during each year of the driver training, the number of claims diminished.

Total reduction in claims = 567

Total direct savings = $1,637,967

Table 2 shows the program savings . The total cost of Company A's driver training program was $542,076. The total direct savings that Company A realized were $1,637,967. This represents a savings of $1,095,891, approximately a 62 percent return on the investment.

The average cost per crash is $16,500 [quoted from the Web site for the Network of Employers for Traffic Safety (NETS)]. Another $4000 can conservatively be added to each incident to cover medical costs, lost time on the job, workers' compensation, and claims and litigation resulting from the collisions. Multiplying that number ($20,500) by the number of claims Company A avoided (567), the estimated total savings is $11,623,500.

TABLE 1

Results of a Fleet Driver Training Program

Year	Training (in $)	Number of Claims	Fleet Size	Crash Rate
Year 1	75,860	632	1664	38%
Year 2	41,442	576	1747	33%
Year 3	91,860	517	1847	28%
Year 4	141,890	525	1945	27%
Year 5	100,612	492	2054	24%
Year 6	90,412	483	2198	22%

TABLE 2

Claims Reduction and Direct Cost Savings

Year	Reduction in Claims	Average Claim Cost (in $)	Savings (in $)
Year 1	Year program started	--	--
Year 2	56	3224	180,544
Year 3	115	2695	309,925
Year 4	107	2971	317,897
Year 5	140	2851	399,140
Year 6	149	2889	430,461

Step 5: Develop Fair and Comprehensive Policies

Safety professionals must help their organizations to create fair and comprehensive driver-safety policies. These policies will evolve over time, but it is important to set a base from which to start. Policies should include driver's license requirements, standards for driver's license records checks, hiring standards, an action plan for problem drivers, training requirements, and safety incentives.

Step 6: Require Drivers' License Records Checks and Set Consequences for At-Risk Drivers

It is absolutely imperative to run drivers' license records checks on employee drivers, and systems must be in place to manage these records. The organization must also be prepared to take immediate action regarding drivers with poor driving records.

There are fifty states, and each has a different motor-vehicle code. Organizations must have systems in place that interpret their state's driving records and provide a point-scoring system for various violations. This scoring system should assign points that are appropriate to the seriousness of each infraction. For instance, a driver who has a stop-sign violation might receive two points, but one who drives under the influence of drugs or alcohol would receive ten points. There are vendors that offer this type of system.

All crash data must be recorded on employee drivers' records. Only *reportable* crashes will show up on a driver's record check. Reportable crashes are those that involve injury or death and those in which vehicles must be towed. Crashes in which nobody is hurt and the cars drive away will not show up in a driver's record check, but there are vendors that can help collect all crash data, even the data that does not show up in the records.

Once drivers receive a certain number of points, an intervention should take place that is equivalent to their level of risk. Organizations should classify drivers in three risk groups based on the number of violation points on their records. Suggested interventions are:

- Level I (smallest number of points): Consider an intervention that includes a computer-based training program.
- Level II: Consider a more active intervention such as a classroom program and a behind-the-wheel program.
- Level III: Consider termination or one-on-one training.

Step 7: Educate Drivers

Step 6 will identify and help drivers who are having problems—and encourage driver accountability. It is not possible to hold drivers accountable if they do not have a base of knowledge regarding safe driving. Just because drivers are licensed does not mean they are safe drivers. If drivers are unaware of basic safe-driving principles, it is difficult to hold them accountable for collisions that might have been avoided had they been aware of those principles.

Organizations should provide all drivers with basic safe-driving information and keep records documenting that they received this knowledge. Once this is accomplished, drivers should be held accountable for driving safely.

Step 8: Begin at the Beginning

Statistics prove that new hires are involved in more crashes than established employees (Volpe 1998). According to this report, the crash rate for employees within their first twelve months of employment is higher than for employees who have been driving for a company longer. This stands to reason, because many of these new employees are learning new jobs in unfamiliar vehicles, possibly in unfamiliar areas. Also, many of these newly hired drivers are young people who fall within an age range that statistically has a higher crash rate than other age ranges.

For this reason, new hires should be provided with safe-driver training right from the start. This accomplishes two things: (1) they will gain some very important information that will help them to stay safe when they get behind the wheel, and (2) they will understand the tone of the organization from the beginning—that safe driving is considered very important.

Step 9: Ensure that Field-Level Managers Convey the Right Message

People who have direct managerial responsibility for an organization's drivers can make or break a driver-safety initiative. Some managers tell drivers to GO, GO, GO; others say, SAFETY, now GO, GO, GO. If safe driving is not important to a driver's immediate manager, it will not be important to that driver.

Managers should be taught that they play a vital role in helping to keep employees safe. They should have instruction on how to conduct safety ride-alongs and be required to conduct ride-alongs at least twice a year. The results of ride-alongs should be an important part of each employee's performance review. This is an extremely important part of any driver-safety initiative.

Step 10: Sustain What Is Achieved

Organizations should not waste time, money, and effort putting together a driver-safety initiative if they do not plan to sustain it. They may identify problem drivers and provide drivers with some initial training with great results, but unless they keep driver safety in front of their drivers, their results will diminish with time.

Sustaining a safe-driving initiative can be done very cost effectively. Newsletters, e-flashes, periodic testing, and recognition of safe driving are all effective measures that can be taken to help an organization maintain a safe driving record.

Addressing Safe Driving Is Worth the Effort

Addressing driver safety is a formidable but very achievable task. For organizations that have addressed driver safety and are still looking for ways to improve, this chapter will provide some assistance. Safety professionals in an organization can make a big difference in this area of safety.

DRIVER-SAFETY POLICY GUIDELINES

The following sections should be included in a comprehensive driver-safety policy. Some may not apply to all organizations, and additional sections may be necessary for some organizations.

1.0 Purpose

This section provides reasons for the policies that help to ensure the safe operation of vehicles, including those owned or leased by the organization and those used to conduct business for the organization.

- The ultimate goal of these policies is to promote and maintain the well-being of the employees.
- By reducing the number of collisions, the risks of employee injury and death are reduced.

2.0 Scope

In this section the organization explains to whom the policy applies and what vehicles are affected. It should include company-owned, leased, and rented vehicles as well as those that are used to conduct business for the organization.

3.0 Definitions

Some definitions may clarify which employees and vehicles are affected by the policy. Others may describe serious infractions and immediate-action incidents.

4.0 Hiring Requirements

These are clear guidelines that are to be followed regarding employee license requirements and driving history, and how they affect the consideration of those applying for employment.

5.0 Driver Records Checks

Organizations must spell out Department of Motor Vehicle (DMV) check timelines. Wording should be included that makes it clear that DMV checks will be run on a regular basis and at other times when determined necessary. Wording should cover the Fair Credit and Reporting Act regulations.

6.0 Violation Point Assessments

Organizations should develop point codes that rate violations and crashes. Point codes are utilized to determine level of discipline/retraining. The point codes should reflect the severity of each type of incident.

7.0 Risk Levels

Organizations should develop a system that rates the number of points accumulated by drivers and defines risk levels based on the number of points.

8.0 Risk-Level Interventions

This policy describes the interventions that will take place for each level of risk.

9.0 Dispute of Findings

This policy sets a time during which a driver can dispute the findings of a DMV driver records check. It should specify that no record can be changed internally until the governing body that issued the record has changed the official record.

10.0 General Compliance

A general policy should be included that states all employee drivers must comply with all laws related to the legal operation of motor vehicles.

11.0 Family Members Operating Organization Vehicles

This policy states whether family members (spouses, common-law spouses, life partners, and driver-age children) may operate the organization's vehicles. If family members are sometimes allowed to operate company vehicles, the policy must specify how DMV-check regulations affect family members and how their driving records will affect whether they may operate the organization's vehicles.

12.0 Collision Reporting

This policy describes employees' responsibilities for reporting work-related collisions and other collisions involving the organization's vehicles. It should define the steps that employees must take when a collision occurs, including notification of the proper authorities and notification of the employer.

13.0 Violation Reporting

This policy should require that all moving violations be reported to the employer within a given time period, both those that occur during work time and those that occur during personal time. The reasoning behind this is that any violation that affects a person's driving record affects the person's ability to drive for the organization.

14.0 Personal Vehicle Use

Some organizations allow employees to use personal vehicles for work-related activities. This policy defines insurance and vehicle maintenance requirements and describes reimbursement policies. The organization's tax department should make sure the policy complies with all applicable tax codes.

15.0 Collision Classifications

Many organizations determine whether an employee driver could have prevented a collision. There is a distinct difference between fault and preventability. It may be found that a driver is not at fault for a collision but could have prevented it from happening.

16.0 Collision Deductibles

Some employers charge a deductible to employees who are involved in preventable collisions in organization vehicles. Some states regulate this practice and may prohibit it.

SAMPLE POLICY

The following policy is a blueprint for a comprehensive fleet safety policy. Items covered in this sample policy may not apply to every organization, and some organizations may need to add policies to address their specific needs.

1.0 Purpose

(Organization Name) is committed to promoting the safe, proper, and professional operation of all motor vehicles that it owns, leases, or rents, and any other vehicles used for (Organization Name) business. These vehicles are operated by its employees, client employees, vendors, and other authorized operators for business and personal use.

(Organization Name) has an obligation to make sure anyone driving an (Organization Name)-owned or -leased vehicle, or anyone driving on (Organization Name) business has a valid driver's license. (Organization Name) also has an obligation to make sure that its drivers do not have a history of unsafe driving.

(Organization Name) has enacted a policy for the purpose of implementing procedures for drivers' license records checks. This policy also institutes an action plan for drivers who have a history of unsafe driving. This policy will be referred to as the *DMV Policy*.

2.0 Scope

The DMV Policy is applicable to the following:

- All persons who drive an (Organization Name)-owned or -leased vehicle for business or personal use
- All spouses who, in accordance with this policy, are permitted to drive an (Organization Name)-owned or -leased vehicle
- All persons who drive personal vehicles for (Organization Name) business
- All persons who drive any other vehicles for (Organization Name) business

3.0 Definitions

The following definitions apply to the DMV Policy:

3.1 *(Organization Name) Motor Vehicles* includes all motor vehicles that are owned, leased, or rented by (Organization Name) and any other vehicles used for (Organization Name) business.

3.2 *Drivers* refers to all persons described in section 2.0 of the DMV Policy.

3.3 *Administrative Suspension of Driving Privileges* includes any suspension of a driver's operating license as the result of administrative actions. They include nonpayment of child support, nonpayment of taxes, and any other instance that does not involve a motor-vehicle violation.

3.4 *Suspension of Driving Privileges* includes any suspension, revocation, or other loss of a driver's operating privileges as a result of a motor-vehicle violation(s).

3.5 *Preventable Collision:* A collision is preventable when it is determined that a driver's actions (or inactions) put him or her into a position in which a collision occurred.

3.6 *Nonpreventable Collision:* A collision is nonpreventable when no matter what action the driver took, he or she could not have avoided a collision.

3.7 *At-Fault Collision:* A collision is at-fault with respect to a driver when the investigating authority determines that the driver was responsible for at least 51 percent of the cause of the collision.

3.8 *Not-at-Fault Collision:* A collision is considered not-at-fault with respect to a driver when the investigating authority determines that the driver was responsible for less than 51 percent of the cause of the collision.

3.9 *Serious Driving Infractions* include the following:

- any suspension of driving privileges
- any driving-under-suspension violation
- any driving-under-the-influence violation
- any offense involving fleeing or evading police, or related actions
- any violation involving leaving the scene of a motor-vehicle collision
- any reckless driving violation*
- any homicide-by-vehicle or vehicular manslaughter violation
- any speeding violation of 30 or more miles per hour (mph) over the speed limit
- any vehicle-related misdemeanor or felony violation

*Reckless driving is included under *Serious Driving Infractions* because it is defined as "The willful and wanton disregard for safety of persons or property" (Pennsylvania Consolidated Statutes, Vehicle Code, Title 75). It is not the same as inattentive driving.

4.0 Requirements for Consideration of Employment

4.1 Scope

This section of the DMV Policy is applicable to all persons who operate vehicles within the scope of their employment with (Organization Name) and is a consideration of employment to any person who has been given a conditional offer of employment by (Organization Name).

4.2 General Requirements

- Any person who falls under the scope of this section must possess a current and valid driver's license that is issued by the controlling authority where the applicant currently resides.
- Persons who fall under the scope of this section must give written permission to conduct a check of their motor-vehicle record (MVR). The federal Driver's Privacy Protection Act (DPPA) of 1994 is the primary law governing a fleet manager's ability to collect and use employees' MVRs. Under this

law, state DMVs are restricted from disclosing personally identifiable driver records without first obtaining the driver's expressed written consent (Alaniz 2008). This is a condition of employment.

4.3 Considerations

Persons who have received a conditional offer of employment will not be eligible for employment if, within the past three years, they

- received a conviction for any serious driving infraction as defined by the DMV Policy, such as collisions for which they were convicted of driving under the influence (DUI)/driving while intoxicated (DWI).
- received three or more convictions for a speeding violation in excess of 20 mph.
- received four or more convictions for moving violations.
- were involved in more than two preventable collisions.

5.0 Driver License Records Checks

On an annual basis, or more frequently, (Organization Name) will run a check on the drivers' licenses of all individuals who fall under the scope of the DMV Policy Violations, and collisions that have occurred over a rolling three-year period will be considered for the purposes of these checks.

6.0 Risk-Level Classifications

In order to effectively manage drivers with motor-vehicle violations and/or collisions, the following risk-level classifications will be used to determine which interventions will result in accordance with each driver's activities:

- 0–3 points—No risk
- 4–6 points—Level I
- 7–9 points—Level II
- 10-plus points—Level III

7.0 Risk-Level Interventions

All interventions must be communicated to the drivers with a clear expectation for improvement.

7.1 Level I

Drivers will complete a computer-based training program that addresses the specific problems they are experiencing. This training will include testing to document the results of the training.

7.2 Level II

Drivers will complete an instructor-led, eight-hour classroom and behind-the-wheel training program that addresses the specific problems they are experiencing.

7.3 Level III

Drivers will participate in a one-on-one, full-day training session that addresses the specific problems they are experiencing. A comprehensive report will be filed that details the driver's driving habits. Level III drivers also face further disciplinary action up to and including termination of employment.

7.4 Spouse/Domestic Partner Risk-Level Drivers

Spouses or domestic partners of (Organization Name) employees who receive violations that put them in any of the risk levels outlined in this policy will not be permitted to operate (Organization Name)-owned or -leased vehicles until they have proven that they are no longer risk-level drivers.

8.0 Dispute of Findings

Once a risk-level driver is notified of the findings from a driver's license records check, he or she has 30 days to dispute the findings. To be removed from a risk-level category, a driver's violation(s) must be removed from the driver's license records by the issuing authority that posted them. If, within the 30 days, a driver notifies (Organization Name) that the violation(s) have been removed, (Organization Name) will conduct another driver's license records check. If the driver no longer falls under a risk-level category, no further action will be taken. If the driver still falls under a risk-level category, the appropriate action will take place.

(Organization Name) may remove the driver from all (Organization Name) driving responsibilities during the 30-day dispute period.

9.0 Violation Point Assessments

The following is an example of a violation-point system to classify motor vehicle violations and collisions:

9.1 No Points

Nonmoving violations, including equipment violations
Other nonmoving actions

9.2 Two Points

One preventable collision in a year
Windshield/window obstruction

Speeding (one to ten mph over speed limit)

Driving with expired driver's license

Stop-sign violations

Driving while fatigued

Red/yellow light violations

Backing-up violation

Failure to yield

Seatbelt violation

Improper lane change

Following too closely

Improper turn

Improper lane use

Improper passing

Headlight violation (nonequipment)

Disobedience of traffic devices

One-way street violation

Blocking intersection

Failure to obey police officer

Improper signaling

Littering from vehicle

Obstructing traffic

Other moving violation

Vehicle license class violation

9.3 Four Points

Driving too fast for conditions

Passing school bus

Speeding (eleven to twenty mph over speed limit)

Failure to yield to emergency vehicle

Speeding (school zone)

Unrestrained child

Inattentive driving

9.4 Six Points

Two preventable collisions in a year

Speeding (twenty-one to thirty mph over speed limit)

9.5 Ten Points

Three preventable collisions in a year

Fleeing or evading police and related offenses

Speeding (thirty-one to forty mph over speed limit)

Driver's license suspension

DWI/DUI and other alcohol-use violations

Driving while license is suspended

Hit-and-run violations

False reports

Reckless driving

9.6 Twenty Points

Four preventable collisions in a year

Any misdemeanor or felony charge except DUI/DWI

Speeding (forty-one or more mph over speed limit)

10.0 Driver's License Requirements

Drivers who fall under the scope of the DMV Policy must, at all times, possess a valid driver's license issued by the authority that has jurisdiction where the driver resides. The license class must be appropriate for the class of vehicle the person drives for (Organization Name).

11.0 Vehicle-Law Compliance

Persons who fall under the scope of the DMV Policy must, at all times, comply with all traffic laws that pertain to the area where they are driving.

12.0 Spouse Use of (Organization Name) Vehicles

The spouse or domestic partner of an (Organization Name) employee may operate a vehicle that has been assigned to that employee. This policy pertains to (Organization Name)-owned or -leased vehicles and does not include vehicles that bear (Organization Name) decals.

13.0 Reporting Violations

Drivers who fall under the scope of the DMV Policy must report to their immediate manager when they are charged with motor-vehicle violations as follows:

- Within 72 hours of their first reporting workday, they must report any moving violations they have been charged with.
- They must immediately report any suspension of driving privileges.
- Within 24 hours of their first reporting workday, they must report any serious motor-vehicle infraction as defined by this policy.

Any violation that affects a person's driver's license status affects the person's ability to legally operate a vehicle for (Organization Name). Therefore, reporting of violations includes violations that occur during either company or personal time and includes incidents that involve either company or personal vehicles.

13.1 Managers' Responsibility

Managers who receive a self-reported notification of a violation from an employee will, as soon as possible, report this information to the (Organization Name) Fleet Services and/or Risk Management Department.

14.0 Motor-Vehicle Collision Reporting

Persons who are involved in motor-vehicle collisions while operating any vehicle on (Organization Name) business or at any time while operating an (Organization Name)-owned or -leased vehicle must immediately report the collision to the (Organization Name) Fleet Services Department or its designee.

15.0 Seatbelt Usage

Drivers and passengers traveling in vehicles that are being driven on (Organization Name) business or in vehicles owned or leased by (Organization Name) must properly wear seatbelts while vehicles are in operation.

16.0 Vehicle Maintenance

Vehicles that fall under the scope of the DMV PolicyÁmust be properly maintained as described by the (Organization Name) Fleet Services Department.

17.0 Privately Owned Vehicles Used for Business

Persons who, with the approval of (Organization Name), use a privately owned vehicle for (Organization Name) business will receive a predetermined per-mile reimbursement for this use.

18.0 Collision Classifications

It is the responsibility of the (Organization Name) Fleet Services Department or its designee to determine whether an (Organization Name)-related motor-vehicle collision was preventable or nonpreventable as defined under sections 3.5 and 3.6 of the DMV Policy.

19.0 Driver Deductibles

19.1 If, within a three-year period, an employee is involved in a preventable collision while operating an (Organization Name) vehicle or while driving on (Organization Name) business, that employee will be charged a deductible fee of ???. [The fee is determined by individual organizations and typically increases with each offense.]

19.2 If, within a three-year period, an employee is involved in two preventable collisions while operating an (Organization Name) vehicle or while driving on (Organization Name) business, that employee will be charged a deductible fee of ???. [The fee is determined by individual organizations and typically increases with each offense.]

19.3 If, within a three-year period, an employee is involved in three preventable collisions while operating an (Organization Name) vehicle or while driving on (Organization Name) business, that employee will be charged a deductible fee of ???. [The fee is determined by individual organizations and typically increases with each offense.]

19.4 If, within a three-year period, an employee is involved in more than three preventable collisions while operating an (Organization Name) vehicle or while driving on (Organization Name) business, that employee will be charged a deductible fee of ??? and will face possible termination. [The fee is determined by individual organizations and typically increases with each offense.]

COMMERCIAL VEHICLES

Department of Transportation (DOT) Regulations

The regulations covering commercial vehicles are extensive. Areas covered in these regulations include, but are not limited to, driver licensing; hours of service; weight, height, and length restrictions; vehicle inspection; and driver alcohol and drug violations.

For the purposes of this chapter, the focus will be on hours of service, alcohol and drug regulations, and driver licensing requirements.

Visit the Federal Motor Carrier Safety Administration (FMCSA) Web site at www.fmcsa.dot.gov for a complete view of commercial vehicle regulations.

Figure 2 is an excerpt of the Commercial Motor Vehicle Safety Act of 1986; it is taken from the Federal Motor Carrier Safety Administration Web site (FMCSA 2008).

CDLIS CLEARINGHOUSE

States must be connected to the Commercial Driver's License Information System (CDLIS) and the National Driver Register (NDR) in order to exchange information about CMV drivers, traffic convictions, and disqualifications. A state must use both the CDLIS and NDR to check a driver's record, and the CDLIS to make certain that the applicant does not already have a CDL. Members

COMMERCIAL MOTOR VEHICLE (CMV) SAFETY ACT OF 1986

The Commercial Motor Vehicle Safety Act of 1986 was signed into law on October 27, 1986. The goal of the Act is to improve highway safety by ensuring that drivers of large trucks and buses are qualified to operate those vehicles and to remove unsafe and unqualified drivers from the highways. The Act retained the State's right to issue a driver's license, but established minimum national standards which States must meet when issuing CDLs.

The Act addresses circumstances that existed prior to 1986 by making it illegal for CDL holders to possess more than one license, requiring States to adopt knowledge and skills testing to ensure that individuals required to have a CDL are qualified to operate heavy trucks and buses, and establishing minimum licensing standards and information requirements for the CDLs.

It is important to note that the Act does not require drivers to obtain a separate Federal license; it merely requires States to upgrade their existing testing and licensing programs, if necessary, to conform to the Federal minimum standards.

The CDL program places requirements on the CMV driver, the employing motor carrier and the States.

THE DRIVER

Drivers have been required to have a CDL in order to drive certain CMVs since April 1, 1992.

The Federal Motor Carrier Safety Administration (FMCSA) has developed and issued standards for testing and licensing CDL holders. These standards require States to issue CDLs to certain CMV drivers only after the driver passes knowledge and skills tests administered by the State and related to the type of vehicle the driver expects to operate. Drivers are expected to obtain and hold a CDL if they operate in interstate, intrastate, or foreign commerce if they drive a vehicle that meets any of the classifications of a CDL:

Classes of License:

The Federal standard requires States to issue a CDL to drivers according to the following license classifications:

Class A – Any combination of vehicles with a gross vehicle weight rating, GVWR, of 26,001 or more pounds provided the GVWR of the vehicle(s) being towed is in excess of 10,000 pounds.

Class B – Any single vehicle with a GVWR of 26,001 or more pounds, or any such vehicle towing a vehicle not in excess of 10,000 pounds GVWR.

Class C – Any single vehicle, or combination of vehicles, that does not meet the definition of Class A or Class B, but is either designed to transport 16 or more passengers, including the driver, or is transporting material designated as hazardous under 49 U.S.C. 5103 and is required to be placarded under subpart F of 49 CFR Part 172 or is transporting any quantity of a material listed as a select agent or toxin in 42 CFR Part 73.

Endorsements and Restrictions:

Drivers who operate special types of CMVs also need to pass additional tests to obtain any of the following endorsements on their CDL:

- T - Double/Triple Trailers (Knowledge test only)
- P - Passenger (Knowledge and Skills Tests)
- N - Tank Vehicle (Knowledge Test only)
- H - Hazardous Materials (Knowledge Test and TSA Threat Assessment)
- X - Combination of Tank Vehicle and Hazardous Materials
- School Bus (Knowledge and Skills Tests)

If a driver either fails the air brake component of the general knowledge test or performs the skills test in a vehicle not equipped with air brakes, the driver is issued an air brake restriction, restricting the driver from operating a CMV equipped with air brakes.

THE STATES

Knowledge & Skills Tests:

States develop their own tests, which must meet the Federal standards provided for in Subpart G and H of 49 CFR Part 383. Model driver and examiner manuals and tests have been prepared and distributed to the States to use, if they wish.

- Each basic knowledge test, i.e., the test covering the areas referred to in 49 CFR 383.11 for the applicable vehicle group, shall contain at least 30 items, exclusive to the number of items testing air brake knowledge.
- To pass the knowledge tests (general and endorsement), applicants must correctly answer at least 80 percent of the questions.
- To pass the skills test, applicants must successfully perform all the required skills (listed in 49 CFR 383.113 through 49 CFR 383.123). The skills test must be taken in a vehicle representative of the type of vehicle that the applicant operates or expects to operate.

Third-Party Skills Testing:

A State may authorize a person (including another State, an employer, a private driver training facility or other private institution, or a department, agency, or instrumentality) to administer the skills tests, if the following conditions are met:

- Tests must be the same as those given by the State.
- Examiners must meet the same qualifications as State examiners.
- The third party has an agreement with the State containing, at a minimum, provisions that:
  - States must conduct an on-site inspection at least yearly.
  - At least annually, State employees must evaluate the programs by taking third party tests as if they were test applicants, or by testing a sample of drivers tested by the third party and then comparing pass/fail rates.
- The State's agreement with the third-party skills tester must allow the FHWA and the State to conduct random examinations, inspections, and audits without prior notice.

FIGURE 2. Excerpt from Commercial Motor Vehicle Safety Act of 1986

Exemption of Skills Testing Requirements:

States have the option to exempt certain individuals with good driving records from the skills testing requirements (commonly known as "grandfathering"). The State shall impose conditions and limitations to restrict the applicants from whom a State may accept alternative requirements for the skills test described in 49 CFR 383.11. Such conditions must require at least the following:

Driver has a current license at time of application; and Driver has a good driving record and previously passed an acceptable skills test; or driver has a good driving record in combination with certain driving experience.

"Good driving record" means:

A driver can certify that, during the 2-year period immediately prior to applying for a CDL he/she:

- Has not had more than one license;
- Has not had any license suspended, revoked, or canceled;
- Has not had any convictions in any type of motor vehicle for major disqualifying offense;
- Has not had more than one conviction for any type of motor vehicle for a serious traffic violation;
- Has not had any violation of State or local law relating to motor vehicle traffic control arising in connection with any traffic accident, and has no record of an accident in which he/she was at fault.

"Driving experience" means:

A driver can certify and provide evidence that:

- He/she is regularly employed in a job requiring operation of CMV, and that either:
- He/she has previously taken and passed a skills test given by a State with a classified testing system, and that the test was behind-the-wheel in a representative vehicle for that applicant's driver's license application; or
- He/she has operated a representative vehicle for at least 2 years immediately preceding application for a CDL.

Commercial Driver's License Document:

A State determines the license fee, the license renewal cycle, most renewal procedures, and continues to decide the age, medical and other driver qualifications of its intrastate commercial drivers. Interstate drivers must meet the longstanding Federal driver qualifications (49 CFR 391).

All CDLs must contain the following information:

- The words "Commercial Driver's License" or "CDL";
- The driver's full name, signature, and address;
- The driver's date of birth, sex, and height
- Color photograph or digitized image of the driver;
- The driver's State license number;
- The name of the issuing State;
- The date of issuance and the date of the expiration of the license;
- The class(es) of vehicle that the driver is authorized to drive;
- Notation of the "air brake" restriction, if issued;
- The endorsement(s) for which the driver has qualified.

States may issue learner's permits for purposes of behind-the-wheel training on public highways as long as learner's permit holders are required to be accompanied by someone with a valid CDL appropriate for that vehicle and the learner's permits are issued for limited time periods.

Waiver Provisions:

All active duty military drivers were waived from the CDL requirements by the Federal Highway Administrator. A State, at its discretion, may waive firefighters, emergency response vehicle drivers, farmers and drivers removing snow and ice in small communities from the CDL requirements, subject to certain conditions.

In addition, a State may also waive the CDL knowledge and skills testing requirements for seasonal drivers in farm-related service industries and may waive certain knowledge and skills testing requirements for drivers in remote areas of Alaska. The drivers are issued restricted CDLs. A State can also waive the CDL hazardous materials endorsement test requirements for part-time drivers working for the pyrotechnics industry, subject to certain conditions.

OTHER REQUIREMENTS

There are a variety of other requirements related to this legislation which affect the commercial drivers, their employing motor carriers and the States.

Penalties:

The Federal penalty to a driver who violates the CDL requirements is a civil penalty of up to $2,500 or, in aggravated cases, criminal penalties of up to $5,000 in fines and/or up to 90 days in prison. An employer is also subject to a penalty of up to $10,000, if he or she knowingly uses a driver to operate a CMV without a valid CDL.

CDLIS Clearinghouse:

States must be connected to the Commercial Driver's License Information System (CDLIS) and the National Driver Register (NDR) in order to exchange information about CMV drivers, traffic convictions, and disqualifications. A State must use both the CDLIS and NDR to check a driver's record, and the CDLIS to make certain that the applicant does not already have a CDL. Members of the law enforcement community seeking access to CDLIS data should visit the FMCSA Technical Support Web site. Carriers needing CDLIS data should seek a commercial company that provides a clearinghouse service for this information, or contact the driver's State of licensure.

FIGURE 2. Excerpt from Commercial Motor Vehicle Safety Act of 1986 (cont.)

of the law-enforcement community seeking access to CDLIS data should visit the FMCSA Technical Support Web site. Carriers needing CDLIS data should seek a commercial company that provides a clearinghouse service for this information, or contact the driver's state of licensure.

HOURS OF SERVICE REGULATIONS

The rules governing hours of service were changed in 2005. The last changes had been made in 2003. Figure 3 offers a snapshot of the new regulations.

Short-Haul Hours-of-Service Provisions

Short-haul drivers are drivers of property-carrying CMVs who do not require a commercial driver's license for operation and who operate within a 150 air-mile radius of their normal work-reporting location. They

- may drive a maximum of ten hours after coming on duty following ten or more hours off duty
- are not required to keep records of duty status (RODS)
- may not drive after the fourteenth hour after coming on duty five days a week, or after the sixteenth hour after two days a week

In place of RODS, these employers must maintain and retain accurate time records for six months that show

2003 Rule Property-Carrying CMV Drivers (compliance through 09/30/05)	2005 Rule Property-Carrying CMV Drivers (compliance on and after 10/01/05)
May drive a maximum of eleven hours after ten consecutive hours off duty	No change
May not drive beyond the fourteenth hour after coming on duty following ten consecutive hours off duty	No change
May not drive after 60/70 hours on duty in a seven/eight-consecutive-day period after taking 34 or more consecutive hours off duty	No change
CMV drivers using a sleeper berth must take ten hours off duty, but may split sleeper berth time into two periods provided neither is less than two hours.	CMV drivers using the sleeper berth provision must take at least eight consecutive hours in the sleeper berth or off duty or any combination of the two.

Passenger-carrying carriers/drivers are not subject to the new hours-of-service rules. These operators must continue to comply with the hours-of-service limitations specified in 49 CFR 395.5.

FIGURE 3. Hours-of-service regulations (*Source:* FMCSA 2005)

Result:	Action:
Less than 0.02%	No action required under CFR Part 40
0.02%–0.039%	Varies among DOT agencies. For example, FMCSA states that a driver may not resume safety-sensitive functions for twenty-four hours (382.505), while the Federal Railroad Administration (FRA) requires eight hours (219) .101 (a)(4). The Federal Transit Administration (FTA) and Pipeline and Hazardous Materials Safety Administration (PHMSA) require only that a driver test below 0.02%. A driver who does not pass that test cannot work until the next scheduled duty period, which cannot be less than eight hours from the time of the test (655.35 and 199.237 respectively).
0.04% or greater	Drivers must immediately be removed from safety-sensitive functions and may not resume them until they successfully complete the return-to-duty process.

FIGURE 4. BAC finding and subsequent actions

what time duty periods began and ended and the total hours on duty each day.

Drivers who use this short-haul provision are not eligible to use the 100 air-mile provision (395.1(e)) or the current sixteen-hour exception in 395.1(o).

DRUG AND ALCOHOL REGULATIONS FOR CDL DRIVERS

The laws regulating the use of drugs and alcohol are much more stringent for CDL drivers than for drivers with standard licenses. Preemployment testing, testing on the job, and lower blood-alcohol-concentration allowances are a few examples of these stricter provisions. The regulations are extensive and complicated. To obtain the full text of these regulations, visit this section of the FMCSA Web site: (www.fmcsa.dot.gov/safety-security/safety-initiatives/drugs/drug-guidelines.htm).

Figure 4 provides an overview of the laws regarding blood-alcohol-concentration (BAC) limitations for CDL drivers.

REFERENCES

Alaniz, Richard. 2008. "Striking the Balance: MVR Checks and Privacy Laws." *Automotive Fleet* (retrieved February 9, 2008). www.automotivefleet.com

American National Standards Institute/American Society of Safety Engineers (ANSI/ASSE). 2006. ANSI Z15, *Safe Practices for Motor Vehicle Operations*. Des Plaines, IL: ANSI/ASSE.

Bureau of Labor Statistics (BLS). 2014. *Census of Fatal Occupational Injuries, 2013* (retrieved December 20, 2014)). www.bls.gov/news.release/pdf/cfoi.pdf

Bureau of Transportation Statistics (BTS). 2003. *U.S. Business Travel.* www.bts.gov/publications/america_on_the_go/us_business_travel/

Code of Federal Regulations (CFR) Title 49 (Parts 40, 171–180, 325, 380–399).

Federal Motor Carrier Safety Administration (FMCSA). 2008. "Commercial Driver's License Program (CDL/CDLIS)" (retrieved February 8, 2008). www.fmcsa.dot.gov/registration-licensing/cdl/cdl.htm

John A. Volpe National Transportation Systems Center (Volpe). 1998. "New Entrant Safety Research." Report prepared for the Federal Highway Administration. Cambridge, MA: Economic Analysis Division, Volpe National Transportation Systems Center.

National Highway Traffic Safety Administration (NHTSA). 2008. *Fatality Analysis Reporting System Encyclopedia* (retrieved June 29, 2010). www-fars.nhtsa.dot.gov/Main/index.aspx

_____. 2007. *The Economic Burden of Traffic Crashes on Employers: Costs by State and Industry and by Alcohol and Restrain Use.* www.nhtsa.dot.gov/people/injury/airbags/EconomicBurden/pages/WhatDoTCCost.htm

_____. 2009. *Traffic Safety Facts.* DOT HS 811 291. Washington, D.C.: NHTSA's National Center for Statistics and Analysis (retrieved June 29, 2010). www-nrd.nhtsa.dot.gov/Pubs/811291.pdf

National Safety Council (NSC). 2010. *Injury Facts, 2010 Edition.* Itasca, IL: NSC (www.nsc.org).

Occupational Safety and Health Administration (OSHA). 2006. "Guidelines for Employers to Reduce Motor Vehicle Crashes." www.osha.gov/Publications/motor_vehicle_guide.html

Pennsylvania Consolidated Statutes. 2007. *The Vehicle Code* (Title 75). www.law.onecle/pennsylvania/vehicles/index.html

RECOMMENDED RESOURCES

There is a growing awareness in the once-forgotten area of driver safety. Because of this, numerous organizations, both private and government, provide information that can help with driver safety programs. The sources below provide a wealth of information.

Traffic Accident Reconstruction Origin (TARO). www.tarorigin.com

Transit Cooperative Research Program, www.trcponline.org

Transportation Research Board (TRB). www.trb.org

U.S. Bureau of Labor Statistics, U.S. Department of Labor. www.bls.gov

U.S. Department of Transportation (US DOT). www.DOT.gov

ADDITIONAL READING

HOW PERDUE FARMS INC. IMPLEMENTED A VIDEO-BASED DRIVER RISK MANAGEMENT PROGRAM*

Del Lisk
Vice President, Safety Services
DriveCam

Frank Cruice
Senior Director, Corporate Safety & Security
Perdue Farms

Tommy Pollard
Corporate Fleet Safety Manager
Perdue Farms

Introduction

Perdue Farms faced increasing driving accidents at one particular facility, resulting in an increase in vehicle accident costs and negative safety behaviors. The company investigated various options to improve driver safety and evaluated a video-based driver risk management system at that facility, which eventually spread to the entire fleet. This paper will illustrate how Perdue navigated throughout their organization to implement a process that improved driver safety behaviors and results. In this paper, we will:

- Learn about new safety technologies and how to evaluate them
- Understand how a video-based driver risk management system improves driver behavior and reduces claims costs
- Learn how to navigate throughout an organization to implement a new program – from executive management (C-level) to drivers, including Risk, Human Resources, Safety and Transportation/Logistics

First, we begin with a look at the solution that Perdue adopted and some of the data already gathered about driver risk management.

The Solution

DriveCam customers deploy in-cab video technology and objective third-party analysis as a means to improve driving, as well as capture the truth if a collision occurs. The video camera is commonly affixed to the windshield and is loop recording in front, as well as inside, the vehicle. When the vehicle experiences substantial force, such as hard braking or swerving, the device is triggered to save the 8 seconds before the moment of force as well as an additional 4 seconds afterward. The net result is a video that reveals what happened and why. This video is then uploaded to a review center, where it is objectively reviewed and assessed for risk. Events with a significant level of concern are then directed to the client for driver coaching via a web platform. Exhibit 1 illustrates this process.

DRIVER SCIENCE ENGINE

DRIVER SCIENCE PROGRAM

Exhibit 1. Process of Review of Risky Driving Behavior

DriveCam has analyzed approximately 30 million risky driving clips, and has learned a tremendous amount about driver behavior and what can be done to make drivers safer and more fuel efficient.

Armed with the ability to isolate and correct risky driving before it leads to a crash, clients report tremendous improvements in fleet safety as well now having the ability to protect themselves and their drivers against false claims:

- Heritage Propane reduced collisions by more than 60%
- Orange County, Florida, reduced cost of accidents by 81% in the first year
- Amerigas reduced the number of risky driving incidents by almost 60%
- Mactec reduced collisions by 75%
- TXI reduced accidents by almost 50%

As with any impactful safety process, there are challenges. Discussed below are the most common challenges:

Getting the Funding

Budgets are generally tight so getting funding can be a challenge. Organizations are demanding that all investments—including investments in safety—must have a measurable positive financial impact for the organization. It's important that the returns on investment expectations are presented internally to the decision-makers. This is a simple process of taking historical costs of traffic accidents and showing what the impact of reducing costs by 30-50% would be. In many cases, the program has paid for itself in one year or less. Lloyd Pest Control, a California-based pest control service with 300 vehicles, reports the program paid for itself in the first 90 days.

Often, there are concerns internally from the legal department. The concern is, "What if a serious accident happened and the video showed it was our fault? How would the video impact an award if this went to trial?" Every one of our clients has considered this and decided the positives far outweigh this concern. The positives that need to be factored in are:

- Reduced collisions—the best way to reduce the cost of an accident is to prevent it altogether
- Ability to more effectively defend against false claims
- Even if at fault, with the video, clients quickly know the facts and can move immediately to a quick settlement. Sometimes they can settle before the other party gets a lawyer involved.

- Far less investigative costs. The video shows what really happened, so the need for an accident reconstructionist, investigators or others to assist with the case is greatly reduced.

Impacts on Operations

Organizations are running lean and mean. There are scant resources to dedicate to managing new processes. Consequently, it is essential that a process such as this does not put too many demands on management. DriveCam long ago recognized this and designed tools that make it easy for management to quickly identify what the issues are and what needs to be done. Also, most of the heavy lifting occurs in the first few weeks when driver coaching begins. This workload drops dramatically as drivers quickly improve and there are far fewer risky driving incidents to require coaching. It is common for clients to see risky events and the subsequent workload drop by 50 percent just one month after program launch.

Some companies wonder if their culture meshes with a solution like this. It's a good question. Looking at the vast array of cultures within our 500+ clients, we've come to realize this is the wrong question to ask. Instead, the question should be, "can this solution be adapted so it meshes with our company culture?" Our clients adjust the program in many ways to align with their culture –

- Some only coach, others tie in discipline when errors are more serious
- Some have drivers "self-coach"
- Some work closely with labor to review and adjust the program on an on-going basis
- Some tie in manager bonuses to risk reduction
- Some leave expectations and oversight at the local level; others design corporate oversight that cascades down through the organization

Another common concern or challenge is how a program such as this will be received by labor. If the driver force is unionized, this concern is usually higher. The key is to have open, early communication with union leaders and employees long before equipment is installed in vehicles. We find there is more push back from labor when early communication did not occur.

Most of the concerns are due to misconception, misinformation or lack of experience with the program and relate to two issues:

1. *The technology*: Drivers mistakenly think the technology has the ability to record everything, all the time, or that management can trigger it remotely to record or look in live. It doesn't have these capabilities. An event is only triggered when a vehicle experiences unusual force or is excessively speeding.

2. *The video will be used against them:* It's important to emphasize that the intent of the program is to improve driving behavior through coaching and training. Statistics prove that drivers do become safer with this solution. Safer drivers have fewer accidents than drivers who are having problems, and therefore their jobs are more secure, not less. It's also important to recognize that video may protect the driver in an incident that may otherwise been blamed on him/her.

The Perdue Farms Story

Perdue Farms is the third largest producer of poultry food products in the U.S. The Perdue Family of Companies includes Perdue Farms, Perdue AgriBusiness, and shared services organizations. Since its beginning on Arthur Perdue's farm in 1920, through expansion into agribusiness and the introduction of the PERDUE® brand of chicken and turkey under Frank Perdue, to today's third-generation of family leadership with Chairman Jim Perdue, the company has remained a family-owned entity dedicated to making Perdue the most trusted name in food and agricultural products.

Dedicated equally to the safety of its associates as to its product, Perdue recognized a need to improve upon its fleet safety process in order to decrease associate injuries, and reduce operational costs from crashes that were negatively impacting the bottom line. In order to leverage current staffing while allowing that staff to become more effective, Perdue sought to develop a fleet-driven, behavioral based safety (BBS) process. The company was looking to leverage a technology solution to help achieve those objectives.

As with most companies, staff was already stretched. "We were stretched for people, time and resources, and with a mixed fleet of 1,200 commercial and non-commercial vehicles, we knew the only way we would be able to make an impact with our drivers and improve driver behavior without adding staff would be to leverage technology," said Frank Cruice, senior director corporate safety and security for Perdue.

Perdue had employed driving simulators in the past and has strategically installed various vehicle-based safety systems, such as lane departure warning systems, on-board diagnostics, blind-side sensing systems, and front-facing radar. These tools were valuable, but ultimately

Perdue decided to implement a driver risk management solution at two sites where risky driving incidents were highest, in an effort to truly change driver behaviors.

Now that a need had been established for a Driver Risk Management solution, both Frank Cruice and Tommy Pollard, corporate fleet safety manager at Perdue, conducted an assessment of available service providers. Once service providers were sourced, they conducted vendor presentations to the implementing staff in order for them to take ownership in the decision as to what product/vendor they felt could deliver and provide the most value for their investment. Ownership by a site in selecting a service provider is paramount to ensuring a successful beta test within your organization. Based on the presentation and capability of its global driver risk management system, DriveCam was selected to implement their technology solution within Perdue's pilot fleet of 37 commercial vehicles dispersed within three separate types of short haul operations.

DriveCam combines audio and video event capture with expert analysis and driver coaching to identify and correct risky driving behavior before a collision occurs. DriveCam's palm-sized, exception-based video event recorder is mounted in vehicles behind the rearview mirror and captures sights and sounds inside and outside the vehicle. Exceptional forces trigger the video event recorder to save critical seconds immediately before and after the triggering event. Saved events are downloaded, reviewed, assigned a risk score and used to coach drivers to operate more safely. DriveCam's driver risk management solution has helped more than 1,500 fleets reduce vehicle damages, workers' compensation, personal injury and claims cost by as much as 50 percent in nearly 100,000 vehicles.

Pollard knew nothing could compare to the power of sight and sound when reviewing an incident and determining the root cause of a collision or risky driving event. "Nothing affords us the data and insight that video does," said Pollard. "As we evaluated alternative solutions, it became very clear that DriveCam gave us the best data to get into the dugout with the driver and change that behavior for the better. How can you beat video? As the adage goes, a picture is worth 1,000 words... especially when that picture happens to be video."

Cruice secured approval from senior management to test the DriveCam solution at the pilot sites that were experiencing a higher than usual number of risky driving incidents. Perdue deployed the solution in three different types of vehicles: hatchery, dry bulk feed and live haul trucks. Prior to deployment, Pollard brought the solution to the site managers and the drivers themselves. He introduced DriveCam and discussed the benefits of

the solution for each driver, allaying any concerns and misperceptions they might have had. Pollard shared video clips with the drivers and discussed the benefit of incident exoneration. Local managers would be responsible for reviewing video from the DriveCam Risky Driving Analysts, and then coaching drivers accordingly. They supported the program and were instrumental in the selection process because they felt a sense of ownership and involvement from the outset. This also helped impact overall driver acceptance.

Perdue saw a distinct reduction in the number of incidents incurred among fleets outfitted with the DriveCam solution. The company experienced an 88 percent reduction in vehicle incidents compared to the previous year without DriveCam. Additionally, the first collision that occurred following implementation of the DriveCam solution was one in which the video evidence exonerated the driver. This immediately justified the need for the solution in the Perdue fleet.

By implementing the DriveCam solution, Pollard feels that drivers have the much-needed reminder to make conscious decisions while driving, as if he was in the vehicle with them.

"How do you be there without really being there?" Pollard asks. "Our commercial drivers are out there alone, but DriveCam helps them make conscious decisions about their driving because they know the event recorder is there."

The data gathered from each recorder is used to decide where to focus training time, and has helped Pollard determine why incidents are occurring.

Pollard reports that drivers have been receptive to the coaching and appreciate the evidence exonerating them and helping them maintain their safety records. In the case of Perdue's short-haul fleet, often the roads that drivers travel are winding with little to no shoulder or room for error. As these particular vehicles often travel at night, Perdue relies on its drivers to be alert and aware, to keep both themselves and their vehicles safe. Implementing the DriveCam solution allowed Perdue to identify the riskiest behaviors seen on these types of roads and coach drivers to safely operate their vehicles.

Initially, Perdue recognized that one of their largest motor vehicle losses came from single vehicle accidents classified as "run off road and rollover." Nearly 1/3 of these types of accidents were stemming from the selected project site. The DriveCam solution validated that the root cause of these incidents was driver distraction. This evidence showed the company what the leading indicators were and, consequently, Perdue was able to strategize a Crash Reduction Plan based on facts. Pollard says,

"In the past, we spent over 80 percent of our time on investigating and debating what happened, and now with the naturalistic data that the camera produces, we spend less than 20 percent of the time on that. Most all of our time is spent on preventing reoccurrence. The camera inverts this equation and puts the emphasis on preventing reoccurrence versus trying to figure out why!"

"Bottom line is, the DriveCam solution gives us the feedback as to why, and provides the data to help us understand what's going on and where to focus our efforts," said Pollard.

While reviewing incidents for coaching, Perdue began to revise other areas of its safety policies, including seat belt and cell phone usage. The camera evidence allowed Perdue to take direct action under its driver policies for these types of violations and turn their focus towards changing driver behavior through a behavioral management approach versus a "discipline" approach. Using the DriveCam solution, Perdue managers monitor severity and repeat behaviors. When a driver reaches a predetermined level, managers step in and develop a performance improvement plan, or PIP, for that driver instead of punitive measures and disciplines. This reinforces the process by showing the driver the company is not just looking to discipline, but rather to create a culture of safety and driver improvement.

"The DriveCam solution became a hub for the driver safety process," said Pollard. "It brought all entities—drivers, managers and senior management—to the same table, allowing us to review our safety processes comprehensively and identify the areas in need of attention."

Through the use of this technology, Perdue continues to embed a culture of safe driving behavior within its company. They have begun a journey to level the playing field between the drivers and managers by instituting a parallel using defensive driving education as the coaching platform for managers. When managers see the videos and in turn coach their drivers, they use defensive driving as the primary communication. Pollard says, "It's not about right or wrong, it's about, did we have an opportunity to drive defensively to prevent the incident?" Using the defensive driving platform during coaching also puts the manager and driver on the same level. Pollard says that whether you are driving a scooter, car, SUV or the big truck, defensive driving is still defensive driving. "Yes, stopping distances may vary between the big truck and car but following distance is the coaching moment," said Pollard. Using the data from the DriveCam solution

and the defensive driving platform, the focus turns away from the big truck and onto following distance. Thus, both manager and driver are on equal footing. The bottom line is that you don't have to have big-truck experience to coach big-truck drivers.

Summary

Driver safety efforts tend to go through periods where one issue reaches a critical mass in awareness and goes viral. This is a positive phenomenon in that it draws many different stakeholders into the issue and causes changes to happen more quickly than they may otherwise have. But it can also lull fleet operators into thinking they've solved the problem. Some may overlook other crucial safety issues and will later be disappointed when the results they were expecting don't follow.

Until the day when technology takes driving decisions out of the hands of the operator, a key focus of safety efforts needs to be on insuring drivers are using the fundamental safe driving skills that have separated the "good driver" from the "bad driver" since the invention of the automobile. Vehicles and technology have changed dramatically over the years, but the underlying causes for people making mistakes behind the wheel have not.

In the case of Perdue Farms, it was one specific facility where critical mass got the attention of fleet safety, which led to a technology solution deployment at that facility, and ultimately to fleet-wide deployment. *Perdue measured an ROI of 406% after the first two years and an 88 percent reduction in vehicle incidents compared to the previous year without DriveCam. Frequency and severity were measured for the three (3) years prior and after implementation and returned extremely favorable results.* Best seen in the chart below, Perdue measured the longevity of the process and experienced fewer accidents and less cost because driving behaviors were addressed. The frequency was reduced by 60 percent, and severity was reduced by 86 percent.

- Frequency at three (3) years prior to implementation of DriveCam averaged 15.3 incidents/year; (vs.) three (3) year post implementation averaged 6.3 incidents/year.

- The project site had been averaging $420,716 in accident costs for the three prior fiscal years. Since implementation, vehicle accident costs have been reduced to an average of $59,671 per year.

History

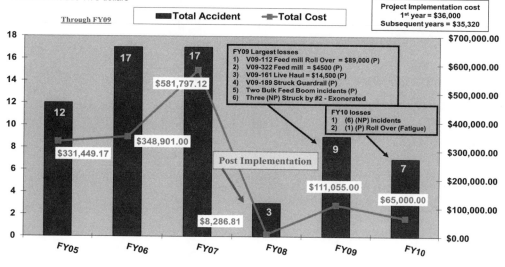

For (37) cameras covering Short Haul Operations, (Feed & Livestock tractor trailer.)
Includes all <u>commercial</u> vehicle accidents for periods measured (excluding animal strikes & Off Hwy non-serious incidents)
Cost are estimated, based on available maintenance records & Insurance data sources (paid & accrued)
Does not include W/C dollars

Exhibit 2. Truck Mounted Camera Pilot Project: Total Accident & Total Cost Before/After Implementation

As an advocate for safety across the company, Cruice is always looking for a new process to maintain Perdue's high standard of safety. He believes the DriveCam solution supports and enhances the company's existing process.

"At Perdue, we measure the four P's – People, Products, Profitability and Planet," said Cruice. "DriveCam is an integral part of our corporate behavioral-based safety process, and is used to constantly to monitor, coach and improve our driver's behaviors. Thus keeping Perdue a company deeply engaged in employee safety that always puts its associates—and those we share the roads with—first."

Index

Notes

Notes